THE CHILDREN'S HOUR

Volume One
FIRST STORY BOOK

Volume Two
FAVORITE FAIRY TALES

Volume Three
OLD TIME FAVORITES

Volume Four
CARAVAN OF FUN

Volume Five
BEST-LOVED POEMS

Volume Six
STORIES OF TODAY

Volume Seven
FAVORITE MYSTERY STORIES

Volume Eight
MYTHS AND LEGENDS

Volume Nine
FROM MANY LANDS

Volume Ten
SCHOOL AND SPORT

Volume Eleven
ALONG BLAZED TRAILS

Volume Twelve
STORIES OF LONG AGO

Volume Thirteen
ROADS TO ADVENTURE

Volume Fourteen
FAVORITE ANIMAL STORIES

Volume Fifteen
LEADERS AND HEROES

Volume Sixteen
SCIENCE FICTION — GUIDE

Science Fiction
& Readers Guide

A BOOK TO GROW ON

CONSULTANT EDITORS FOR
THE CHILDREN'S HOUR

CAROL RYRIE BRINK
Author
Newbery Prize Winner

JULIA M. H. CARSON
Author and Biographer

FLEUR CONKLING
Editor and Author

IRVING CRUMP
Editor and Author

HELEN DEAN FISH
Editor and Author

WILHELMINA HARPER
Anthologist, Librarian
Redwood City, California

WILLIAM HEYLIGER
Author,
Editor of Literature for Youth
The Westminster Press

SIDDIE JOE JOHNSON
Children's Librarian
Dallas Public Library

CORNELIA MEIGS
Author and Teacher
Newbery Prize Winner

NORMA RATHBUN
Chief of Children's Work
Milwaukee Public Library

MABEL L. ROBINSON
Author, Associate Professor
Columbia University

MARGARET JONES WILLIAMS
Director of Elementary Education
Cornell College, Iowa

THE CHILDREN'S HOUR

MARJORIE BARROWS, *Editor*

Science Fiction
& Readers Guide

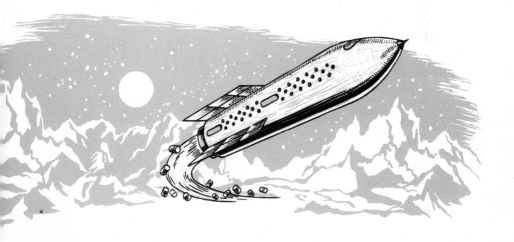

MATHILDA SCHIRMER
Associate Editor

DOROTHY SHORT
Art Editor

THE SPENCER PRESS, INC. • *Chicago*

Acknowledgments

The editor and publishers wish to thank the following publishers, agents, authors, and artists for permission to reprint the following stories, articles, and illustrations:

LURTON BLASSINGAME for "Black Pits of Luna" by Robert A. Heinlein, first published by *The Saturday Evening Post.*

DOUBLEDAY & COMPANY, INC., for "Lancelot Biggs on the *Saturn*" from *Lancelot Biggs: Spaceman* by Nelson Bond, copyright, 1950, by Nelson Bond.

HENRY HOLT AND COMPANY, INC., for "The Child's Personal Library" from *About Books and Children* by Bess Porter Adams, copyright, 1953, by Henry Holt and Company, Inc.

THE HORN BOOK, INC., and Herman Schneider for "What Is a Good Science Book?", reprinted from *The Horn Book Magazine*, September, 1951. The Bibliography was revised and brought up to date by Mr. Schneider, February, 1954.

LANTERN PRESS, INC., for "What Time Is It?" from *Teen-Age Science Fiction Stories* by Richard M. Elam, Jr., copyright, 1952, by Lantern Press, Inc.

THE MACMILLAN COMPANY for "Children's Interests in Reading" from *Story and Verse for Children* by Miriam Blanton Huber.

McGRAW-HILL BOOK COMPANY, INC., for "Mars and Miss Pickerell" from *Miss Pickerell Goes to Mars* by Ellen Macgregor and for six pictures by Paul Galdone from this book.

THE NEW AMERICAN LIBRARY OF WORLD LITERATURE for "Biographies Bring New Companions" by Marchette Chute, from *The Wonderful World of Books*, copyright, 1952, by Alfred Stefferud, published by The New American Library of World Literature, Inc., and Houghton Mifflin Company.

STORY PARADE, INC., for "Adventure on Mars" by Richard M. Elam, Jr., copyright, 1952, by Story Parade, Inc.

A. P. WATT & SON for "The Truth about Pyecraft" from *Twelve Stories and a Dream* by H. G. Wells.

BILL BROWN for "The Star Ducks," first published in *Fantasy and Science Fiction.*

PADRAIC COLUM for "Imagination and Children's Literature," first published in *Child Life Magazine*, and "Poetry and Childhood," first published in *Child Life Magazine.*

CLOYD HEAD for "The Poetry of Young Children" by Eunice Tietjens, first published in *Child Life Magazine.*

BURR W. LEYSON for "Trail to the Stars," first published in *Boys' Life Magazine.*

BERTHA MAHONY MILLER for "Fairy Tales and the Spirit," first published in *Child Life Magazine.*

ARTHUR PEDERSON for "My First Book Friends" by Rachel Field.

H. PERCY WILKINS for "Is There Life on the Moon?", first published in *Collins Young Elizabethan.*

We thank Ewing Galloway for permission to reprint pictures of Robert Browning, George Gordon Lord Byron, Lewis Carroll, Samuel Clemens, Daniel Defoe, Alexander Dumas, Ralph Waldo Emerson, Eugene Field, Jacob Grimm, Wilhelm Grimm, Nathaniel Hawthorne, Oliver Wendell Holmes, John Keats, Charles A. Lindbergh, Henry Wadsworth Longfellow, Edgar Allan Poe, Theodore Roosevelt, Sir Walter Scott, Percy B. Shelley, Robert Louis Stevenson, Alfred Lord Tennyson, and John Greenleaf Whittier; we also thank the many publishers who provided us with pictures of their various authors and artists, and acknowledge the following photographers: Bunny Adler, Arni, Bachrach, Barde, Victor Barnaba, Charles Bentley, Blackstone Studios, Bobbs-Merrill, Wesley Bowman Studio, Inc., Frederick Bradley, Bruno, Burnell, Cerro Studio, Conway Studios, Charles M. Daugherty, J. M. Egbert, E. G. Fine, Forde and Garter, Foster Studio, John French, Georgeson, Gibson Studios, Gitchells' Studio, Frederick Hamilton, Harcourt Paris, Harris and Ewing, Herndon, Jay Hyde Bernum, Robert Janssen, Keystone Pictures, Inc., Koehne, Russell O. Kuhner, Lehman, Don Loving, Earle Lyon, Pirie MacDonald, Mardis Studio, E. F. Marten, Mishkin, Moffett Studio, Carl Moon,

Nicholas Muray and Associates, Office Appliances, Oscar and Associates, Bee Pancoast, Parsons Studio, Barbara Perine, Bernice B. Perry, Pinchot, Rayhoff-Richter, Ryan Aeronautical Company, Jean Sardon, John D. Schiff, Howard G. Schmitt, Viola Semlar, Clara E. Sipprell, William A. Smith, Swisher Studio, Bill Tague, U.S. Coast Guard, Martin Vos, and Maynard Washslof.

Great pains have been taken to obtain permission from the owners of reprint material. Any errors that may possibly have been made are unintentional and will gladly be corrected in future printings if notice is sent to the Spencer Press, Inc.

The editor is deeply grateful to Sanford Cobb and Leonard S. Davidow for the help they have given in compiling these sixteen volumes of *The Children's Hour*.

She is also grateful for the help from her staff, (Mathilda Schirmer, Walter Eckart, Nancy Porter, Denise Giraud, and Suzie Snider), and for the help she has received from Ernest Frawley, the Reference Staff of the Chicago Public Library, The Thomas Hughes Room of the Chicago Public Library, and the Children's Room of the Evanston Public Library. She also wishes to express her thanks to Walter R. Barrows, Jane Beglen, Meg Carr, Herma Clark, Pauline Dubkin, Mary Dupre, Edward Fitzgerald, Rollo Fogarty, William E. Hill, Nettie King, Barbara Landy, Joan Pontius, Johanna Porter, Esther Reno, Eleanor Senn, Max Siegel, and Helen Wohlberg. The editor also thanks one hundred and twenty thousand school children, teachers, and librarians throughout the country who offered helpful suggestions for *The Children's Hour*.

Contents

WHAT TIME IS IT?　　　　　RICHARD M. ELAM, JR.　　1
    Illustrated by Hardie Gramatky

ADVENTURE ON MARS　　　　RICHARD M. ELAM, JR.　　21
    Illustrated by Seymour Fleishman

MARS AND MISS PICKERELL　　ELLEN MACGREGOR　　36
    Illustrated by Paul Galdone

THE STAR DUCKS　　　　　　BILL BROWN　　59
    Illustrated by Hardie Gramatky

LANCELOT BIGGS ON THE SATURN　　NELSON BOND　　70
    Illustrated by John Dukes McKee

THE TRUTH ABOUT PYECRAFT　　H. G. WELLS　　102
    Illustrated by John Dukes McKee

THE BLACK PITS OF LUNA　　ROBERT A. HEINLEIN　　115
    Illustrated by Brinton Turkle

IS THERE LIFE ON THE MOON?　　H. PERCY WILKINS　　132
    Illustrated by Ann Davidow

TRAIL TO THE STARS　　CAPTAIN BURR LEYSON　　134
    Illustrated by John Merryweather

GLOSSARY　　141

PAGES FOR PARENTS
  Fairy Tales and the Spirit　　BERTHA E. MAHONY　　144
  Poetry and Childhood　　PADRAIC COLUM　　147
  Biographies Bring New Companions　　MARCHETTE CHUTE　　151
  The Child's Personal Library　　BESS PORTER ADAMS　　153
  Your Child and World Neighborliness　　AGATHA L. SHEA　　159
  What Is a Good Science Book?　　HERMAN SCHNEIDER　　162
  My First Book Friends　　RACHEL FIELD　　170
  Imagination and Children's Literature　　PADRAIC COLUM　　173
  Children's Interests in Reading　　MIRIAM BLANTON HUBER　　176

WHO'S WHO IN THE CHILDREN'S HOUR　　186

CONSULTANT EDITORS FOR THE CHILDREN'S HOUR　　287

AUTHOR-TITLE INDEX　　290

SUBJECT INDEX　　334

THE CHILDREN'S HOUR ILLUSTRATORS　　374

Richard M. Elam, Jr.

WHAT TIME IS IT?

ILLUSTRATED BY *Hardie Gramatky*

"THIS IS the house," Tom Lester said, pointing to the big, rambling, Spanish-style home surrounded by date palms.

"A college engineering teacher's pay must be good these days," quipped Chuck Parker, as they walked up the winding flagstone path to the house.

Tom, who was tall with wavy blond hair, looked down on his shorter, freckle-faced companion. "A professor's pay couldn't afford this, Chuck. Dr. Haley's one of the outstanding scientists in the country. It's his great inventions in electronics that have brought him the extra cash."

"Wonder what he wants to see a couple of high-school goofs like us for?" Chuck muttered.

"We'll know in a few minutes," Tom answered.

They rang the bell, and the door was opened by a girl their own age.

"Hi, Jean," Tom said. "Will you tell your father we're here?"

She smiled and invited them in. Leading them through the house she said mysteriously, "You two are really in for a surprise!"

The boys looked at one another in wonderment. But they said nothing until Jean led them into the presence of Dr. Haley in his laboratory, which was located in the west wing of the house.

He was a heavy-set man in a soiled smock, and his hair, graying along the sides, was in disarray. He smiled in greeting and shook hands with the boys as they entered. Only after their eyes had become accustomed to the bewildering litter of vac-

1

uum tubes, generators, and mechanical equipment did the boys notice the giant aluminum box sitting in the corner.

"I see you're interested in the big box," Dr. Haley said. "I don't blame you. That object holds the secrets of the past and future."

"Huh?" Chuck gasped, rubbing a hand through his red crew cut.

"What do you mean, Dr. Haley?" Tom asked.

The scientist approached the box. "Help me roll it into the middle of the floor, will you, fellows, and then I'll show you all about it."

The three of them had no trouble pushing the bulky object, measuring about six feet high by some four feet square, farther into the room, as it was resting on a low platform equipped with rollers. Jean was still present, looking on with an amused glance.

"Watch," Dr. Haley said and simultaneously pressed two buttons on the side of the aluminum box. Two opposite sides began rolling up like curtains. They disappeared into the top, revealing an inner framework of braces wrapped in copper wire. A narrow panel, containing gauges and a back-and-forth lever, ran from top to bottom on the opposite side.

"Wh-what is it?" Chuck asked, completely baffled.

"I call it the Time Traveler," Dr. Haley answered.

"*A time machine?*" Tom asked, astonished.

"Exactly," the scientist said. "I've been working on it during my past sabbatical year away from the Institute. It works too. I've sent guinea pigs into the past and the future."

"It's incredible!" Tom breathed.

"Meaning unbelievable?" Dr. Haley said. "I think you will believe it tonight when I put on my demonstration before a science convention in the auditorium of Southwest Institute."

"Dad's been working in secret with the Time Traveler," Jean said, "the whole year. See, the windows are blacked out. He worked under mercury-vapor lights all the time."

"But why have you told us two all this, Sir?" Tom asked.

"Tonight I'll be plagued with questions no end from scien-

2

tists and reporters. I'll need you two to help Jean explain some of the more elementary facts of the Traveler to these men, especially the reporters. Also I'll need some help in operating the machine for the demonstration."

"How did you know about us?" Chuck asked.

"I asked Jean if she knew of a couple of above-average science students in her class at school who could keep their mouths shut until the proper moment, and she suggested you two. Will you take the job?"

"Will we?" Tom said enthusiastically.

"Let's get started!" Chuck put in.

"I won't go into the complicated physics of the project," the professor said, "because you wouldn't understand them in the first place." He put his hand on the aluminum box. "This is only the insulating cover. The machine itself is the inner part. The electronic system that operates it is located in the top and bottom portions. When the current is on, an electromagnetic field is set up between those coils that resemble a framework, and that's what transports you through time."

He showed them the back-and-forth lever that operated the Traveler. Its box was calibrated in approximate ages, the present being in the center. "I haven't used the lever yet," he said. "That's for a human traveler to use should we ever dare send human beings through time. I have a remote-control panel I've been using on the guinea pigs."

The explanations went on for another half hour. When they were over, Dr. Haley lowered the shutters, closing the box. Experimentally, he pressed the buttons to raise the sides again, but he found that they wouldn't move.

"I was afraid of that," he said. "The switch is faulty and I don't have time to work it over. I'm glad now I put a mechanical lid on top of the box so that we can get into it when the sides fail to open."

Under the scientist's directions, Tom climbed in through the top and adjusted the switch so that it worked again.

Dr. Haley gave his final instructions to the boys before he dismissed them. "Come by about seven. We'll load the Traveler on a panel truck I've rented, and then we'll take it over to the college."

At eight o'clock the auditorium of Southwest Institute was packed with scientists who buzzed in anticipation. To avoid a crowd of the merely curious, the fact that the most remarkable invention of the century was about to be revealed had not been let out. So far as the audience knew, they were about to hear merely another lecture.

Tom and Chuck felt a certain amount of pride as they sat beside the Time Traveler in the company of Dr. Haley, his family, and the regents of the Institute. Dr. Haley was introduced as one of the most learned physicists in the country and an honored member of the college staff.

When Dr. Haley described his earth-stirring invention, the auditorium burst into an outspoken mixture of reactions:

"A time machine! Fantastic!"

"Entirely fictional!"

"This is the greatest thing since radio!"

Slowly then, the incredulous and believing alike subsided as Dr. Haley went into details. Before long he had an openmouthed audience who sat in silent, awed attention. He still had not revealed the inside of the aluminum box.

"The energy for driving the Traveler takes many months to store up in the special generator required," he continued. "For the demonstration tonight I will send a guinea pig into the past and another into the future, just as I was able to do in my laboratory. The generator is loaded to seventy-five per cent of its capacity, which will just about take care of our two journeys. Now to reveal the inside of the Time Traveler." He pressed the two buttons on the case, but the sides failed to lift.

He grinned at Tom and Chuck. "It's acting up again," he said to them. "You'll have to climb inside, Tom."

The scientist explained the situation as a chair was placed beside the box and Tom climbed onto it with a kit of tools. Lifting the lid and throwing it back on its hinges, he dropped to the metal floor inside and began work on the defective switch.

4

Then he saw that it would take an extra hand to hold one of the springs in place. He called to Chuck, and his friend's face appeared at the top.

"Give me a hand, will you, Chuck?" Tom asked.

The shorter youth was blushing as he struggled into the case. "I feel like an acrobat performing before all these people," he grunted, dropping to the floor beside Tom.

It was a tight fit for the two of them. Tom handed Chuck a screw driver and showed him what he wanted. Chuck lifted the spring, but it popped back into his face. Chuck swung his arm back, startled.

And then it happened.

The boys' eyes suddenly became blurry, and they felt as though they were going down in a whirlpool. Their knees buckled, and they alternately felt terrible heat and icy cold. Then they blacked out. . . .

Tom was the first to come to. Slowly, his daze left him, and the first things that focused before his eyes were the calibrated markings on the lever box. The soft metal was dented, and the lever was shoved nearly as far back into the past as it would go!

He shook his friend, whose eyes opened in wonderment. "What happened?" he asked in a weak voice.

"Your arm struck the lever," Tom replied. "We're probably thousands—maybe millions—of years back in time!"

Chuck tried to say something, but only a frightened croak came out of his mouth. It looked to Tom as though his freckles had become more vivid in his fear. They looked around them. They were at the mouth of a cave in a forest area. Patches of strange, high grass and dense brush grew out of marshy ground. Gnarled trees with thick boles dotted the area. Through the trees Tom sighted a rugged mountain range several miles away.

"Look!" he exclaimed. "That range over there looks just like Spice Mountain! If it weren't so rugged it would be identical with it!"

"It *is* Spice Mountain, Tom," Chuck said positively. "Only one mountain in the world could ever look like that!"

Then it came to Tom. "I've got it! This spot is the same that the college is on, only many, many years earlier! Spice Mountain is younger now; that's why it's less eroded!"

"This may be the same spot, but it sure doesn't look familiar!" Chuck muttered, peering back uneasily into the cave. "I think we'd better get back to the present—I mean the future. Hang it, I don't know what I mean!"

"Hold on, then!" Tom said. "We're going back."

He shoved on the lever, but it would not move. He pushed

6

again, but it was still stuck. "It looks like you jammed it, Chuck, when you hit against it. I don't know whether we'll ever get out of here or not!"

Just then a chilling growl raised the hair on their necks. The sound had come from deep within the cave.

"Tom!" Chuck cried. "This is the den of a wild animal!"

Then they heard it again. It was just like a deep, ragged note on a bass viol. Tom's eyes searched the forest and lighted upon a big tree, not far off, with a lot of low branches and foliage.

"We've got to make it to that tree!" Tom whispered urgently to his friend. "Come on!"

They climbed out between the coils of the machine and started running swiftly across the soft ground toward the tree. Chuck tripped and fell when they were about halfway across, and Tom had to help him up and drag him the rest of the distance. Tom swung up in the branches and leaned down to grasp Chuck's hands.

A full roar burst on their ears. They turned; the most formidable creature they had ever seen came bounding out of the cave. It was catlike and as big as a small horse, massively built, and sprouting a pair of foot-long tusks from the upper jaw. When the beast caught sight of the boys, he roared again and plunged after them.

Tom strained and finally got his shorter companion off the ground. The big cat sprang, and his raking claws grazed the youth's back. When the boys were at a safe height they looked down, panting heavily, at the fearsome attacker.

"It's—it's a saber-toothed tiger!" Tom said. "Remember the picture in our zoology book? It looks a lot like this big fellow!"

"Ugh, what a brute!" Chuck said with a shudder. "He almost made ribbons of my back!"

"Look at those terrific shoulders—and the size of him!" Tom murmured. "No two tigers in our time would be a match for this one!"

"What're we going to do, Tom?" Chuck asked gloomily. "He may sit under this tree indefinitely!"

"I don't know," Tom answered gravely. "We've just got to

7

get back to the Traveler. I guess the tiger will leave to eat sometime."

The saber-tooth started back to his cave, glancing back occasionally as though making sure that his treed victims did not try to escape.

"Look, Tom!" Chuck suddenly said, pointing at the trees.

What appeared to be two walking tanks were passing through the forest. They were plated all over, and on the end of each one's tail there was a bristly club. The beasts were fully fifteen feet long and stood about six feet tall.

"Giant armadillos!" Tom said. "They're called glyptodons!"

The beasts passed, but it seemed to be only the beginning of a parade of fantastic creatures. A herd of tiny animals resembling miniature rhinoceroses trotted past. Behind them plodded a massive bearlike creature with very long claws. He was easily twenty feet in length. From his zoology training, Tom was certain he was watching a giant ground sloth of the Pleistocene epoch.

"The saber-tooth is pawing at the Traveler!" Chuck shouted. "If he damages it, we're stuck here for the rest of our lives!"

Tom watched in helpless silence as the prehistoric beast growled and struck at the mechanism with his broad forepaws. A single torn wire could mean disaster for the boys, because neither of them knew how to repair the complicated time machine.

Suddenly, to the boys' vast relief, the big cat paused stock-still and lifted his nose into the air as though sniffing. Tom and Chuck heard a drumming sound, as of numerous small tom-toms, and looked into the distance. On a grassy plain a herd of odd antelope flitted into view. The saber-toothed tiger left the cave and slunk into invisibility through the high grasses in the direction of the antelope herd.

"He's gone to catch himself a meal!" Tom said. "We'll wait a few minutes, then try to make a break for the machine."

Just as they were getting ready to descend from the tree, the largest brute they had yet seen emerged from some thick brush across the way.

8

"We've got to make it to that tree!"

"Jiminy!" Chuck cried. "What a whopper of an elephant!"

It was an elephant rightly enough but, more specifically a wooly mammoth, with enormously long hooked tusks. The huge beast was every bit of thirteen feet in height. His mountainous bulk thrashed through the brush, snapping saplings like matchsticks. As soon as he spotted the boys, he snorted and threw up his trunk in a bellow.

"We've got to get higher in the tree!" Tom said.

They climbed higher, until they ran out of branches. All they could do was hope the animal's long trunk could not reach that far up. The mammoth hooked his gracefully curling tusks around the upper slenderer part of the bole and began pulling. The youths felt the tree bending and themselves swaying over toward the animal.

"You don't think he'll snap it off, do you?" Chuck cried in terror.

"He's sure trying to!" Tom answered tightly.

It was a nightmare for the next few minutes. The mammoth squealed in rage as the stubborn tree refused to snap under his repeated efforts. Once or twice he let go suddenly, and the boys felt themselves whipped back in the opposite direction so forcefully that they nearly lost their clutch on the tree.

Finally the mammoth gave up trying to break the tree and began probing with his hairy trunk up through the foliage. The fingerlike tip was so close to Tom he could see the quivering pink flesh inside. The tip was barely short of reaching him. The elephant's red-rimmed eyes burned with hatred. He withdrew his trunk and, with a furious bellow, crashed off through the trees.

When the noise of his passing was gone, Tom said to Chuck, "Let's get out of here—we don't know when that saber-tooth will be back!"

They scrambled with almost reckless haste down the trunk of the tree and, after a cautious look around, set out across the area toward the cave. Tom entered the Time Traveler first and desperately wrenched at the operating lever.

"Get in here with me, Chuck," Tom said. "I think it's beginning to budge." When his friend had crowded in beside him, Tom studied the energy-supply gauge. "We've got only forty per cent power left. We used almost half getting here. We can't afford to be careless setting it now."

Tom was trying to work the dent out of the lever box when Chuck suddenly dug an elbow fiercely into his side. Tom whirled. The giant tiger was back. He stood only a few yards away, a large antelope in his jaws. He studied the boys with baleful eyes. The sunlight, filtering through the trees, gleamed on his yellow saber fangs. The slain antelope slipped from his teeth. Then he advanced on the youths, lips drawn back.

Tom had no other choice but to jerk the lever as hard as he could. In his haste he tried to set it approximately in their own lifetime, but even as the lever slid across and he felt that whirl-pool sensation taking hold of him, he knew he had missed the date. . . .

Tom came out of his blackout in the same sort of daze that had marked his last journey through time. He shook his head to clear it. He started to rouse Chuck, but this time his companion had been the first to waken. They both stared out over a sun-baked desert.

"We missed it!" Tom groaned, looking at the gauge. "There's only seven per cent energy left in the machine now!"

"I don't think we missed it very far," Chuck remarked. "This is a whole lot like the country around the Institute. Look at the yucca plants and prickly pear cactus. And there's Spice Mountain again, a little more smoothed off than it was way back there!"

Tom scarcely heard him. He was studying an adobe-walled village in front of them, mentally reviewing his archeology and trying to place the exact period. Then Tom noticed a river in the distance and a network of canals.

"The ancient Canal Builders!" Tom said suddenly. "This is six or seven hundred years before our time. Some of this race's artifacts were recovered on the northwest corner of the campus last year—just about the spot where that village is!"

10

"It seems peaceful here," Chuck said, stepping out of the Traveler. "Maybe we'll be able to get the lever straightened out without having anything bother us. I think I'll look around a little if you can handle it by yourself."

"Go ahead," Tom said.

He began working on the lever, and Chuck scrambled to the top of the hill on which they were perched. It seemed that the ancient saber-toothed tiger's den had grown into a sizable mound over the years.

Tom had hardly started before he was startled by a panicky shout from his friend and saw him come hurtling down the sandy incline. At the same time Tom heard a throb of drums and saw that the wall of the village was covered with shaggy-haired Indians, clothed in animal hides and brandishing bows and spears.

When Chuck reached Tom's level, he pointed up the slope. Lined against the deep-blue sky on the hill's summit was a solid rank of grim-faced painted figures, as shaggy as those who stood on the village wall. They, too, were armed to the teeth. The next instant the air was filled with arrows and the most blood-chilling shrieks the youths had ever heard.

Down the slope the attackers plunged, obviously heading for the village. They appeared unaware of the cringing youths and their curious machine. In a moment Tom knew they would be on top of them.

He yanked the fear-paralyzed Chuck into the Traveler. An arrow from the village defenders skimmed so close to Tom he could see the turkey-feathered shaft. His hands trembling, he seized the lever and shoved it forward. Once again they were hurled into the stream of time. . . .

The next thing Tom knew, he was in a place that seemed strangely familiar. The Time Traveler was on the stage of a huge auditorium. The platform had a lot of features like those at Southwest Institute, but they seemed to be finished off in more modern designs.

"Where are we now?" Chuck asked.

11

"I don't know, but this sure looks like the auditorium at the Institute, only all dressed up," Tom answered. "Look how many more seats there are out there and how comfortable they look, just like easy chairs!"

"Tom!" Chuck exclaimed. "There's only two per cent power left in the machine!"

"That means we used only a little to get here," Tom said. "We overshot our mark. We're in the future!"

They had been so interested in their surroundings, they were just noticing that it was nighttime. The auditorium was lighted by an invisible soft radiation. Through long panorama windows, sparkling city lights were visible. The huge room was utterly deserted except for themselves.

"Let's take a look around!" Chuck suggested excitedly.

"Hadn't we better be getting back—or trying to get back—to our own time?" Tom asked. "I guess Dr. Haley is still wondering what's happened to us."

"We've got time for that," Chuck said. "We may never get a chance to see this age again."

"It seems to be a late hour," Tom said reflectively. "There aren't any sounds in the building or any people around. I don't suppose there's anybody to notice us."

They walked down the steps of the stage toward the windows.

"Look at the floor, Chuck," Tom said. "It looks like glass." They stooped and examined it. "Plastic," Tom said. "Unscratchable green plastic."

The windows were huge, long rectangles that were crystal clear. The boys decided that these must be a kind of Plexiglas. They looked out one of the windows and gasped at what they saw.

It was definitely the future. The air was full of low winking lights that turned out to be helicopters. It seemed as though nearly every family in the city must own one. There were a number of triple-decked highway trestles, completely lighted, over which sped teardrop-shaped automobiles.

"There's Spice Mountain again!" Chuck said.

"Look at the houses!" Tom pointed out. "They reflect the city lights just like metal! They *are* metal—prefabricated, probably."

"I wonder what year it is," Chuck said.

"I don't know," Tom answered. "It's sure hard to think of our town ever looking like this."

Every thoroughfare was evenly illuminated by brilliant lamps on tall posts located at regular intervals. There were no dark streets whatsoever. Like a giant reposing wheel, what appeared to be an immense airport lay in the center of the city.

The spokes radiated out into city streets, making the airport the major feature of the metropolis. Sleek planes and buzzing helicopters rose and landed on the airstrips.

But the greatest drama was yet to come. Both boys saw it the instant it happened. A vertical thread of light rose swiftly in the air, and several moments later there was a loud roar. Tom and Chuck watched the silvery object at the top of the thread until it was lost from sight in the immense starry night.

"A rocket!" Tom cried. "That was a rocket ship!"

13

"I wonder where it's going!" Chuck said.

Their enthusiasm for the wonders of this new age meant further postponement of their trip back to their own times. They decided to go out into the corridor of the Institute and see what was out there.

The floor of the hall was of the same plastic as the auditorium floor, and there was not a scratch on it, although it carried the dusty footprints of many feet. The same soft, invisible lighting prevailed here as well. The boys paused before a bulletin board containing some typed items. They looked them over interestedly.

Tom read the beginning of one aloud: "At 2300 on March 3, 2007, Dr. Leeds, professor of chemistry, blasts off for Luna on a research expedition. . . ." A card pinned over the bulletin board carried the same date.

"That 2300 figure is the armed service's method of counting time," Chuck said. "I guess the people of the future have adopted it—or will adopt it. There I go getting mixed up on tenses again!"

"That rocket we just saw must have been the professor taking off," Tom said. "Twenty-three hundred means eleven P.M. our time. I suppose that's why the college is deserted."

They moved down the corridor and came to what appeared to be a classroom. They pushed open the door. In the light of the hallway they could see much of what the room contained.

"Look at that double-lens camera," Tom said, pointing to an object at the back of the room. A double screen was at the front. "Stereo motion pictures!" he said, as it came to him.

Chuck sat down at one of the desks. The seat was soft foam rubber, and the desk itself was of mirror-smooth blue plastic. "If we had desks like this back in our time, going to school would really be a pleasure," he commented.

He found that the desk lid raised. Out of the compartment underneath he pulled a thick, strange-looking book. The metallic pages contained only chapter headings, and opposite each item there was a push button. Into the side of the book ran two wires to which were attached a pair of lightweight earphones.

14

Chuck hooked the earphones over his head. He found a switch on them and snapped it on. He opened the book and pressed one of the buttons. Tom saw an attentive, pleased look on his friend's face.

"Boy, what a way to study!" Chuck said. He handed the earphones to his companion. "Listen."

Tom pulled them on and listened to a soothing voice lecturing on history. They examined the book and found a tiny mechanism between each page that probably was the source of the material.

The two suddenly heard a jarring buzz that nearly startled them out of their wits.

"What in the world was that?" Chuck asked.

They rushed over to the door and looked out into the corridor. What they saw caused chills to race up their spines. Clicking down the hall were a dozen shiny mechanical men—*robots*. They were far from manlike, having only a knob for a head and stiff-looking arms and legs. In their claws were long-handled instruments.

Tom's breath squeezed tightly in his chest. "Those things are heading this way! Let's get out of here!"

They ran down the hall. Just as they were about to go into the auditorium they turned for a last look. The robots had dispersed and were disappearing into various rooms along the hall.

"They weren't after us!" Chuck said. "Let's go back and see what they do."

They looked into one of the rooms and saw a robot pushing his instrument swiftly, expertly along the floor. Where the instrument had passed, the floor began to gleam brightly.

"They're floor cleaners!" Tom exclaimed. "They probably clean the whole building in nothing flat!"

"I wonder how they knew when to start," Chuck said.

"That buzz we heard might have actuated some mechanism in their bodies so that they started operating," Tom suggested.

"Could be," Chuck agreed.

"There's no telling what else is liable to go on here tonight," Tom said. "I think we'd better try to get the Traveler working.

16

We've only got two per cent energy left, remember. If we miss our date next time, we're sunk."

"I'm for it," the little redhead said. "Let's go."

They started back down the corridor and passed a door that was differently colored from the others along the hall. This piqued the boys' curiosity, and they stopped. Tom thumped on the door with his fist.

"It's solid metal!" he said. "Wonder why?"

Chuck hit it experimentally. To their surprise, the heavy door fell open.

"If this is a special room, somebody forgot to lock it," Tom said.

They entered cautiously. The hall lighting revealed a giant showcase on the other side of the room. The youths approached the case.

"The windows are barred," Chuck said. "Whatever's in that case must be awfully valuable."

They ventured closer. There was a plate at the bottom of the case, reading: "The Housman Cosmic-ray Battery. This model electronic instrument absorbs raw cosmic rays out of the upper atmosphere and stores their tremendous energies. When released instantaneously, these energies are the most potent force ever harnessed by man. When released slowly, the energies are capable of unparalleled industrial power."

"Jiminy!" exclaimed Chuck. "I should think this thing would be terribly valuable!"

He leaned closer to examine the instrument within the case when suddenly a clanging bell went off loudly in the building.

"We must have set off an electric-eye alarm or something!" Tom said. "Let's get out of here—fast!"

They dashed through the open doorway into the hall and headed for the door leading to the auditorium. To their dismay, the door was locked fast. "The alarm must have automatically locked all the doors in the building," Tom said.

"What'll we do, Tom?" Chuck asked desperately. "How will we get to the machine?"

"I don't know, Chuck!" Tom answered glumly. "But we'll

sure have trouble explaining our position if we're caught! They'll think we're spies who came here to steal that cosmic-ray thing!"

The alarm continued to peal. It sounded loud enough to arouse everyone in the city. The boys ran down the hall toward another exit door, but it too was locked. They were absolutely trapped.

Suddenly the huge double doors of the building's entrance were flung open, and the boys got their first view of the people of the new century. There were about five men, probably college teachers or officials who lived near by. Their clothes were not cut so very differently from what Tom and Chuck were used to seeing; the main difference seemed to be in the type of material, which had a shiny cast to it and was brightly colored.

The men spied the boys and ran toward them. They appeared to be unarmed. "There they are!" one of them shouted.

The boys frantically tried all the doors around them, but none would yield to their tugs.

Tom spoke swiftly to Chuck, "When they get close, let's dive right through them and try to make it out the front door!"

When Tom gave the word, the two darted straight toward the elderly men. The suddenness of the motion caught them unprepared, and they fell away. The boys raced down the corridor and burst through the swinging doors in front of them. They ran down the steps of the building and ducked into some shrubbery near by.

"I'm glad they were *old* men," Chuck said, breathing hard.

"Don't forget," Tom told him dryly, "we'll be as old as they are in 2007—that is, if we get out of this jam."

"Say, that's right!" Chuck answered, with some dismay.

Just then a car, its siren dying, whirled up in front. The automobile was teardrop-shaped like the others the boys had seen, and it was painted white. On the side of it were the familiar words, "Police." Five policemen in gray uniforms jumped out of the car and ran up the steps.

"We'd better find some place else before the men tell them we've left the building!" Tom whispered. "This is the first place they'll look!"

18

"Why not hide in the car?" Chuck suggested. "That's the *last* place they'll look!"

Tom nodded. "If they get far enough away from the building, we may be able to make a dash for the auditorium."

They slipped quickly into the police car, closed the door, and knelt down in the roomy front flooring. A moment later the policemen came out of the building and began beating the bushes. By now, other people had come running from all directions. Lifting his head cautiously, Tom could see, through the glass of the building's front door, that the door into the auditorium from the hall was ajar.

"They won't suspect us of trying to get back into the building," Tom whispered. "I guess that's why the hall isn't guarded. Let's slip out of the other side of the car and mingle with the people watching until we can make a break up the steps."

This they did, and finally saw their chance. There were some men talking at the end of the corridor, but Tom felt they wouldn't be bothered by them before they gained the auditorium. The boys dashed up the steps. Just as they went through the doorway, they heard a cry from outside, "There they go!"

"They've seen us!" Tom cried as they ran for the auditorium door.

The men down the hall then spotted them and gave chase, calling loudly all the time to attract the police. The boys ran into the assembly room and made for the stage. As they climbed onto it, the police burst in. Tom and Chuck got inside the framework of the Time Traveler, and Tom desperately fiddled with the operating lever.

"Make sure you set it right this time!" Chuck warned. "This is the last trip we can make on our low power supply!"

Despite the urgency of their plight, Tom concentrated carefully on what he was doing. Slowly, he moved the lever across the box until it stood straight up. This time it *must* be right. The last thing Tom saw was a mass of florid faces, topped by gray caps, bearing down on him and his friend. . . .

As Tom came to, his first impression was that of being in a prison. After observing worriedly that the reading on the lever box was zero, he looked around and found himself hemmed in on all sides. Then he breathed easier as he looked up and recognized the light bulbs of Southwest Institute's auditorium. They were back in their own time.

"I guess we made it this time," Chuck said. "We seem to be in the aluminum case."

They heard Dr. Haley's voice say, "Have you fellows got it repaired yet?"

"Got what repaired, Sir?" Tom asked, puzzled.

They heard the scientist chuckle. "Why, the switch that lifts the sides of the box, of course. You've been in there two minutes."

"*Two minutes!*" Tom said to Chuck. "Is that all the time we've been gone?"

Suddenly Chuck burst out laughing.

"What's funny?" Tom asked.

"They are," Chuck answered, grinning. "They haven't even *missed* us!"

20

Richard M. Elam, Jr.

ADVENTURE ON MARS

ILLUSTRATED BY *Seymour Fleishman*

LOOK, Ray, the sun is out!" Jenny Colby exclaimed to her older brother. She pointed through the large picture window of their Martian home into the violet sky, where the tiny, faraway sun had broken through the clouds.

"It's about time," Ray grumbled. "This house is like a prison. Nothing interesting ever happens." For two long days the children had had to stay inside because of the terrible arctic windstorm.

"Cheer up," said Mrs. Colby. "Perhaps our luck will change now that the wind has stopped. It made me nervous, too!"

A loud clucking filled the room. It was Flatfoot, the Colby's little Martian pet, who was just like another member of the family. He had come to the Colbys eight months before, in the year 2054, soon after their arrival on the planet. The Colbys had rescued him from a rock slide that had wiped out the rest of his colony.

Now Flatfoot had seen the sun too, and being an igyat, and therefore very excitable, he stood up to his full three-foot height and began hopping up and down on his broad pancake feet. His enthusiastic chatter was deafening.

"Be quiet, Flatfoot, please!" begged Jenny, covering her ears.

Flatfoot stopped clucking and looked up at her. His large golden eyes, set in a rabbit-like face, brimmed with tears. Remembering how sensitive an igyat is, Jenny dropped on her knees beside the little animal and put her arm lovingly around his white neck. Flatfoot purred and was contented again.

Ray patted the sheep-like wool of the igyat. "You're the funniest thing ever, Flatfoot," he laughed. "There's nothing like

21

you on Earth—or on Mars, either. If it weren't for you, life would be just too dull."

At these words, the igyat twitched a powder-puff of a tail much like that of a rabbit, and unrolled two antennae that were kept curled into springs on his head. These were the igyat's organs of hearing and were uncoiled when needed, like a radio aerial, to pick up distant sounds. In the thin atmosphere of Mars, where sound did not carry very well, Flatfoot could hear noises the Colbys could not.

"Flatfoot is restless," Mrs. Colby said. "Why don't the three of you go for a long hike?"

"That'll be super!" Ray was always ready for a hike, and Jenny hurried to get dressed. The two of them pulled on their heavy boots, which were light as slippers on their feet in Mars' low gravity. Then came the triple-lined coats made from the shaggy hides of the rovers, animals like the old American bison. Jenny envied Flatfoot's being able to stand the very coldest Martian weather while she had to bundle herself up to the ears like an Eskimo.

"Don't stay too long," Mrs. Colby warned, helping Jenny on with her roverskin parka. "I don't want you to be caught in that subzero afternoon cold."

A pair of thick gloves completed their outfit, and they were ready to go. As she opened the door for them, Mrs. Colby said to Ray, "Take care of Jenny and Flatfoot, too. Remember, you are the oldest."

Jenny's face tingled at the first exposure to the crisp, cold air. Ray buried his face in his tan parka, then broke into a grin as they started walking. "Look at Flatfoot! He's going to enjoy the hike!"

Jenny laughed. As soon as he had come out into the cold, the igyat had tucked his white forepaws into the warm kangaroo pouch on his chest. Now he tramped along on his big pancake feet, like a stooped old man bundled up in a thick overcoat.

The three walked over to the great Lockard Canal. Last spring, when the Polar Cap had melted, they had watched it flow with clear water and replenish their underground spring and those of the other colonists. Ray knew that water had been more dear to the ancient inhabitants of Mars than gold to the Earthmen, and that its scarcity had led to building a network of canals all over the planet.

As they walked along, Jenny asked, "Isn't it funny, Ray, that no one has ever found a statue or a picture of a Martian? Or any graves, either?"

"Dad and the other archeologists believe it was part of their religion not to make any statues of themselves," Ray replied. "And the last Martian died thousands of years ago. It will be hard to find a cemetery."

For a while they hiked on aimlessly, and then Jenny said, "I thought of something, Ray! Why don't we walk over to the old ruin where Dad is working? Perhaps we'll have time to explore a bit, and then ride home with him."

"Sounds good," Ray agreed.

They set off toward the narrow passage running between two low hills east of their home.

"Dad's been on that job a month now, hasn't he?" Jenny asked as they headed into the pass.

"Uh huh. He's just about given up hope of finding any Martian statues."

"It would be the greatest discovery ever made on Mars if he found one," Jenny said.

"No such luck," Ray grunted.

They plodded along between the low hills, following a faint trail. After some time they came out upon a flat red desert. Here Ray suddenly grabbed Jenny's arm. A towering plant armed with long spikes stood about fifty yards away.

"Look out!" Ray warned Jenny. "There's one of those shooting cactus plants." No sooner had he spoken than he saw several "arrows" whirring through the air and headed in their direction.

"Quick, that boulder over there!" he shouted, grabbing Jenny's hand and pulling her toward a big heap of rocks across the way. "Come on, Flatfoot!"

Flatfoot's forepaws were out of his pockets, and he squawked in terror as he padded after the children. The air was now full of flying spines which whistled dangerously close to them. Just as they reached the safety of the boulders, Flatfoot squalled like a pig.

Crouching behind their fortress, the young Colbys saw that Flatfoot had been hit! He was grabbing with his short chubby paws at the shaft that had struck him. Ray pulled him to safety and looked him over.

"He's—not—hurt!" cried Jenny with relief, in between moments of catching her breath. "See—the arrow is stuck—in the woolly part of his tail."

Ray jerked out the barb and Flatfoot chuckled gratefully. He began smoothing out the ruffled wool of his round little tail with his paws.

When they were breathing normally again after their tiring sprint in the thin air, Ray ventured to look out.

"The Indian attack seems to be over," he said. "I think it's safe enough to go along if we circle around a bit."

They started out again, and after about fifteen minutes' walking they were able to make out a sprawling dark shape on the horizon.

"That must be the ruin!" Ray said. "Are you game to keep going?"

"Of course." Jenny was getting tired, but wouldn't admit it.

"It doesn't look far away," Ray went on. "We've still got about two hours before it gets too cold."

They knew that after two hours there would come the dry-ice cold that no human being could stand. They had checked the night temperature on their thermometer and had seen it register as low as a hundred and twenty degrees below zero!

As they hiked along, Ray studied the frosty, clear sky. The veil of atmosphere was so thin that the brighter stars gleamed through the upper ice vapors. He watched the faint movement of Phobos, the closest of Mars' two small moons, and the bright green spark that was Earth. The sight of it brought a wave of homesickness. Jenny had enjoyed their life on Mars from the beginning, but Ray found the new life dull. He missed his old friends and the school games.

24

Finally, the ruin was just ahead. Their father's rocket car was out front; he must be inside the building. The temple, built of huge red blocks of stone, was in an advanced stage of decay. The roof was partly gone, and the sides had gaping holes torn in them from long sieges of bad weather.

Deep in thought, Ray hadn't noticed that Flatfoot had dropped behind. He turned now and saw him standing tensely with his hearing organs uncoiled.

"What the dickens is the matter with him?" Ray burst out.

The igyat began to jump up and down, clucking in joy. He smiled as much as his rabbit-like features would permit.

"Maybe he hears Dad," Jenny suggested.

Without warning, Flatfoot suddenly uttered a piercing whistle. The whistle was answered from a low hill beyond the ruin where a colony of igyats was stretched out comfortably, absorbing the weak sunlight. Their paws were in their chest pouches and they looked like lazy workmen loafing on the job.

"That's what Flatfoot was shouting about," Jenny said, grinning. "Must be his cousins or something. They'll be having a family reunion, next."

Ray pointed to a forbidding black doorway at the top of about fifty sagging steps. Huge red rock pillars framed the entrance. "We haven't much time left," Ray said. "You're not afraid to go inside, are you, Sis?"

"If Dad's in there, I'm not," Jenny replied. "Come along, Flatfoot."

The three of them started the long climb. Both the young folks were winded when they reached the top. Inside the building, it was almost dark.

"Let's call Dad," Ray said. They did call, but all they heard in reply was their echo rolling off ancient walls.

"Funny he doesn't answer," Ray said. "This is a pretty big place, though."

"It sure is creepy in here," Jenny whispered. "I don't know whether I want to go on, after all."

"Let's go a little farther," Ray said. "As long as we keep in sight of the door, we won't get lost."

Flatfoot inched along with them, clucking in a low tone. Jenny and Ray felt a softness beneath their feet and looked down. The floor was covered with red sand. The huge gallery was full of grotesque shapes and carvings. Yet no shape resembled a human being.

At the end of the big room, a wide doorway led down a flight of stone steps that curved out of sight.

"Look at that strange eerie light shining up the steps," Jenny said.

The three descended the winding stairs cautiously.

"Look at the walls," Ray said. "That odd strip running along both sides is where the light is coming from. It must be a phosphorescent mineral."

"It makes your skin look awful!" Jenny was trying to be flip and casual.

Ray cautiously touched the strange strip. "It's not hot. It must have been glowing for thousands and thousands of years."

At the foot of the stairs the young explorers found themselves in a broad hallway. Strips of the mysterious mineral circled the top of the high ceiling and bathed the space below in the same eerie light. There were gloomy doorways along both sides of the hall. The orange tile floor was covered by a shallow layer of red sand. Ray examined some carved forms and pottery.

"Look, Ray," Jenny said. "Flatfoot's gone off on an expedition of his own." The igyat was at the far corner, down on all fours, probing with his nose.

"Maybe he's caught Dad's scent!" Jenny said. "Oh, I hope, I hope . . ."

Flatfoot suddenly backed sharply into a long narrow pedestal that was supporting a big stone block. The pedestal tottered and fell with a crash. Ray laughed as Flatfoot looked up in frightened amazement at what he had done.

But his laughter choked in his throat. A big hole opened in the tile floor right where the stone had fallen. Flatfoot, just inside the sloping cavity, scrambled to get free.

"Flatfoot, watch out!" Jenny screamed in terror.

27

It was too late. Flatfoot clawed frantically for a hold. Then
he disappeared into the darkness below.

"Oh, Ray, we'll never see him again!" Jenny sobbed as Flatfoot disappeared.

Ray called the igyat's name but got no reply. "If we only
had a light!" he said desperately.

Jenny's tearful eyes brightened. "I wonder if we could use
that odd light on the walls, somehow."

Ray ran to the staircase and tried to pry some of the queer
strip from the wall. "Even if I get a piece loose," he told her,
"I don't know if it'll keep shining." But when he dug out a strip
about two feet long, it continued to glow.

Cautiously Ray advanced toward the hole. On hands and
knees he carefully tested the weakened tiling before placing
his weight on it. Just above the dark opening, he dropped the
torch. By its light Ray could see Flatfoot sitting on the stone
floor about ten feet below.

"Flatfoot seems to be all right," Ray said. "I was afraid he
might be knocked out by his fall." He twisted around toward
Jenny. "Hand me that pedestal, will you, Sis?"

Ray lowered the pedestal into the hole, hampered in his

efforts by the bulky clothing he wore. The stone slab was just out of Flatfoot's reach, but after several jumps, the igyat was able to grab it. Ray tugged with all his strength but could lift the little fellow only a few inches.

"Give me a hand, Jenny," Ray said. "The pedestal is so clumsy."

Cautiously Jenny came up behind Ray. When her arms were around Ray's waist, they pulled together. Up came the pedestal, four, eight, twelve inches . . .

Then it happened. With a rending sound, the tiles ripped loose under them! Children and stones crashed to the floor below.

Slowly Ray got to his feet. "Are you all right, Jenny?" he asked shakily.

"I think so," Jenny answered, gingerly feeling a long rip in her heavy parka. "All that padding helped."

Flatfoot had run to her, chattering as usual. She rubbed his woolly top and looked around at the darkness that closed them in from all sides. "Now we're all three down here with no way of getting out!" she cried.

Ray picked up the bright, glowing torch and started exploring their surroundings. He found an archeologist's pick lying nearby. "This is Dad's!" he exclaimed.

"That must have been why Flatfoot was sniffing around!" Jenny said.

They called their father. Getting no answer, they turned to explore the space around them and found a doorway.

"There ought to be some stairs somewhere that lead up to the top floor," Ray said. "We may as well try this way."

Jenny was beginning to feel the subzero cold of the afternoon. Her feet were icy. "I'm getting cold, Ray! What if we're trapped down here!"

"We'll find a way out," Ray told her. "Don't worry." He wished he felt as confident as he spoke.

With his light held before him, and still carrying the pick, Ray led the way along a corridor of rock. As they followed its course, the children smelled the mustiness of countless ages.

At last a metal door, covered with green lichen, barred their way. Ray gave it a sturdy push, and the whole thing fell inward with a crash. "Everything is rotten in this place," he muttered.

He held the light out in front of him and walked slowly forward. Suddenly he dropped the pick and stopped. Jenny bumped into him and screamed.

"It's a giant!" Jenny cried. "A horrible giant!"

Then they both turned and ran out of the room, dragging the igyat with them. They kept going down the long corridor until they were forced to stop for breath. Ray peered back into the darkness. "He doesn't—seem to be—following."

"Look at Flatfoot!" Jenny said.

In the feeble light of the torch, the children saw the igyat with his antennae fully extended. He was staring down the corridor in the opposite direction.

"He seems glad!" Jenny's fear evaporated as the igyat hopped up and down.

"Do you suppose the igyats we saw outside have come into the ruins?" Ray asked.

"If they have, that means Flatfoot can lead us to them and show us the way out!" Jenny returned hopefully. She looked uncomfortably behind her. "Who in the world could that man be, Ray?"

He shrugged. "Anybody's guess. Let's just hope that Flatfoot leads us as far away from him as possible!"

Ray took the lead with his light and Flatfoot followed, his antennae uncoiled. At the spot where they had fallen through the floor, they watched Flatfoot's hearing organs quiver in the direction of another passageway. Following it, they came into a circular open space. From it branched corridors like the spokes of a wheel. The place was lighted overhead with the glowing blue mineral.

Here Flatfoot really became excited. He hopped and clucked with joy.

"Never mind the rhumba," Ray told him. "How about showing us the way out?"

31

This time Flatfoot went ahead of them down one of the corridors. Ray walked behind, holding the torch to light their way. Suddenly they came to a dead end. But Flatfoot continued to hop up and down. Ray pushed on the rock wall. Suddenly, to his amazement, a door of stone swung open right in front of him!

The twins heard a familiar voice calling. They went through the doorway and hurried down a blue-lighted passage. The calling voice became stronger, nearer.

"Dad!" cried Jenny. "It's Dad!"

They broke into a run and were brought up short before a heavy door that had been cut from a solid slab of Martian ebony. Fancy grillwork was carved all the way through it.

"Ray!" came the familiar voice again. "I can't tell you how glad I am to see you!" Through the grillwork Ray saw his father's cold-reddened face buried in a rover parka.

The boy's questions tumbled out so fast, Mr. Colby had to slow him down. The archeologist explained that he had been exploring the room when a gust of wind slammed the door shut. The rusty lock had shattered, wedging the door tightly, so that he could not push it open.

The children and Flatfoot pulled on the corroded knob while the father shoved from inside. But the door didn't budge.

"I've got it!" exclaimed Ray. "The igyats outdoors! They can help us pull."

They explained to Flatfoot what they wanted, cupping their hands to their mouths and trying to copy his peculiar calling whistle. Flatfoot finally got the idea and nearly burst their eardrums with his piercing call.

Presently, down the corridor, came the pad-pad of running pancake feet. The igyats burst upon the Colbys in a chattering little army.

Since Ray had had no trouble showing Flatfoot how to pull on the door, he got him in position again. He placed him behind Jenny and put his forepaws around her waist. As though expecting great fun, the other igyats fought one another to encircle Flatfoot's waist in the same manner. Ray lined them up

32

in single file. Then he stood behind the last one and started
pulling. The line tensed, and after a steady strain for several
moments, the grilled door tore open with a creak. The little
animals fell in a heap, tumbling back on top of each other.

Jenny ran to her father and threw her arms around him. She
laughed with relief, "It's a good thing we brought Flatfoot
along, Dad."

Ray told his father about their own adventure in the ruin.
When he mentioned seeing the strange man, Mr. Colby could
scarcely wait for him to finish.

"Can you find that room again? I want to see that giant for
myself!"

Ray and Jenny looked at one another fearfully. Mr. Colby
chuckled. "The man's harmless. Let's go." He brought out a
flashlight and they led him down the corridor to the spot where
the mysterious door had opened in the wall.

"By Jove!" their father exclaimed as he examined the stone door. "So that's why I never found this passageway! When the door is closed, it becomes invisible."

They hurried down the corridor and after several minutes approached the entrance to the room of mystery. The cone of Mr. Colby's light bit into the darkness and fell upon the pick Ray had dropped. Then it lifted and shone on the giant Ray and Jenny had seen. Only it wasn't a giant. In the brighter light they saw that it was a *statue*.

"What a stroke of luck!" Mr. Colby exclaimed. "Do you realize we're the first Earthmen to know how a Martian really looked!"

Their fears gone now, the children examined the statue closely. The giant Martian was not quite Earth-like. His ears were extra large and his chest was very broad and deep. He stood fully seven feet tall.

"If the Martians didn't believe in making statues of themselves," Ray said, "how come this?"

"This man was Mars' greatest hero, according to writings we've deciphered," answered Mr. Colby. "See the name *Estaz* carved there? He's an exception to the rule. What a lucky find!"

"The archeological society will be happy," Jenny remarked.

"They've got ways of showing it, too," her father replied. "There's a big reward coming for you two that will boost those college savings. On top of that, you've earned me a promotion I was promised if the statue was found. But there's something else you'll be glad to hear."

"What's that?"

"A furlough to Earth. That was promised, too."

"Whoopee!" shouted Ray. He began to plan immediately the stories he would tell his old school friends about his life on Mars.

"Flatfoot is really the one to thank," Jenny reminded them. "It was he that broke the hole in the floor."

"Speaking of Flatfoot," said Mr. Colby, looking around, "what's become of him and his buddies?"

They searched the passageways but found no trace of the

igyats. Anxiously, Mr. Colby led them out of the building, and the children were relieved to see the igyats gathered a short distance from the ruin.

As they approached the rocket car that was to take them home, the Colbys called to Flatfoot. He ignored them!

"Don't tell me he's going to stay with the other igyats!" Jenny groaned.

Ray called to the Martian animal again. But the little fellow just looked around and then turned back to chatter with his relatives.

"That's too bad!" Mr. Colby said, shaking his head in regret. "But if he prefers his own kind, we must let him go."

"What'll we do without him?" Jenny said, close to tears. "He's like a member of the family. I thought he liked us!"

"We can't wait around any longer, I'm afraid," her father told her. "It's dropping ten degrees by the minute now."

Sadly the three of them climbed into the rocket car. Then with a *swoosh* of propelling jets, the Colbys were headed homeward. Suddenly there was a boisterous squawking in the rear.

Ray and Jenny turned in their seats and saw Flatfoot padding along as fast as he could, clucking angrily that they should even think of leaving him behind!

Miss Pickerell, driving back from a month-long visit with her nephews, gives a lift to a mysterious scientist named Haggerty. When she arrives home, she discovers that her farmhouse has been used during her absence and that her cow pasture has been converted into a take-off place for a rocket ship. She protests the use of the pasture without her permission to Wilbur, the guard outside the ship, but he cannot help her. When he is called away by the captain she climbs into the rocket ship herself. The captain, mistaking her for Haggerty, gives the order to take off. Her first encounter inside is with Mr. Killian, Executive Officer of the ship.

Ellen Macgregor

MARS AND MISS PICKERELL

ILLUSTRATED BY *Paul Galdone*

"P ASSED the stratosphere," Mr. Killian said, "long ago."

Miss Pickerell said, "I believe I'll send my nieces and nephews a telegram when we land. How soon will that be, Mr. Killian? And just where is it we are going, anyway?"

"Be a long, long time before we land," Mr. Killian said darkly, "*if* we ever do; and where we're going you won't be able to send any telegrams."

Miss Pickerell saw something moving out of the corner of her eye. She turned her head and gasped at what she saw. What she saw was the young man Wilbur. But Wilbur was not walking. Wilbur was swimming—yes, actually swimming—right across the room, without even touching the floor. He had emerged from one of two openings in a partition beside the panel of instruments.

"Why, hello there, Miss Pickerell!" Wilbur said. He tipped his cap, and then, instead of putting it back on, he released it from his fingers. The cap remained suspended in the air.

"Forevermore!" Miss Pickerell said.

Wilbur turned to Mr. Killian. "Did you tell the captain Miss Pickerell came with us? Was he mad?"

"Haven't told him yet," Mr. Killian said. "Not supposed to interrupt him. Still busy over there in his own compartment. What's he doing in there, anyway?"

"Writing a speech," Wilbur said. "To give when we get back to earth."

"Back to earth!" Miss Pickerell exclaimed. "Why, what are you talking—"

"Might as well save himself the trouble," said Mr. Killian. "Probably never get there now. Not without Haggerty."

Wilbur's face went quite white. He reached up to a ring in the ceiling above him and steadied himself in the air. He spoke in a hoarse, frightened voice. "You mean we left Haggerty behind? Why, Mr. Killian! Who's going to do the calculations for our flight?"

"I'm not," Mr. Killian said flatly. "I don't know how. All I know how to do is tell if we're on our course, or off it. Guess I'd better check the instruments."

He unfastened the strap which had been holding him down and floated across to the instrument panel. Wilbur, nervous and frightened, swam along close beside him. Neither man paid any further attention to Miss Pickerell.

She thought this was extremely rude of them. They hadn't even given her a chance to tell them that Mr. Haggerty was right down there on the ground, and all they had to do was to go back and get him—if it was so important.

From across the room came a low buzz of conversation, where Mr. Killian and Wilbur were floating in front of the instrument panel and earnestly studying various dials and gauges. Miss Pickerell decided this would be a good time to have a talk

37

with the captain. The men might be afraid to interrupt him, but she certainly wasn't.

It seemed quite warm in the space ship, and Miss Pickerell took off her pink sweater and pressed it down against the surface of her bunk. She unclamped the belt across her lap.

At first, Miss Pickerell wasn't quite sure how she should leave her bunk: whether she ought to put her feet out first, or whether she should go head first. And for one awful moment, she thought, "What if the air doesn't hold me up?" But she knew that was silly. If Wilbur and Mr. Killian could swim through the air, she certainly could too.

Miss Pickerell put her hands beneath her and pushed herself up. But this was unnecessary. Now that the belt was unfastened, she simply floated right out into the room. She held her breath.

"Why, it's magic!" she said to herself. "I've never felt anything like this. And I'm not a bit dizzy." She bounced delicately against the ceiling, feeling exactly as if she were a balloon.

In a few moments, Miss Pickerell learned how to guide her movements. The rings she found set at intervals across the ceiling were a help. She noticed, too, that there were handholds all around the circular wall of the room.

The men were conferring at the instrument panel. They seemed to have forgotten all about Miss Pickerell.

She was about to ask where she would find the captain, when a crisp sharp voice called out, "Mr. Haggerty! Come here immediately."

The voice seemed to come from one of the openings in the partition. Miss Pickerell swam toward it.

"You tell him, Wilbur," she heard Mr. Killian say.

"No, you," said Wilbur. "You're the executive officer."

"Don't bother," Miss Pickerell called out. "I'll explain." She swam through the opening just as the voice was calling again.

"Mr. Haggerty. Come *here!*"

This enclosure was much smaller than the large room. Around its edges were a number of very complicated-looking pieces of equipment, none of which made much sense to Miss Pickerell.

In the middle of this small compartment was an adjustable cushioned chair. The chair was turned with its back to the opening so that all Miss Pickerell could see of the man sitting in it was that he had short iron-gray hair and a fat red neck.

The man called again, "MR. HAGGERTY!"

Miss Pickerell, looking down from over the top of his head, saw him angrily unsnap a belt which had been holding him in the chair. He pushed himself up with his hands.

"Careful!" Miss Pickerell said. "Don't bump your head on the ceiling."

The man turned around in the air and stared at her. Miss Pickerell thought she had never seen such a startled man. Beneath the short crew cut of his iron-gray hair, his bright blue eyes bulged wide in his plump red face.

"Good gracious!" he said, almost in a whisper. "Who in the world are you?" And then, even before Miss Pickerell could answer, he shouted so loud that it hurt her ears, "MR. HAG-GERTY!"

"It won't do you any good to shout like that," Miss Pickerell said. "Mr. Haggerty can't possibly hear you from down there on the ground." She steadied herself by holding a ring in the ceiling.

The captain reached out one hand to the chair below him, and with the other, he held his forehead. "This can't be happening!" he said. "It can't really be!" Then he called in a lower tone of voice, "Mr. Killian! Wilbur! Come here."

Mr. Killian and Wilbur floated in immediately.

"Has anybody made the introductions?" Wilbur asked. "Miss Pickerell, this is Captain Crandall."

"How do you do, Captain Crandall," Miss Pickerell said. "I really just came in here to ask you about how soon it will be before I can get home again, and to tell you—"

"Who let this happen?" asked the captain in a stern voice.

"Nobody," Mr. Killian said. "She just got on all by herself."

"That's not what I'm talking about," said the captain. "We'll go into that matter later. What I want to know now is how we happen to have left without Mr. Haggerty."

39

"It's very easy to understand, Captain Crandall," Miss Pickerell said. "These men just made a very natural mistake. When they heard me get on, they thought I was Mr. Haggerty, and started the ship. I don't imagine any real harm's been done, because I saw Mr. Haggerty coming into the pasture just as I got to the top of the ladder. I'm sure he'll wait until you go back for him."

Captain Crandall looked at Mr. Killian. "Are we on our course?"

Mr. Killian nodded. "Guess so. Near as I can tell. But say—"

"Do not address me as 'Say,'" said Captain Crandall. "Let us try to maintain a little dignity on this voyage—even if we have left our navigator behind, and even if we do have a stowaway."

"Yes, Sir," Mr. Killian said. "I only wanted to call your attention, Sir, to the instruments."

"What about them?"

"Some of them don't seem to be giving the right readings. If anything happens to the instruments, Sir, we're sunk, Sir."

"I don't think you need to worry about that," Miss Pickerell said. "I'm sure Mr. Haggerty can fix any instruments that might go wrong. He seems to be very good at that sort of thing. At least he fixed my car very easily. So, as soon as you take me back—"

The captain looked at her icily. "Would you mind keeping still for just a minute, Miss. . . ."

"Pickerell," said Wilbur.

"Miss Pickerell?"

"I'm only trying to help," Miss Pickerell said. "Naturally, I'm sorry if you have been inconvenienced, but it just happens that it wasn't very convenient for me, either. I have a sick cow down there on the ground. Besides that, I want to get my rock collection ready for the state fair. That's one of the reasons I came in here. I wanted to ask you how soon—"

"She talks about inconvenience!" the captain said through clenched teeth. "Miss Pickerell! Do you have any idea at all of the seriousness of what's happened?"

40

"Only that I think you're making too much of this thing, Captain Crandall. Everybody makes mistakes. It surely can't matter a great deal if you have to go back and make a second start. You'll only be a few hours later getting to wherever you're going."

"A second start, she says!" Captain Crandall held his head with both hands as if he were afraid it might split apart.

"I don't want to be unreasonable," Miss Pickerell said. "If it's really so important for you to keep right on going, I won't insist that you take me back. But I should think you'd want to go back, on account of Mr. Haggerty."

"Miss Pickerell," Captain Crandall said, "nothing would give me greater pleasure than immediately returning you to wherever it is you came from. Even disregarding the matter of Mr. Haggerty. But the inescapable fact is that we can't go back."

"That's right," Mr. Killian said. "Course was pre-set before we started."

"How ridiculous!" Miss Pickerell said. "If you're using some kind of an automatic pilot, you can certainly turn it off and pilot the ship yourselves!"

"It's scarcely a question of piloting," Captain Crandall said. "When you start out on such an expedition as ours—when you set out in a space ship to go to another planet—then everything must be very carefully worked out in advance. Even then, something could go wrong with the calculations. That is why we would never have dreamed of starting without Mr. Haggerty."

"What was that you said about a planet, Captain Crandall?"

"Mars is a planet, Miss Pickerell."

"Mars!" Miss Pickerell exclaimed. "Why, Captain Crandall! I never heard of anything so ridiculous as expecting to get to Mars. Have you ever looked at Mars up in the sky?"

"It happens, Miss Pickerell, that I have made a rather exhaustive study of Mars."

"Then I don't see how you could ever have such a silly idea as trying to go to that tiny little bit of a red star. I know it's called a planet, but it looks just like all the other stars, except

41

that it's redder than most of them. Even the time I saw it through a ten-cent telescope at the state fair, it didn't look any different. Why, Mars must be millions of miles away!"

Mr. Killian said, "I'm going out to look at the instruments."

"Miss Pickerell," Captain Crandall said, "if you come to a good stopping place, I'd like to say a word. Is it your habit to talk constantly?"

"Why, I hardly talk at all," Miss Pickerell said. "I don't usually have anyone to talk *to*, living all alone the way I do. And that reminds me, Captain Crandall, I have a bone to pick with you for trespassing on my farm. Now, as soon as we get back, I want you to—"

A frightened shout from Mr. Killian at the panel of instruments in the larger room interrupted them. Without even excusing themselves, the captain and Wilbur swam rapidly away.

Miss Pickerell sighed. Captain Crandall was certainly a very difficult man to talk to. She hadn't settled a thing with him about getting back to her cow and her rock collection. . . .

[DURING the trip Miss Pickerell busied herself fixing meals and taking her turn standing watch. She was the first to sight the small red globe of Mars, and her idea of letting gravity pull the ship down was used in preparing to land.]

Much to Miss Pickerell's surprise, their approach to Mars was rather unexciting.

From inside the space ship, there was no way of telling where they were, or even in which direction they were pointing, except by looking through the eyepiece. And Miss Pickerell was now denied this privilege. The men divided the watches between themselves, and carefully rehearsed each step of their landing procedure.

Miss Pickerell spent much time in her bunk, either sitting up crocheting or lying down sleeping.

Once, when she awoke, she could tell by the tenseness of the men that something important was happening. Wilbur was pulling levers and punching buttons. Mr. Killian was faithfully studying the instruments. The captain was at the eyepiece.

"You've done it, Wilbur," the captain said finally in a low voice. "You've turned us around. Now Mars is beginning to draw us down."

Very shortly, Miss Pickerell began to notice strange sensations in her body. No one had prepared her for the effect of Mars's gravity, and as they came closer and closer, Miss Pickerell grew heavier and heavier in her body, and more and more sluggish in her mind. She noticed that her body sank lower into the cushions of her bunk. It became an effort to turn over. She slept a great deal.

"This is it!" she heard someone shout. "We're here! We've landed."

With great effort, Miss Pickerell managed to turn her heavy head in the direction of the men.

Wilbur and Mr. Killian were standing upright, close together, clapping each other on the back. The captain stood slightly apart, and each man in turn took his hand and shook it solemnly and respectfully.

Miss Pickerell tried to sit up, but she couldn't. She seemed to weigh tons. She lacked the strength to move her heavy body.

"Help!" she called. "I can't move! I'm paralyzed!"

"No, you aren't, Miss Pickerell," Wilbur said, as he walked toward her with tired-seeming steps. "It just seems that way

44

because we've been without gravity for so long. As soon as you get used to it, you'll feel wonderful. You'll feel a lot lighter than you did on earth."

Wilbur was right. Very soon, Miss Pickerell was able to sit up. She stepped down to the floor of the room. It was a strange sensation to be using her leg muscles again after such a long time of floating through the air.

"Well," she said to the captain who was looking across the room at her. "What are we waiting for? Let's open the door and go out."

The captain walked slowly toward her.

"Now, Miss Pickerell," he said. "I expect you to be reasonable about this and not make a fuss. I cannot allow you to leave the ship."

"If you think for one minute, Captain Crandall, that I am going to come all the way to Mars without getting out to see what it's like, you are very much mistaken." She reached into her bunk for her pink sweater and began to put it on.

The captain said, "Do you see those bulky suits with transparent helmets that the men are putting on? Those are pressure suits. Each person who leaves the ship must wear one, in order to remain alive."

"I don't mind," Miss Pickerell said. "I'll wear Mr. Haggerty's suit. Which one is his?"

"Now, listen, Miss Pickerell—"

"Couldn't she come, Captain?" Wilbur asked. "I'll watch out for her."

"No," Captain Crandall said firmly. "This is a scientific expedition. We are explorers. We cannot be watching out for tourists."

"But, Captain Crandall," Miss Pickerell said, "that's not fair. Don't you remember that it was I who—"

"I remember that it was you who came on board our ship, when you weren't supposed to, and that if you hadn't done so, we would have had Mr. Haggerty with us."

"But you didn't need Mr. Haggerty—as it turned out," Miss Pickerell said.

45

"That's beside the point. I cannot take the responsibility of letting you leave the ship. However, you may listen to our conversation on the walkie-talkie set. All of our pressure suits have walkie-talkies connected to one in my compartment. You can hear everything that we say to each other, and if you get too lonely, you may speak to us."

"Thank you," Miss Pickerell said stiffly. "That will be a great pleasure, I am sure!" She decided not to argue with the captain any more at present. She would wait until he had returned. Perhaps he would be more approachable then.

She watched the men getting ready to leave the ship. Each man put on a bulky-looking suit and fastened a transparent helmet over his head. Inside each helmet was a small microphone just in front of the man's mouth.

Wilbur kept his helmet off till the last, so that he could explain things to Miss Pickerell.

He told her about the atmospheric pressure of Mars—how it was much less than that of the earth. He explained that for that reason the pressure suits must maintain the same pressure as that of the earth. He told her how the atmosphere of Mars did not contain enough oxygen. He showed her the oxygen tanks. Each man carried one of these tanks in a large pocket on the back of his suit. Wilbur showed Miss Pickerell how the oxygen tank was connected to the suit. Also he explained that the temperature of Mars, during most of the day and all of the night, would be far too cold for comfort or safety, which was why the suits were heated.

Then he took her to the door of the ship and explained the pressure lock to her. Mr. Killian was just entering the lock. Miss Pickerell wouldn't have known it was Mr. Killian if he hadn't turned around so that she could see his face through the transparent front of the helmet. In the bulky suits, they looked alike.

"See, Miss Pickerell," Wilbur said. "He opens the inside door of the pressure lock and goes in. He closes the door and adjusts the pressure valve. The outside door of the lock won't open until the pressure in there is the same as that outside. Do you understand, Miss Pickerell?"

46

"Not very well," Miss Pickerell said. "But it's nice of you to try to explain it to me, Wilbur."

The last person to leave the ship, the last person to go through the pressure lock, was the captain. "We won't be gone long, Miss Pickerell," he said. He was talking into his microphone because he had already fastened his helmet. It sounded strange to hear his voice coming out of the walkie-talkie in the captain's compartment behind Miss Pickerell, when she could see his lips moving as he stood directly in front of her.

"We'll be back within half an hour," the captain said. "Half an hour at the most." Then he stepped into the pressure lock and closed the inside door.

Miss Pickerell was left alone.

Almost immediately, Miss Pickerell heard the voice of the captain coming from the walkie-talkie in his compartment.

"Miss Pickerell," he said. "Did I leave my watch in there?"

Miss Pickerell hurried into the captain's compartment. The watch was on a bench. She noticed that it was just half past twelve.

"Yes, Captain," she said, stooping to speak into the microphone on a bench before the captain's chair. "I'll bring it to you. I'll put on Mr. Haggerty's suit and bring it right out."

"Miss Pickerell," the captain said in his customary sharp voice, "you are to remain on the ship. Those are my orders. I merely wanted to be sure that my watch was there. Do not leave the ship under any circumstances."

Miss Pickerell did not answer. The captain had no right to talk to her like that. He had no right to give her orders. She was not a member of his crew. If she chose to get out and see what Mars looked like, he had no authority to prevent it. She went back to where Mr. Haggerty's pressure suit was lying in an open chest. She reached down to pick it up, but then she changed her mind.

"I suppose it would be wrong," she said. "I suppose it would be more honest to wait until the captain gives me permission to go outside."

She went back and sat down in the captain's chair. From

time to time she heard the men speaking into their microphones. Sometimes they addressed remarks to her and she answered them. "Don't tell me what it's like," she said. "I want to see for myself, when the captain lets me go out."

"I'll bring you a souvenir, Miss Pickerell." It was Wilbur's voice. "How would you like a rock?"

"A rock!" Miss Pickerell exclaimed. "Are there rocks right out there?"

"All kinds," Wilbur said. "Red, mostly. They're very pretty. I'll bring you one."

Now Miss Pickerell was twice as eager to get outside. Red rocks from Mars would make a wonderful addition to her rock collection at home.

"Come back, Wilbur." This was the captain's voice. "You're getting too far away from us."

"All right," Wilbur said. "I'm just getting a red rock for Miss Pickerell."

"Miss Pickerell. What time is it?" the captain asked.

Miss Pickerell looked at the captain's watch. "It's a quarter to one," she said.

"All right, men," the captain said. "Everybody turn around and go back to the ship. We'll run out of oxygen if we stay away any longer."

Miss Pickerell heard Wilbur's voice. "Captain, something's happened. I'm stuck. My foot is caught between two big rocks. Help me, Captain."

Miss Pickerell listened for the captain's answer. "Here we come, Miss Pickerell," was all he said.

"Captain!" Miss Pickerell shrieked. Something must have happened to his walkie-talkie. He must not have heard Wilbur's call.

Miss Pickerell remembered that once before this had happened. On the very first day of the flight, when Wilbur had tried to report her from the pasture gate to the space ship, the walkie-talkie had been out of order at first.

Again she heard Wilbur's voice. "Please, Captain. I need help."

49

"What is it, Miss Pickerell?" said the captain's voice. "Is anything the mat—" There was a sharp click and complete silence. The walkie-talkie had gone dead. Miss Pickerell shouted into the mouthpiece, but there was no answer from the captain, or from Wilbur, or from Mr. Killian.

For seconds, Miss Pickerell sat there, stiff with horror. Unless the captain turned around, he would never know that Wilbur was not right behind him. Wilbur would run out of oxygen. . . .

"Wilbur," Miss Pickerell said, just in case he was still able to hear her voice. "Don't be frightened! I'm coming. I'm coming to help you."

She dashed to where she had left Mr. Haggerty's pressure suit. She picked it up. It was clumsy and heavy. She struggled into it, one foot at a time. She had no time to take off her clothes, and her skirts made a bulky wad around her waist. She took an oxygen tank and put it into the big loose pocket on the back of the suit. She lifted the helmet over her head and fastened it, though this was hard to do because of the thick gloves that sealed the ends of her sleeves.

Last of all, Miss Pickerell connected the oxygen tank to its opening in the suit, the way Wilbur had showed her. She hurried to the pressure lock, but just before she entered it, she went back and gathered up another oxygen tank in her arms. This would be for Wilbur in case he ran out of oxygen before they could free his foot.

Inside the pressure lock, she closed the inner door. She remembered Wilbur had said something about adjusting the pressure valve. In the wall of the lock was a small handle and Miss Pickerell turned this. Immediately there was a hoarse sucking sound, and in a few moments, Miss Pickerell was able to open the outer door.

She almost fainted when she saw how high above the ground she was. There was a thin ladder leading down to the red rocky waste below, and she would have to descend this, wearing the bulky pressure suit, and carrying the extra tank of oxygen for Wilbur.

But Miss Pickerell did not hesitate. Somehow, slipping and

50

clutching at each rung and keeping her eyes tight closed to fight against her dizziness, somehow, she managed to get to the ground. She opened her eyes.

Far in the distance, she could see Wilbur. He was alternately waving his arms in the air and stooping down to try to free his trapped foot.

Between Wilbur and the space ship, and coming toward her, Miss Pickerell saw the other men. Neither one had missed Wilbur. Apparently each man thought Wilbur was following behind.

Clutching the extra oxygen tank, Miss Pickerell lumbered toward the men. It was hard to walk in the heavy suit. The ground was rough and rocky, and now and then strong gusts of wind blew thick clouds of red dust across the front of her helmet.

She waved and pointed, trying to make the men turn around and look back. But this only made them walk faster. As they neared each other, Miss Pickerell could identify the face of the captain in the lead. He took long angry steps and his blue eyes were blazing. His lips, inside the transparent helmet, were moving, and although Miss Pickerell could not tell what he was saying, she knew he must be expressing his indignation at her for defying his orders about leaving the ship.

"Captain!" she shouted. "Captain!" If only the walkie-talkie would work.

The captain had almost reached her now. He tried to take hold of her arm, but Miss Pickerell squirmed away. She said the word "Wilbur" over and over, stretching her lips wide each time, hoping that the captain would understand.

Then she suddenly grasped the captain by the sleeve of his suit and partly turned him around. She pointed again, and this time the captain saw.

The captain hesitated for only a second. Very quickly and deftly he disconnected his oxygen tank and substituted it for the one Miss Pickerell was wearing. After he had connected the tank he had been wearing to her suit, he took the extra tank from her arms and hurried out across the rocks toward Wilbur.

51

Miss Pickerell started to follow, but a gentle pull restrained her. It was Mr. Killian. Miss Pickerell turned back toward the ship. She realized that the captain's depleted tank of oxygen would not take her far. She would have to go back and wait inside the ship until the captain and Wilbur returned.

Mr. Killian gestured that she was to climb the ladder and enter the pressure lock. From the top of the ladder, Miss Pickerell took one look back. She had the satisfaction of seeing that the captain had reached Wilbur. With one powerful tug, he freed Wilbur's trapped foot, and the two men stood together a moment while the captain connected the extra oxygen tank to Wilbur's suit. Then, as Miss Pickerell stooped through the outer door of the pressure lock, they hurried to the ship.

From that day on, nothing was too good for Miss Pickerell. Mr. Killian, who still addressed the others in short, choppy sentences, became very talkative with Miss Pickerell, and told her the complete story of his life, bit by bit. Wilbur waited on Miss Pickerell hand and foot. And the captain, even before he began repairing the walkie-talkie set, made her a stiff little speech of apology.

"I have misjudged you, Miss Pickerell. I hope you will forgive my abruptness to you earlier in the flight. I doubt very much if even Mr. Haggerty could have thought and acted as quickly as you did to save Wilbur's life. It is an honor to have you as a member of our expedition."

Now each time any of the men went outside Miss Pickerell was allowed, and even urged, to accompany them. She made so many trips up and down the ladder between Mars and the space ship that she quite overcame her dizziness and was never troubled by it again, so long as she lived.

During their stay on Mars, Miss Pickerell had plenty of opportunity to see what the planet was like. She observed that it was dry, rocky, dusty, and flat.

As far as the expedition could tell, there was no animal life on Mars. And Miss Pickerell saw for herself that the only plant life was a sort of dry moss that grew around some of the rocks.

There were no clouds, except dust clouds. There was no rain.

Miss Pickerell decided that the earth was a much pleasanter planet than Mars. She was glad she lived on the earth.

However, Miss Pickerell did find many beautiful red rocks on Mars. And the men were so generous about adding to her collection that within a few days her bunk was nearly filled with rocks. There was just a narrow space next to the wall, for Miss Pickerell to sit and lie.

Mars and the earth were different in so many ways that Miss Pickerell was a little surprised to learn that the days on Mars were almost exactly the same length as the days on earth.

"Only thirty-seven minutes longer," Captain Crandall said one day when she asked him about it. "You see, both Mars and the earth are spinning around all the time, just like tops. That's what makes—"

"Yes," Miss Pickerell said. "That's what makes night and day."

"And they both spin at just about the same rate. That's why days here on Mars are almost the same length as the days on earth. And by the way, Miss Pickerell, I'd advise you to do something with those rocks of yours before tomorrow. We're going to start home tomorrow, and if you leave your rocks where they are, they'll be all over the place the minute we get away from the gravity of Mars. Maybe Wilbur can show you a chest or cupboard to put them in."

Miss Pickerell saved out the seven finest specimens, the ones she was going to give her nieces and nephews for souvenirs, so that she would have something to admire on the trip home. The rest of the rocks she and Wilbur locked away inside a chest.

When it was time for the take-off, Miss Pickerell strapped herself firmly back against her bunk, closed her eyes tightly, and prepared herself for the explosion.

This time, too, although she had been determined not to, Miss Pickerell lost consciousness and wakened to find that once more they were without the pull of gravity.

On the return trip, everyone was excited and happy—even the captain. He kept flitting back and forth between the main room and his own compartment, where he wrote page after page after page with his blue pencil.

"This is going to be one of my finest lectures," he said one day. "And, Miss Pickerell, sometime when I am lecturing in the vicinity of Square Toe Mountain, you must come and sit on the platform with me and let me introduce you to the audience as the first woman who has ever been to Mars. You'll be famous, you know."

"How soon will we be home, Captain Crandall?" Miss Pickerell asked.

"Just a few days more, Miss Pickerell. Aren't you excited?"

"A little," Miss Pickerell admitted. But Miss Pickerell was also worried. The nearer they came to the end of their trip, the more Miss Pickerell worried.

"It's about my cow," she confided to Wilbur. "I should never have left her all alone down there with a strange man. Oh, I do hope she'll be all right."

"You didn't mean to come, Miss Pickerell," Wilbur said. "It was an accident. It wasn't your fault."

"I hope Mr. Haggerty won't be mad at me," Miss Pickerell said, "for coming in his place."

Just then the captain called out from the instrument panel where he and Mr. Killian had been conferring.

"We're approaching the earth now, Miss Pickerell. We're going to have to get used to gravity all over again. Why don't you try to go to sleep while we land?"

Miss Pickerell did go to sleep, and when she woke up, she knew by the heaviness of her body that they had returned. The pull of gravity was more than she could cope with.

Even the men were having trouble moving this time. She saw Wilbur trying to walk along the edge of the room. But he was pulling himself along by using the handholds on the wall, as if he lacked the strength to move otherwise. He reached the pressure lock and opened both doors. A path of sunlight fell across the floor.

Wilbur looked out. "Hi! Haggerty!" he shouted, and Miss Pickerell heard Mr. Haggerty answer him. Then she heard another sound. A welcome sound. She heard the contented mooing of her cow. Miss Pickerell sighed with relief. Now all she had to worry about was apologizing to Mr. Haggerty for taking his place so that he had to stay behind.

By the time they were ready to leave the space ship, Miss Pickerell had begun to regain the use of her arms and legs. She was beginning to get accustomed to her own heaviness again. She stood up.

The captain emerged from the door of his compartment. He crossed to Miss Pickerell's bunk and picked up her pink sweater. He held the sweater for her so that she could slip her arms into the sleeves.

"Captain Crandall," Miss Pickerell said, "promise me one thing. Promise you won't move this space ship out of my pasture until my nieces and nephews have a chance to come and see it."

"I promise," said the captain.

Down on the ground, Miss Pickerell hurried toward Mr. Haggerty and her cow. Mr. Haggerty held the cow's rope in one hand. His other arm lay affectionately along her back. Miss Pickerell could see that the cow was well and happy.

"Miss Pickerell," Mr. Haggerty said, "I just can't thank you enough for—"

"Mr. Haggerty," said Miss Pickerell, "I do want to apologize—"

They both stopped and looked at each other.

"Thank me for what?" Miss Pickerell asked.

"For the chance to take care of your cow," said Mr. Haggerty. "Do you know what I've decided, Miss Pickerell?"

"No," said Miss Pickerell.

"I've decided to go back to college and study to be a veterinarian after all. And it's all because I've had such a good time making your cow well again. I just love farm animals."

"And you're not mad because you didn't get a chance to go to Mars?"

"Certainly not," said Mr. Haggerty. "And by the way, I have a message for you, Miss Pickerell. I wrote it down and put it in my brief case. My brief case is over there by the fence. It was a telephone message."

"Oh, mercy!" said Miss Pickerell. "Was it from the governor?"

"I remember now," Mr. Haggerty said. "It was from the governor's wife. I told the governor what had happened the day he called you back—the first day of the flight. Then the governor's wife called. She told me to tell you they want you to come and visit in the governor's mansion when you get back. That was what I wrote down in my brief case."

Miss Pickerell stroked her cow's neck. She looked around her beautiful green, sunny pasture. She heard the cow pulling off a mouthful of grass, with a noisy tearing sound.

"It's so good to be home," Miss Pickerell said. "Do you know something, Mr. Haggerty? There isn't even any *grass* on Mars!"

In the next few months, Miss Pickerell made several visits to the governor's mansion. The following year, at the state fair, her collection of red rocks from Mars won not only the blue ribbon, but also the special gold medal given each year for the most outstanding exhibit of the whole fair. The governor himself made the awards. And Mr. Haggerty spent his first college vacation on Miss Pickerell's farm.

In fact, Miss Pickerell's life was never the same as it had been before she went to Mars.

But the biggest change, and the one Miss Pickerell liked the best, was in her nieces and nephews. From the moment she called them up by long-distance and invited them to come and see the space ship in her pasture—from that moment on—her seven nieces and nephews never tired of hearing Miss Pickerell tell them about her wonderful trip. They admired the blue ribbon and the gold medal. And all their lives long, they treasured the souvenirs Miss Pickerell gave them—the seven beautiful red rocks brought from the planet of Mars.

Bill Brown

THE STAR DUCKS

ILLUSTRATED BY *Hardie Gramatky*

WARD RAFFERTY's long, sensitive news-
hawk's nose alerted him for a hoax as soon as he saw the old
Alsop place. There was no crowd of curious farmers standing
around, no ambulance.

Rafferty left *The Times* press car under a walnut tree in the
drive and stood for a moment noting every detail with the effi-
ciency that made him *The Times'* top reporter. The old Alsop
house was a brown, weathered, two-story, with cream-colored
filigree around the windows and a lawn that had grown up to
weeds. Out in back were the barn and chicken houses and fences
that were propped up with boards and pieces of pipe. The front
gate was hanging by one hinge, but it could be opened by lifting it. Rafferty went in and climbed the steps, careful for loose
boards.

Mr. Alsop came out on the porch to meet him. "Howdy do,"
he said.

Rafferty pushed his hat back on his head the way he always
did before he said: "I'm Rafferty of *The Times*." Most people
knew his by-line and he liked to watch their faces when he
said it.

"Rafferty?" Mr. Alsop said, and Rafferty knew he wasn't a
Times reader.

"I'm a reporter," Rafferty said. "Somebody phoned in and
said an airplane cracked up around here."

Mr. Alsop looked thoughtful and shook his head slowly.
"No," he said.

Rafferty saw right away that Alsop was a slow thinker so he

59

gave him time, mentally pegging him a taciturn Yankee. Mr. Alsop answered again, "Noooooooooooo."

The screen door squeaked and Mrs. Alsop came out. Since Mr. Alsop was still thinking, Rafferty repeated the information for Mrs. Alsop, thinking she looked a little brighter than her husband. But Mrs. Alsop shook her head and said, "Noooooooooooo," in exactly the same tone Mr. Alsop had used.

Rafferty turned around with his hand on the porch railing ready to go down the steps.

"I guess it was just a phony tip," he said. "We get lots of them. Somebody said an airplane came down in your field this morning, straight down trailing fire."

Mrs. Alsop's face lighted up. "Ohhhhhhhhhh!" she said. "Yes it did but it wasn't wrecked. Besides, it isn't really an airplane. That is, it doesn't have wings on it."

Rafferty stopped with his foot in the air over the top step. "I beg your pardon?" he said. "An airplane came down? And it didn't have wings?"

"Yes," Mrs. Alsop said. "It's out there in the barn now. It belongs to some folks who bend iron with a hammer."

This, Rafferty thought, begins to smell like news again.

"Oh, a helicopter," he said.

Mrs. Alsop shook her head. "No, I don't think it is. It doesn't have any of those fans. But you can go out to the barn and have a look. Take him out Alfred. Tell him to keep on the walk because it's muddy."

"Come along," Mr. Alsop said brightly. "I'd like to look the contraption over again myself."

Rafferty followed Mr. Alsop around the house on the board walk thinking he'd been mixed up with some queer people in his work, some crackpots and some screwballs, some imbeciles and some lunatics, but for sheer dumbness, these Alsops had them all beat.

"Got a lot of chickens this year," Mr. Alsop said. "All fine stock. Minorcas. Sent away for roosters and I've built a fine flock. But do you think chickens'll do very well up on a star, Mr. Rafferty?"

60

Rafferty involuntarily looked up at the sky and stepped off the boards into the mud.

"Up on a what?"

"I said up on a star." Mr. Alsop had reached the barn door and was trying to shove it open. "Sticks," he said. Rafferty put his shoulder to it and the door slid. When it was open a foot, Rafferty looked inside and he knew he had a story.

The object inside looked like a giant plastic balloon only half inflated so that it was globular on top and its flat bottom rested on the straw-colored floor. It was just small enough to go through the barn door. Obviously it was somebody's crackpot idea of a space ship, Rafferty thought. The headline that flashed across his mind in thirty-six point Bodoni was "Local Farmer Builds Rocket Ship For Moon Voyage."

"Mr. Alsop," Rafferty said hopefully, "you didn't build this thing, did you?"

Mr. Alsop laughed. "Oh, no, I didn't build it. I wouldn't know how to build one of those things. Some friends of ours came in it. Gosh, I wouldn't even know how to fly one."

Rafferty looked at Mr. Alsop narrowly and he saw the man's face was serious.

"Just who are these friends of yours, Mr. Alsop?" Rafferty asked cautiously.

"Well, it sounds funny," Mr. Alsop said, "but I don't rightly know. They don't talk so very good. They don't talk at all. All we can get out of them is that their name is something about bending iron with a hammer."

Rafferty had been circling the contraption, gradually drawing closer to it. He suddenly collided with something he couldn't see. He said "ouch" and rubbed his shin.

"Oh, I forgot to tell you, Mr. Rafferty," Mr. Alsop said, "they got a gadget on it that won't let you get near, some kind of a wall you can't see. That's to keep boys away from it."

"These friends of yours, Mr. Alsop, where are they now?"

"Oh, they're over at the house," Mr. Alsop said. "You can see them if you want to. But I think you'll find it pretty hard talking to them."

61

"Russians?" Rafferty asked.

"Oh, no, I don't think so. They don't wear cossacks."

"Let's go," Rafferty said in a low voice and led the way across the muddy barnyard toward the house.

"These folks come here the first time about six years ago," Mr. Alsop said. "Wanted some eggs. Thought maybe they could raise chickens up where they are. Took 'em three years to get home. Eggs spoiled. So the folks turned right around and came back. This time I fixed 'em up a little brooder so they can raise chickens on the way home." He suddenly laughed. "I can just see that little contraption way out there in the sky full of chickens."

Rafferty climbed up on the back porch ahead of Mr. Alsop and went through the back door into the kitchen. Mr. Alsop stopped him before they went into the living room.

"Now, Mr. Rafferty, my wife can talk to these people better than I can, so anything you want to know you better ask her. Her and the lady get along pretty good."

"Okay," Rafferty said. He pushed Mr. Alsop gently through the door into the living room, thinking he would play along, act naïve.

Mrs. Alsop sat in an armchair close to a circulating heater.

Rafferty saw the visitors sitting side by side on the davenport, he saw them waving their long, flexible antennae delicately, he saw their pale blue faces as expressionless as glass, the round eyes that seemed to be painted on.

Rafferty clutched the door facings and stared.

Mrs. Alsop turned toward him brightly.

"Mr. Rafferty," she said, "these are the people that came to see us in that airplane." Mrs. Alsop raised her finger and both the strangers bent their antennae down in her direction.

"This is Mr. Rafferty," Mrs. Alsop said. "He's a newspaper reporter. He wanted to see your airplane."

Rafferty managed to nod and the strangers curled up their antennae and nodded politely. The woman scratched her side with her left claw.

Something inside Rafferty's head was saying, you're a smart boy, Rafferty, you're too smart to be taken in. Somebody's pulling a whopping, skillful publicity scheme, somebody's got you down for a sucker. Either that or you're crazy or drunk or dreaming.

Rafferty tried to keep his voice casual.

"What did you say their names are, Mrs. Alsop?"

"Well, we don't know," Mrs. Alsop said. "You see they can only make pictures for you. They point those funny squiggly horns at you and they just think. That makes you think, too— the same thing they're thinking. I asked them what their name is and then I let them think for me. All I saw was a picture of the man hammering some iron on an anvil. So I guess their name is something like Man-Who-Bends-Iron. Maybe it's kind of like an Indian name."

Rafferty looked slyly at the people who bent iron and at Mrs. Alsop.

"Do you suppose," he said innocently, "they would talk to me—or *think* to me?"

Mrs. Alsop looked troubled.

"They'd be glad to, Mr. Rafferty. The only thing is, it's pretty hard at first. Hard for you, that is."

"I'll try it," Rafferty said. He took out a cigarette and lighted

63

it. He held the match until it burned his fingers.

"Just throw it in the coal bucket," Mr. Alsop said.

Rafferty threw the match in the coal bucket.

"Ask these things . . . a . . . people where they come from," he said.

Mrs. Alsop smiled. "That's a very hard question. I asked them that before but I didn't get much of a picture. But I'll ask them again."

Mrs. Alsop raised her finger and both horns bent toward her and aimed directly at her head.

"This young man," Mrs. Alsop said in a loud voice like she was talking to someone hard of hearing, "wants to know where you people come from."

Mr. Alsop nudged Rafferty. "Just hold up your finger when you want your answer."

Rafferty felt like a complete idiot but he held up his finger. The woman whose husband bends iron bent her antenna down until it focused on Rafferty between the eyes. He involuntarily braced himself against the door facings. Suddenly his brain felt as though it were made of rubber and somebody was wringing and twisting and pounding it all out of shape and moulding it back together again into something new. The terror of it blinded him. He was flying through space, through a great white void. Stars and meteors whizzed by and a great star, dazzling with brilliance, white and sparkling stood there in his mind and then it went out. Rafferty's mind was released but he found himself trembling, clutching the door facings. His burning cigarette was on the floor. Mr. Alsop stooped and picked it up.

"Here's your cigarette, Mr. Rafferty. Did you get your answer?"

Rafferty was white.

"Mr. Alsop!" he said. "Mrs. Alsop! This is on the level. These creatures are really from out there in space somewhere!"

Mr. Alsop said: "Sure, they come a long way."

"Do you know what this means?" Rafferty heard his voice becoming hysterical and he tried to keep it calm. "Do you know this is the most important thing that has ever happened in the history of the world? Do you know this is . . . yes it is, it's the biggest story in the world and it's happening to me, do you understand?" Rafferty was yelling. "Where's your phone?"

"We don't have a telephone," Mr. Alsop said. "There's one down at the filling station. But these people are going to go in a few minutes. Why don't you wait and see them off? Already got their eggs and the brooder and feed on board."

"No!" Rafferty gasped. "They can't go in a few minutes! Listen, I've got to phone—I've got to get a photographer!"

Mrs. Alsop smiled.

"Well, Mr. Rafferty, we tried to get them to stay over for supper but they have to go at a certain time. They have to catch the tide or something like that."

"It's the moon," Mr. Alsop said with authority. "It's something about the moon being in the right place."

The people from space sat there demurely, their claws folded in their laps, their antennae neatly curled to show they weren't eavesdropping on other people's minds.

Rafferty looked frantically around the room for a telephone he knew wasn't there. Got to get Joe Pegley at the city desk,

65

Rafferty thought. Joe'll know what to do. No, no. Joe would say you're crazy.

But this is the biggest story in the world, Rafferty's brain kept saying. It's the biggest story in the world and you just stand here.

"Listen, Alsop!" Rafferty yelled. "You got a camera? Any kind of a camera. I *got* to have a camera!"

"Oh, sure," Mr. Alsop said. "I got a fine camera. It's a box camera but it takes good pictures. I'll show you some I took of my chickens."

"No, no! I don't want to see your pictures. I want the camera!"

Mr. Alsop went into the parlor and Rafferty could see him fumbling around on top of the organ.

"Mrs. Alsop!" Rafferty shouted. "I've got to ask lots of questions!"

"Ask away," Mrs. Alsop said cheerily. "They don't mind."

But what could you ask people from space? You got their names. You got what they were here for: eggs. You got where they were from. . . .

Mr. Alsop's voice came from the parlor.

"Ethel, you seen my camera?"

Mrs. Alsop sighed. "No, I haven't. You put it away."

"Only trouble is," Mr. Alsop said, "haven't got any films for it."

Suddenly the people from space turned their antennae toward each other for a second and apparently coming to a mutual agreement, got up and darted here and there about the room as quick as fireflies, so fast Rafferty could scarcely see them. They scuttered out the door and off toward the barn. All Rafferty could think was: "My, they're part bug!"

Rafferty rushed out the door, on toward the barn through the mud, screaming at the creatures to stop. But before he was half-way there the gleaming plastic contraption slid out of the barn and there was a slight hiss. The thing disappeared into the low hanging clouds.

All there was left for Rafferty to see was a steaming place in the mud and a little circle of burnt earth. Rafferty sat down in

the mud, a hollow, empty feeling in his middle, with the knowl-edge that the greatest story in the world had gone off into the sky. No pictures, no evidence, no story. He dully went over in his mind the information he had:

"Mr. and Mrs. Man-Who-Bends-Iron. . . ." It slowly dawned on Rafferty what that meant. Smith! Man-Who-Bends-Iron on an anvil. Of course that was Smith. . . . "Mr. and Mrs. Smith visited at the Alfred Alsop place Sunday. They returned to their home in the system of Alpha Centauri with two crates of hatching eggs."

Rafferty got to his feet and shook his head. He stood still in the mud and suddenly his eyes narrowed and you knew that Rafferty brain was working—that Rafferty brain that always came up with the story. He bolted for the house and burst in the back door.

"Alsop!" he yelled. "Did those people pay for those eggs?"

Mr. Alsop was standing on a chair in front of the china closet, still hunting for the camera.

"Oh, sure," he said. "In a way they did."

"Let me see the money!" Rafferty demanded.

"Oh, not in money," Mr. Alsop said. "They don't have any money. But when they were here six years ago they brought us some eggs of their own in trade."

"Six years ago!" Rafferty moaned. Then he started. "Eggs! What kind of eggs?"

Mr. Alsop chuckled a little. "Oh, I don't know," he said. "We called them star ducks. The eggs were star shaped. And you know we set them under a hen and the star points bothered the old hen something awful."

Mr. Alsop climbed down from the chair.

"Star ducks aren't much good though. They look something like a little hippopotamus and something like a swallow. But they got six legs. Only two of them lived and we ate them for Thanksgiving."

Rafferty's brain still worked, grasping for that single frag-ment of evidence that would make his city editor believe—that would make the world believe.

68

Rafferty leaned closer. "Mr. Alsop," he almost whispered, "you wouldn't know where the skeletons of the star ducks are?"

Mr. Alsop looked puzzled. "You mean the bones? We gave the bones to the dog. That was five years ago. Even the dog's dead now. I know where his bones are though."

Rafferty picked up his hat like a man in a daze.

"Thanks, Mr. Alsop," he said dully. "Thanks."

Rafferty stood on the porch and put on his hat. He pushed it back on his head. He stared up into the overcast; he stared until he felt dizzy like he was spiralling off into the mist, spiralling off the earth like a celestial barber pole.

Mr. Alsop opened the door and came out, wiping the dust off a box camera with his sleeve.

"Oh, Mr. Rafferty," he said. "I found the camera."

Nelson Bond

LANCELOT BIGGS
ON THE SATURN

ILLUSTRATED BY *John McKee*

I HAD just finished treating the egg-sized knot on my noggin to an arnica rinse when the door of my radio cabin opened and Cap Hanson—he's skipper of the freight-lugger *Saturn*—shambled in, pawing his gray thatch feebly, and collapsed with a sigh into my most comfortable chair.

"Sparks," he said, "take a good look, then tell me—what am I?"

I stared at him in dismay. Even the best spacemen slip their gravs once in a while, but I never thought I'd live to see the day when Captain Hanson went void-whacky. He'd been with the Corporation, man and boy, for more than thirty years now, and had never spent a day in dry dock.

I reached behind me cautiously and said in a soothing voice, "Why, you're a very nice man, Captain. Now, just sit quiet for a minute. I've got to—"

"Stop bein' a fool, Donovan," said the skipper wearily, "an' lay down that monkey wrench. I ain't a candidate for the paper-doll brigade . . . yet. I'm askin' you a simple question. What do you see?"

I said, "You want facts, Skipper, or flattery? If it's facts, I see a heavy-set, gray-haired guy in his middle fifties who's been through the mill, knows space like a book, and—"

"Wrong!" sighed Hanson. "What you see before you is a broken reed. A creature sadly buffeted by fate an' the fell clutch of circumstance, not to mention meddlesome vice-presidents."

This time I got it. "Biggs?" I asked.

"Yes, Sparks. Biggs. Now tell me, man to man—what did I ever do to deserve Biggs?"

See glossary, page 141.

He had me there. Being the skipper of our space-wallowing old tub is not what I'd call a snap job under the best of conditions. The *Saturn* is an ancient crate, built 'way back in 2084 or '85. Ten or twelve years ago, by order of the Space Safety Control Board, it had been removed from the passenger service and relegated to a freight run. The mere task of keeping it spaceworthy was a king-sized headache for any commander. But to make matters worse, while we were taking on cargo at Long Island spaceport, the skipper had been called into the company offices. When he came out again, he had Biggs in tow.

Biggs was tall. Biggs was lean and lanky and gangling and awkward, and he walked with the lissom grace of a stork on stilts. His chief topographical features were an oversized Adam's apple, ears like a loving cup's handles, and a grin like a Saint Bernard puppy.

But Biggs had his mate's papers and was entitled to be known as Mister Biggs—the title being an alias for his real name, Lancelot. What's more, Biggs was the nephew of old Prendergast Biggs, first vice-president of the Interplanetary Corporation. So when they assigned Biggs to the *Saturn* as fourth officer, there was nothing the skipper could do but gulp and say, "Very good!" —and try to sound as if he meant it.

I asked sympathetically, "What's he up to now, Captain?"

"What isn't he up to?" groaned the skipper. "First he said he could handle the controls when we lifted gravs from Earth. So—"

"Oh!" I glowered. "*He* did that, did he?"

"Stop feelin' sorry for yourself," said Hanson. "You got off lucky. Everybody on the ship went floatin' off to the ceilin', same as you did. Chief MacDougal is nursin' two black eyes. One of the wipers has a busted arm."

"Anything else?" I asked.

"*Everything* else!" growled Hanson. "While we was all scramblin' around in mid-air, Biggs made a grab for the manual controls. He got the trajectory deflector by mistake. Martin has just finished shapin' the flight revision. We're seven degrees off our course; almost a hundred thousand miles. Now we got to waste

71

fuel an' up revs to get back or we'll make Sun City spaceport a day late. An' you know what *that* means."

I knew what that meant. Cap on the carpet before the directors; the rest of us sitting around with our fingers crossed, wondering whether they'd yank the *Saturn* off the Venus run.

"Well, what are you going to do about him?" I asked.

"What *can* I do?"

"There's always the airlock," I suggested.

"This ain't no time to be funny," complained the skipper. "This is a serious problem. We're carryin' a valuable cargo of produce to Venus. But if that guy messes up our flight any more . . ."

He shook his head mournfully. I scratched mine. Then I got a brilliant idea.

"Cargo!" I said. "There's your answer, Captain."

"I'm listenin'," said Hanson.

"Put Biggs in charge of the cargo. That way he won't be in the control turret to get in your hair; he'll be down in the hold throughout the shuttle. There's nothing he can do down there to bother anybody."

"But that's the supercargo's job," frowned the skipper. "Even Biggs knows that."

"Give Harkness a vacation for this shuttle. Tell him to let on he's sick. Then it'll be logical to put Biggs on duty below."

The skipper nodded thoughtfully.

"It might work. It just possibly might work."

"Then you'll try it?"

"Immediately," said Hanson, rising. "Or maybe sooner."

So that was that. At three bells, when my relief came on duty, I went down to the mess hall to ruin my digestion with some of Slops's slumgullion. The first person I met was Lancelot Biggs himself.

"Hello," I said. "What are you doing here? I thought you ate at the skipper's mess?"

"I've been shifted," he grinned shyly. "Harkness was taken ill a few hours ago and the skipper put me on emergency duty in his place."

"Is that so?" I said, making like surprised. "Well, that's quite a responsibility. We're carrying a mighty valuable cargo."

The way his lean face sobered was almost embarrassing.

"I realize that, Sparks. And I'm devoting a lot of thought to the assignment. You know, I'm a bit of an experimenter, and it seems to me—"

One of the mess boys brought our chow then, and I didn't get to hear Biggs expound his theory. Which was a sad mistake. If I had listened, I might have been able to warn Cap Hanson that trouble was on the way.

It was about the third day out that I began to smell the smells. I thought it was odd, but said nothing. I figured they'd go away. But they didn't. They got worse. On the fifth day the Old Man busted into my cabin wearing a look that would have curdled vinegar.

"Sparks," he demanded, "have you been messin' around with some of them chemical experiments of yours again?"

I shook my head. "Not guilty, your honor," I told him. "I thought those smells were coming up out of the galley."

The skipper moaned softly.

"Trouble. Nothin' but trouble. It ain't enough I'm supposed to nurse this leaky old barge between Earth an' Venus; now I got smells to worry about too. Come on. Let's have a look."

73

We went down to the galley. Slops was frying something on the range. I took one look and shuddered. Tapioca again. And don't tell me you're not supposed to fry tapioca. I know it. Tell Slops.

The skipper surveyed our alleged culinary expert with a jaundiced eye.

"O.Q. Slops," he conceded, "we give up. Where did you hide it?"

"Hide what? What is this, a game?"

"That's right," I chimed in. "It's a little pastime called Sniff-the-Atmosphere. You play it by pressing your thumb and forefinger to your nostrils. Then you try to guess what died."

Slops shrugged a surly disclaimer.

"I ain't done nothin'," he protested. "I ain't hid nothin', an' I ain't smelled nothin'. Now, I got a meal on the stove. Go 'way an' leave me alone."

The skipper looked at me, and I shrugged back at him. Both of us realized the same thing at the same time. Slops wasn't lying. The smell *wasn't* as bad here as it had been updeck. Hanson scratched his head. He said suspiciously, "Sparks, do you *swear* you ain't been mixin' chemicals?"

"On a stack of code books," I told him. "That smell came from— Hey! What else besides the galley lies beneath my cabin and the control turret?"

"Let's see," pondered Hanson. "There's the storage closet, the reservoir, the refrigeration tanks, an' the—"

His eyes widened suddenly, fearfully.

"Sparks!" he choked.

"Yes?"

"The storage hold!"

That was it. The minute he said it, I knew. Operation Victuals . . . with Biggs in command!

We hightailed it for the nearest ramp. As we approached the storage hold the smell got worse. Hanson blasted down the corridor like a rogue asteroid, with me trailing along behind. We hit the door, shouldered it open . . .

Biggs was there. The fool was standing in there dressed in

74

mister
mckee

a bulger, calmly spraying the bins of fresh vegetables with a hose!

He turned as we entered, and behind the spacesuit's quartzite visor his eyes lighted. His headset audiophone clacked cheerily.

"Hello," he greeted. "Is anything wrong?"

"Anything wrong!" bellowed Captain Hanson. "He asks if there's anything wrong. That suit! An' that hose—" The skipper's face was a dangerous shade of fuchsia. "An' this *heat!*"

"I turned off the refrigerating unit," nodded Biggs pleasantly. "You see, I have a theory that since hothouses are always warm and moist, we should simulate those conditions aboard ship. So—"

"And the spacesuit?" I asked him. "Why the bulger?"

Biggs moved his hands deprecatingly.

"Why, to guard against possible infection, of course. I didn't want to expose the cargo to any parasitic organisms."

"Infection! Moisture! Heat!" Hanson buried his face in his hands. "Tell him, Sparks. Tell him what he's done."

I said, "Biggs, your theory is no good. Vegetables have to be kept in a cool, dry atmosphere or they rot. As a matter of fact, they *are* rotten. That's why the skipper and I came down here—to investigate the smell. If you weren't wearing a bulger you'd have noticed it yourself."

"Smell?" repeated Biggs. "Why, come to think of it, I *have* noticed a curious odor about the ship from time to time. But I thought it was rats."

That was the last straw for Hanson.

"Biggs," he roared, "you've ruined this cargo, not to mention my blood pressure. You're relieved from your command. But before you report to your quarters, I want this mess cleaned up. An' I mean every last bit, understand? Junk it! Clear it out!"

Biggs faltered, "But, Captain, I was just trying to—"

"You heard me!"

The skipper wheeled, fiery with wrath, and strode to the doorway. I hurried after him. I whispered in his ear, "Remember, Skipper, he's the vice-president's nephew. Maybe you ought to take it easy."

"Easy?" groaned the skipper. "A cargo worth fifty thousand credits ruined, an' you tell me to take it easy? I'll see that knob-jointed son of a space-wrangler blasted out of space if I'm black-listed for it!"

I said nothing more. What was there to say? Fifty thousand credits' worth of cargo rotting in the hold. The Corporation would *love* that.

The next morning I was on the bridge when Cap Hanson had a visitor. MacDougal, the chief engineer. MacDougal practically never came to the bridge, so I knew, the minute I saw him, that something was vitally wrong.

It was. MacDougal glared at the skipper accusingly.

"Captain Hanson," he demanded, "would ye be so kind as to tell me where I can find my Forenzi jars?"

Hanson frowned. "Forenzi jars? What are you talking about, Chief?"

"Ye'll be knowin' wha' a Forenzi jar is, na doot?" asked Mac-Dougal caustically. " 'Tis a lead container for battery solution. Yesterday there were thirty of 'em in the storeroom. Today there are only a half dozen left."

Hanson said pettishly, "Now, Chief, I don't know nothin' about your jars. If you can't watch your own equipment, don't complain to *me* about it."

"I'm complaining to *you*, sir," said the chief, "for the verra simple reason that 'twas one of *your* men who removed them from the locker. Your fourth mate, Mister Biggs."

"Biggs," said Hanson. "Biggs!" His jaw tightened. He walked to the ship's intercommunicating unit, jabbed the button that connected with Biggs's cabin. "Mr. Biggs?" he brawled. "Chief MacDougal is up here in the turret asking about twenty-four lead containers that disappeared from his equipment locker. Do you know anything about them?"

The diaphragm clacked an answer. Hanson started. His eyes bulged. He yelled, *"What?"*

Again some metallic buzzing. This time Hanson didn't try to answer. He tottered away from the phone.

"Chief," he faltered, "will you be needin' the Forenzis before we make port?"

"Well, 'tisna exactly *vital*," admitted MacDougal. "But why do ye ask?"

Hanson made a feeble gesture.

"Because they're . . . out there."

"What?" I exclaimed. "Outside the ship? How come?"

Hanson's eyes were haunted.

"Biggs," he said in a hollow voice, "thought they were garbage cans. He used them to dispose of the rotten cargo!"

Well, some hours later I got a personal solargram for Biggs and took it down to his cabin. Being confined to quarters, he was lonely. He looked so miserable that I felt sorry for him and lingered to talk awhile.

"I guess you think I'm a frightful dummy, Sparks," he said ruefully. "I know Captain Hanson thinks so. But this is my first berth, you know. And no one ever told me what to use for garbage pails."

"Look, Biggs," I told him, "there's no *need* for garbage pails in space. You can't just dump things out the airlock and get rid of them."

77

"But Captain Hanson *said* to junk the spoiled vegetables."

"*Junk*. Not *dump!* They should have been thrown into the incinerator. You see, anything tossed out of the *Saturn* in free space just follows along with the ship." I grinned. "I'd hate to be one of the attendants on Venus when the *Saturn* drops gravs surrounded by twenty-four lead satellites full of garbage."

He picked me up swiftly on that one.

"But they won't be with us when we land, Sparks. As soon as we hit the planet's Heaviside layer, atmospheric friction will destroy the Forenzis and their contents."

I whistled softly.

"By golly, you're right. I clean forgot about that. And Hanson was so sore *he* forgot it too. That means we must get those containers back into the ship before we hit the tropo or we're going to lose a couple hundred credits' worth of equipment."

Biggs said meekly, "I'll be glad to go out and reclaim them, Sparks. Can you fix it with the skipper?"

"I'll try," I told him.

So the next day I told Hanson about it. The captain tugged his lower lip thoughtfully and agreed.

"O.Q., let him do it. Maybe he'll slip into the rocket blasts."

I passed the order on to Biggs, then went back to my radio cabin. Joe Marlowe was calling me from Lunar III. What he

78

had to say drove all other thoughts from my mind. His message came direct from I.P.C. headquarters.

"Please report," it said, *"exact amount and probable value of cargo. Must have immediate reply."*

I relayed the message to the bridge. Then, my curiosity aroused, I contacted Joe on our private conversation band and asked him how come and why. He answered cautiously.

"The New York stock market's taking a nose dive, Bert. Stocks are slipping like a loose garter. The Corporation big shots are gibbering. They need a good profit on this cargo—and they need it bad."

Boy, there was nasty news! It was a private message, but I figured the Old Man ought to know it. So when he came in I passed it along. He stared at me, stricken.

"Sparks! In that case, I can't send *this!*"

"This" was the reply he had intended to send. It said succinctly, *"Cargo ruined. Value zero."*

"If you do," I told him, "we'll all be scanning the want ads as soon as we hit port. Stock markets are screwy. This can't be a real panic, or a fifty-thousand-credit cargo wouldn't be that important. But if the Corporation's under pressure, and the bears learn the *Saturn's* cargo is worthless . . ."

"What will we do?"

"Stall," I suggested. "Maybe the situation will have cleared up by the time we get in."

So we framed a new message that wouldn't upset the applecart. It said, *"Value of cargo estimated Long Island spaceport at 50,000 credits."* And *that* was true enough. . . .

Biggs, with his unerring faculty for selecting the wrong moment, chose this one to come bouncing into my radio room. He had taken off his headpiece but was still wearing his bulger. Its deflated folds hung about him in wrinkles, like the hide of an anemic rhinoceros.

"Sparks," he asked, "do you have a book on energy and radiation?"

"Help yourself," I nodded, pointing to my bookcase. "But why the sudden thirst for learning?"

79

"I have a theory," he began. "I think—"

Captain Hanson let loose a roar like an angry lion.

"Mister Biggs! I thought you was reclaimin' those Forenzi jars?"

"Yes, sir. I was. I mean . . . I am. But—"

"But me no buts. Get back to work!"

"Yes, sir!" Biggs saluted meekly, tossed me a grateful glance. "Thanks, Sparks. I've got an idea, and if I'm right—"

"Get out, Biggs!" roared the skipper.

"Yes, sir." Biggs backed out hastily, thumbing the pages of my textbook as he disappeared. Hanson scowled after him.

"The Corporation goes bust. The *Saturn* goes under the hammer. We're all out of jobs. An' that insane young whippersnapper wants to play school!"

"He seemed mighty excited about something," I said thoughtfully.

"He'll be worse than that," promised the skipper, "if he don't get those jars back on board. Sparks . . . would you happen to have an aspirin tablet around here?"

All this, to wax biblical, took place on the seventh day. The *Saturn* is a ten-day freighter, so we had three more days to run before we slipped into Sun City spaceport. They were three days of headaches, too. The skipper and I spent most of our time huddled over the radio, listening for reports on the stock-market slump in New York. We hoped the situation would ease up so that our making port with a zero-valued cargo wouldn't make any difference. But no such luck. Somehow the rumor had trickled out that the *Saturn's* cargo would not be of sufficient value to keep the Corporation in the black, and the Wall Street wolves were closing in, ready to snap if the rumor were true.

Which was tough enough on me, needing my job as I did, but it was even rougher on Cap Hanson. He was an old spacehound, just barely hanging on. If the *Saturn* were removed from its run, he'd never get another command. He'd be assigned to a watchman's job on a Lunar outpost, or perhaps be made a light-ship keeper on one of the planetoids. And what kind of windup is that for a man who's spent a lifetime pushing gravs?

80

Meanwhile our lumpy-larynxed fourth mate was taking a long time reclaiming those Forenzi jars. It wasn't really a hard job, you know. All he had to do was slip out through the airlock, throw a grapple around each jar and haul it in. But he seemed to be as inept at this as at every other job he had ever attempted. On an off period I went down to watch him. I found he had not yet brought a single one into the ship.

I told him, "You'd better get a wiggle on, Biggs. We make port tomorrow. If those things hit the atmosphere, you'll be able to *pour* them into the airlock."

"I know," he said abstractedly, "but I'm not quite ready yet. Sparks, according to that book you lent me, cosmic rays go down to $1/100,000$ Ångstrom units."

"That's right," I nodded.

"Then they're more than ten times as intense as gamma rays?"

"Right again. Why? What's the pay-off?"

"That's what I'm trying to find out," said Biggs strangely. He finished throwing a hitch around one of the jars, pushed himself toward the airlock.

"Want me to help you drag 'em in now?" I asked.

"No, thanks, Sparks. I think I'll leave them out till tomorrow," he said.

"But Captain Hanson—" I began.

"Tomorrow."

After all, I'm just a radioman. I shrugged. "It's your funeral."

He pulled them inside the next day. I saw them lying in the corridor beside the airlock, covered with a strip of tarpaulin. He got them in just in time, too, for about an hour later we hit the Heaviside layer of Venus. From there on it was an easy glide to the second planet. We threw out our lugsails and applied the power brakes. In a couple of hours we were warping into our cradle at Sun City spaceport.

I closed out my key and locked the radio room. There was nothing more for me to do on this shuttle, so I went up to the control turret and found Captain Hanson gnawing his fingernails down to the second joint.

81

"Any late news, Sparks?" he demanded anxiously.

I shook my head.

"No news but bad news. The Corporation's sending over its appraisers immediately."

He said wearily, "Well, we done our best. If it hadn't been for that madman Biggs, we'd still have our cargo. But as it is—"

"I wonder if International Stratoplanes needs any radio operators?" I wondered gloomily.

We were grounded now. As we walked down the corridor the hypos went off, and I heard the hiss of the airlock opening. We reached the entrance just as the appraisal committee came aboard. Doc Challenger, general manager of the Venus office, was with them, and old Prendergast Biggs himself, our junior officer's big-shot uncle. Challenger stepped forward, beaming.

"Happy landing, Captain!" he chortled. "I need not tell you how glad we are you came in safely. The Corporation has been experiencing bad times in New York, sir; bad times!"

Hanson said dully, "Yes, sir. I got somethin' to tell you, sir—"

"Later, Captain; later. First we must settle this question of your cargo's value. Approximately fifty thousand credits' worth of fresh vegetables—is that right? If your estimate is correct, the Corporation will weather this storm handsomely."

Hanson coughed nervously. He hedged, "Well, now, sir . . . about this here cargo . . ."

You never saw two smiles fade so abruptly. There was dead silence for a minute. Then Challenger asked grimly, "Captain Hanson, there's no *error* in your estimate, is there?"

"No, sir. I mean the *estimate* was right, but—"

It was here that young Lancelot Biggs interrupted.

"Excuse me, gentlemen," he said. "I don't quite understand. Is it important that we land a cargo of *vegetables*?"

Captain Hanson whirled on him.

"That will do, Mister!" he snapped. He turned to old Prendergast Biggs. "Sir," he said, "I've delayed this as long as possible. But now I got to tell you. This here precious nephew of yours—"

The veep smiled fatuously.

82

"Yes, Captain Hanson. A fine lad, isn't he? What were you going to say, Lancelot?"

I grabbed Hanson's arm. I was afraid he was going to blow his tubes and hit somebody right then and there. But before he got a chance, Lancelot Biggs was talking again.

"Captain Hanson," he said seriously, "I wish you'd told me this before. I didn't realize our cargo was so important."

Then he turned to the committee.

"I hope you will not be surprised to learn, gentlemen, that our cargo is *not* fresh vegetables. At the last minute Captain Hanson decided to make a substitution—"

Hanson's face turned assorted shades of lavender—all of them unattractive. He bellowed, "What! Are you trying to shift the blame to me? Why, you—"

Biggs's voice drowned out his protest.

"—and so, gentlemen, we have placed the cargo right here for your inspection. Look!"

With a swift motion he tore the tarpaulin from the Forenzi jars. I looked . . . and gulped! They were the same jars. But with a difference. And *what* a difference! They were no longer the dull grayish color of lead; they had a ruddy, glinting, coppery hue. Biggs patted one of them affectionately.

"Ask your appraisers to estimate the value of these, gentlemen. I think they'll find them to be worth approximately a quarter of a million credits. They are . . . *pure gold!*"

It's a good thing I was holding onto Captain Hanson's arm. For just as the committee was exclaiming, "Excellent! Excellent trading, Captain Hanson!" the skipper's nerves gave out. He collapsed like a punctured bulger. I remember shouting, "Water! Water, somebody!" Then I passed out too. . . .

Afterward, when the three of us were alone in the turret, Hanson asked, "I don't get it. How in blazes did it happen?"

Biggs blushed and looked uncomfortable.

"Why, it's obvious when you analyze it, Captain. I can't understand how in all these years of spaceflight no one ever discovered it before. Perhaps because ships and bulgers are made of permalloy instead of lead. Or it may be that some enzyme secreted by the rotten vegetables acted as a catalyst. Chemists will have to decide that."

"You're *still* not tellin' us what happened."

"Don't you know? It was transmutation induced in the lead Forenzi jars by the action of cosmic rays."

Captain Hanson said in an awed tone, "Exposure to cosmic rays changed lead to gold?"

"That's right. It's always been a theoretical possibility. Artificial transmutations were brought about 'way back in the early twentieth century through bombardment with gamma rays. And cosmic rays are more than ten times as short as gammas.

"I began to suspect something strange was happening to the Forenzi jars when first I went out to gather them in. Their color had changed slightly, and their exterior was rather more granular. That's why I came in to borrow Donovan's book on radiation. What I saw convinced me that the lead was being transmuted; was then in the mesolead stage, approximating an isotope of thallium.

"So," smiled Biggs, "I decided to wait and see if the transmutation would continue. And it did."

Hanson wiped his hand across his forehead.

"Suppose the trip had tooken more time? Suppose the transmutation had gone a step farther? What then?"

Biggs pursed his lips thoughtfully. "Well, now, that's an interesting question. The next element down the periodic ladder is platinum. It's quite possible that—"

"Wait a minute," interrupted the skipper. "Did you say *platinum?*"

"Yes. Why?"

"Nothin'. That is, nothin' much—" The skipper rose and strode to the intercommunicating phone. "MacDougal?" he yelled. "Listen, Chief . . . get this crate ready to roll again. We're liftin' gravs again first thing in the mornin'.

"Where to? Nowhere in particular; we're just cruisin'. Who cares where? An' hey, Chief! Send to the commissary for about five—no, make it six dozen Forenzi jars. Yeah, Forenzi jars, I

said. An' get the biggest ones they got. The Corporation ain't found it out yet, but we're goin' into the transmutin' business. An' Mister Biggs ships with us as our new third mate."

I guess the less said about that transmutation trip, the better. In the first place, our experiment didn't work. In the second place, we wasted six weeks and six dozen Forenzi jars that, lacking whatever mysterious combination of enzymes the garbage had supplied, failed utterly to respond to the cosmic-ray treatment. And in the third place, Cap Hanson caught merry blue from the Corporation officials, who said he shouldn't have gone in the first place.

So we were all in pretty foul humor by the time we gave it up as a bad job and limped back into Sun City spaceport, empty of pocket and full of bicarbonate of soda.

This last because of Slops. Slops wasn't a *bad* cook, you understand. He just wasn't a cook at all, rightly speaking. He had

85

what you might call a tapioca complex. It was tapioca for breakfast, tapioca for lunch, tapioca for dinner. Every day. Boiled tapioca, stewed tapioca, even fricasseed tapioca. . . .

It finally got to be too much for even an iron-bellied old spacedog like Cap Hanson. So when we warped into Sun City spaceport, Cap said firmly, "You're through, Slops. An' I do mean threw!" And he kicked our so-called chef off the *Saturn*, along with his clothing, his back pay, and his harmonica.

Which left us out on the end of a limb, for it turned out that there wasn't a single spaceriding cook dry-docked in Sun City. While the *Saturn* was taking on a cargo for Earth—trade goods, mostly, with one or two bins of medical supplies—the skipper did his best to scare up a grub-wrangler. But no luck.

An hour before we were scheduled to blast off, he ambled up to my radio cabin, scratching his grizzled pate nervously.

"Sparks," he complained, "I thought I was doin' the right thing when I fired Slops."

"You were," I told him. "By chucking that greaseball off the ship, you saved somebody's life. The crew was planning either mutiny or murder—they didn't care which—if they had to eat one more dish of that goo."

"But," he continued fretfully, "in another hour we lift gravs for Earth, an' we ain't got no cook. What the blue space are we goin' to do?"

Our third mate, Lancelot Biggs, had entered as the skipper was talking. Now he suggested helpfully, "I saw Slops at the Palace Bar a few minutes ago, Captain. I'll ask him to come back if you want me to."

"*No!*" said the skipper and I in the same breath.

Biggs looked hurt. He defended, "Well, after all, tapioca's good for you. It contains valuable food elements—"

"Shut up!" howled Cap Hanson. He was in no mood to take advice from anybody, especially Biggs. "I'll kill the next guy who even mentions that—that unmentionable stuff."

Biggs said apologetically, "I was only trying to be helpful."

"You're as much help," the skipper told him, "as fins on a dicky-bird's chest. Now, get out of here. G'wan, beat it."

86

Our lanky third mate turned and started to leave the cabin. Then suddenly . . .

"Wait a minute," yelped Hanson. "I got an idea. Mr. Biggs, do *you* by any chance happen to know anything about the art of cookin'?"

"Who?" asked Biggs. "Me? Why, no, Captain. But I don't imagine it would be very difficult. After all, cooking is simply the practical application of certain elementary chemical processes. By exposing designated organic substances to the action of hydrogen dioxide under suitable thermostatic conditions—"

Cap Hanson's jaw dropped. He goggled at me. "What's he sayin', Sparks?"

"He means," I translated, "that cooking is easy. All you need is victuals, water, and heat."

"Oh?" The skipper grinned ghoulishly. "In that case, our problem's solved. Mr. Biggs, you've just earned a new private office an' a new unyform. You'll find both of 'em below decks, third door to your right."

It was Biggs's turn to look dismayed. His Adam's apple bobbed in his throat like an unswallowed golf ball. "What? But I'm not a cook, Captain. I'm your third mate."

"You *was* my third mate," corrected the Old Man coolly. "The Space Manual gives a ship's commander the right to draft any member of crew or command for any duty in times of emergency. This is an emergency. An' besides, you just got done sayin' that cookin' is simply a matter of exposin' dessicated hoochamacallits to the action of thingamajiggers. So"—he brushed his hairy paws with a gesture of finality—"that's that. To the galley, Mr. Slops!"

So that, as he said, was that. But the funny part of it is that, forced to a showdown, Lancelot Biggs came through.

The first meal out, which was lunch, I went down to the mess hall thinking anything might happen and fearing the worst. I got the shock of my life . . . and shocks are a not inconsiderable part of the life of a freight-lugger radioman.

We had fried chicken with cream gravy, hot biscuits, candied yams, a side dish of stewed okra, creole style, raisin pie, and the best coffee ever served on the wallowing old *Saturn*. After I'd bulged my belt to the outermost notch with fried pullet, I waddled into the galley and confronted the composer of this gastronomic symphony.

"Biggs," I accused, "you've been holding out. Why didn't you tell us you could cook a meal like that?"

He shuffled his feet sheepishly. He asked, "Was it all right, Sparks?"

"All right? It was terrific!"

"I'm glad. Because, you see, that was the first meal I ever cooked."

"*What?*"

"Mmm-hmm. But there are lots of cookbooks here in the galley. And I figured so long as I had to do it, I might as well do it right."

He grinned at me shyly. Every once in a while I wondered, briefly, whether any of us understood this strange, lanky genius, Lancelot Biggs. This was one of the times.

"To tell the truth, Sparks, I found the experiment rather interesting. Cooking is, as I told Captain Hanson, just a practical application of elementary chemistry, with the pots and pans serving as test tubes, the stove as a huge Bunsen burner."

I said admiringly, "I'll hand you one thing, Mr. Biggs. You believe in sticking to theories, don't you?"

"But of course. 'Get the theory first'—that's the secret of success in any undertaking." He looked pleased and a little excited too. "We're going to have a good trip home, Sparks. There's plenty of food here in the galley to experiment with. And in the holds—"

Just then I caught my number being buzzed on the inter-communicating audio. I cut through and called, "Sparks speaking. What's up?"

"Donovan?" It was my relief man calling from the radio room. "You'd better come up here on the double. A message from Sun City, and I think it's bad news."

"Right with you," I acknowledged. I snapped a brief so long to Biggs and hurried to my buzz-bin. My relief man was there, also Cap Hanson and the first mate, Lieutenant Martin. All three of them looked a bit grim and a bit glum and quite a bit apprehensive. My relief shoved a flimsy into my hand. It was a warning from Sun City spaceport.

"Hanson Commander Saturn en route Venus-Earth. Turn back immediately for convoy. Pirate Hake reported on co-ordinates three fifteen plus nine oh nine your trajectory." It was signed, *"Allonby, Comm. Solar Space Patrol."*

I stared at Cap Hanson. I said, "Hake? Runt Hake?"

Hanson said, "Yes. But that's not the worst of it, Sparks. Tell him, Mr. Martin."

Martin wet his lips. "We're in a serious spot, Sparks. We accelerated to max twenty minutes ago and cut hypos for the free run. And since we had—or thought we had—almost nine days of idleness, I told MacDougal he could take down the Number Three hypatomic that's been misfiring."

I said, "So he took it down. So what? He can put it together again, can't he?"

"No. He found the casing worn and melted it down for a recast. We can't reassemble it for at least two days!"

For the sake of you Earthlubbers who don't savvy space lingo, let me say it in words of one syllable. We were in one bad jam. The hypatomics are the motors that operate spacecraft. One of them had shown signs of wear. With the ship freewheeling, so to speak, in space, the engineers had taken down the faulty motor, discovered it needed remolding, and had melted down the casing. As Martin said, it would take at least two days— probably more—to recast the molding and put the hypo together again so we could blast.

But the worst of it was . . . Hake. Runt Hake. There are pirates and pirates in the void between the planets. Some of them are good guys—that is, if an outlaw can ever be considered a "good guy." Like, for instance, Lark O'Day, that debonair bandit who always gives lugger captains a signed receipt for the cargoes he highjacks, and who had once let a tramp freighter go through untouched because the skipper pleaded that his life savings were wrapped up in the cargo. Who had once stopped a luxury liner for the sole purpose of stealing a kiss from its charming passenger, the newly crowned "Miss Universe."

But Hake was something different. Think of the nastiest things you've ever heard of, multiply by ten, add infinity, and you have the square root of Runt Hake.

Hake was a sadist. His idea of good clean fun was to board a freighter like the *Saturn*, unload the cargo, then blast a slow leak through the hull. After, I should mention, first having removed all lifeskiffs and bulgers from the victimized ship. Once in the asteroid Sargossa I saw a ship that had been scuttled by Runt Hake's cutthroats. Its crew still remained with the ship. But not as recognizable human beings.

Oh, a swell guy, this Runt Hake. And now, disabled and helpless, we were drifting right into that sector of space where he awaited us.

Cap Hanson said grimly, "We've got a .20 millimeter rotorgun. We'll give him a taste of that."

"And get ourselves blown to atoms," interjected Martin, "with his pierce-guns? No, Skipper, there's only one thing to do. Send word for the convoy to come on the double . . . and hope it reaches us before we run into Hake."

That was my cue. I shoved the relief man off the bench and got the wobble-bug going. I filled the ether with SOSs, and added a couple of PDQs for good measure. I picked up an acknowledgment from Sun City and threw them a hasty explanation. They wired back that the convoy cruiser would make all haste and not to be frightened . . .

But can I help it if my knees chatter?

There is one thing you can absolutely depend on Lancelot Biggs to do, and that is stick his nose in at the wrong minute. As we three were giving the sob towel a good soaking, the door popped open and in gangled our pro tem Slops. He had a grin on his dial that stretched from ear to there. He chuckled, "Captain—"

"Go 'way," growled Cap Hanson. "I'm thinkin'."

"But look." Biggs opened a clenched fist and displayed a wee gray ship mouse. He placed it on the floor before him. "Look

90

what I found in the aft storage bins. He acts so funny—"

"Go 'way," repeated the skipper gloomily. "I got no interest in mice at a time like this."

Biggs said, "But he *does* act funny." And as a matter of fact, the mouse did. Usually, you know, a mouse is the scaredest thing alive. Put him down in a place like this, surrounded by giant humans, and he'll run like mad to the darkest corner.

But this little twerp didn't run. He deliberately moved to the man nearest him—Martin, that was—and began to nuzzle himself against Martin's shoe as if the first mate were an old and loved acquaintance. Biggs chuckled again.

"See that? Do you know what makes him act that way, Skipper? It's the prol—"

"*Mister Biggs!*" The Old Man's face was fiery. "This is no time for nonsense. Within hours, perhaps minutes, we may all be dead. For the last time, get out o' here!"

Biggs, sort of stunned, said, "Yes, sir." He retrieved his curiously acting little pet from where it rubbed its soft muzzle against Martin's shoelaces, put it in his pocket, and backed out the doorway. As he left he tossed me a beseeching wigwag. I joined him in the runway outside.

"What's the trouble, Sparks?" he demanded.

I gave it to him, both barrels. He had a right to know. Every man has a right to know when it's bye-bye time.

Biggs's eyes were huge and round. "Runt Hake? No wonder the skipper was cross." He plunged into one of his characteristic silences. Then, suddenly, "Sparks!"

"Yeah?"

"They say Hake is a show-off. Likes to crack the whip on a captured ship, ordering up big meals and so on before he scuttles it."

"You think you're going to poison him, maybe? Don't be a dope. He'll make you swallow a sample of everything you serve him."

"Never mind. I'm not sure my idea is any good . . . yet. But do you happen to have a book on physiochemistry?"

"I think so. Yes, I know I have."

91

"Get it for me, will you? I'll explain later."

I got him the book. He jammed it into his pocket and disappeared toward the galley, jogging along like a crane on high heels. But I had no time, just now, to be amused by Biggs's peculiarities, physical or mental. My ears had caught a sound they did not want to hear. The grate of metal on metal near the starboard airlock. The banging of a mailed fist on permalloy, the asthmatic wheeze of the airlock, a crewman's shout ending in a choked gurgle . . .

I plunged back into the radio room. "Cap," I yelled. "Somebody at the airlock. It must be—"

It was. Runt Hake and his pirates.

To look at Hake, you wouldn't think he was a killer. True, he held a hand ray-gun on us as he approached, moving smoothly, lightly, up the runway. A half-dozen men behind him also held their side arms poised, ready for action, while another half-dozen deployed down the corridors toward the engine rooms and control turret. But as Hake came nearer he tossed back the quartzite headpiece of his bulger, and I saw that his hair was wheat-gold; his cheeks smooth, soft, boyish; his lips curved into something like a tender smile.

His voice was gentle, too. He said, "You offer no resistance, Captain? That is wise."

Hanson said, "Hake, I surrender my ship to you freely. But don't harm my men. That is all I ask."

"But, Captain"—the slender little pirate's eyebrows lifted archly—"surely you are premature with your pleas? We have just arrived. There are so many, many things to be done before we enjoy our . . . little pleasures."

And then, as he said that, I saw why men feared Runt Hake. His golden hair, his pink cheeks, his soft mouth—all these were but window dressing, misleading and meaningless. The character of the true Hake was in his eyes, heavy-lidded and ophidian; eyes that glinted in swift-flaming delight as he hinted at that which was to come. I knew, now, that the stories were all true. We could expect no mercy of this man. He would amuse himself with us for a while, toying with us in slow, reptilian

92

mister
mckee

fashion. Then he would leave. And we, like the broken things I had seen in the space ship Sargossa, would remain behind.

He was speaking again. Softly, almost melodiously. "The cargo, of course, is mine, Captain. Even now my men are transferring it to my ship. But there are a few other things we will do while aboard yours. It is lonely, cruising space for months on end. And we do not dine luxuriously. You have, I hope, well-stocked storage bins? A larder provisioned with fine foods? Wines, perhaps, to tempt the jaded palate?"

Hanson tried again.

"We have, Hake. An' they're all yours if you'll assure me my men will be unharmed. Take me as hostage, if you want. But—"

"But no, Captain. That would never do. I think you had best remain . . . with your crew." Again there danced that tiny light in Hake's fanatic eyes. "You see, many know my name, Captain, but none have ever seen my face . . . and lived. It would be unfortunate if ever I were to be identified, would it not?"

He turned to his followers.

"Disarm them." He designated us negligently. "And when the cargo has been transferred, have our men come back to this ship. We will dine aboard the *Saturn*."

You think it strange, perhaps, that we showed no sturdier resistance to Hake's invasion? Well, think it over. The *Saturn* was a lumbering old scow compared to Hake's streamlined man-o'-war. Hanson had adopted the only sane policy. Our best bet was to stall the pirate, try to placate him until the Space Patrol cruiser reached us.

So for more than two hours, unarmed and disconsolate, we sat and twiddled our fingers while Hake's men, using our crewmen and our gang as porters, transferred the more valuable portions of our cargo to their ship. They didn't take the bulk stuff. Just small merchandise that could be fenced from their hide-out on an uncharted rogue asteroid.

Meanwhile, Runt Hake made a special trip to the galley. He took Martin and Cap and me along so he could keep an eye on us. Down there we found Lancelot Biggs quietly reading the

94

book I had loaned him. He glanced up as we entered, rose slowly to his feet as Hake gestured with his ray-gun.

Hake asked in that soft purr of his, "You're the cook on this ship?"

Biggs nodded. "Mmm-hmm."

"You will address me," suggested the little outlaw, "as 'sir.' Very well, Slops. I want you to prepare a meal for us. A *good* meal. Fresh meats and vegetables. You have no idea"—he drawled this last to Hanson—"how one wearies of canned concentrates."

Hanson just glowered. Biggs looked confused. He said, "I—I'll have to get produce from the storage bins if you want a *big* meal. This galley's small." He glanced about him helplessly.

Hake nodded. "Permission is granted. But let me suggest that you attempt no . . . ah . . . medieval toxicological exploits. The chef of the *Spica* tried something of the sort. Poor chap. He screamed horribly at the end. I shall never forget it."

I'll bet he wouldn't, the louse. But I hoped, now, that Biggs would realize I had been right. He couldn't pull any funny business on Hake and get away with it.

Biggs seemed to understand, all right. He said meekly, "I'll do the best I can, sir. It will take a little time, of course."

"We are in no hurry," agreed Hake. "A good meal is worth waiting for. And now, gentlemen . . ."

He motioned us toward the turret. We started to leave the galley. I was the last to pass through the door. As I did so, I felt a fumbling at my side. Lancelot Biggs shoved something into my jacket. He whispered in my ear, "Sparks, give each of our men a piece. Tell them to chew it."

For a moment my hopes flamed high. I didn't know what Biggs had up his sleeve, but I dared dream he had devised some means of thwarting Hake. But when, a few minutes later, I learned what he had thrust into my pocket, my hopes died as swiftly as they had been born. The stuff was nothing but pepsin. Plain, ordinary pepsin. Good for headaches, maybe, but hardly a deadly weapon against a lethal foe.

I was half minded to chuck the stuff away. I suspected that

95

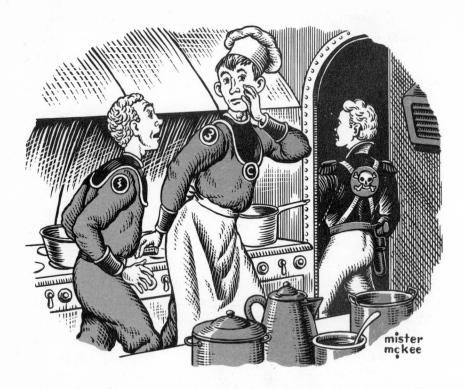

fear, worry, desperation, had made Biggs slip his gravs. Then I thought better of it. After all, he must have had *some* reason for his strange request. And in a spot like this any gamble was worth taking.

So, slowly, cautiously, I started circulating the stuff. I managed to slip half the package to Doug Enderby, the steward, with instructions to get it to the crewmen. I met Chief Mac-Dougal 'tween decks and gave him some for his engine-room gang, the blasters and the wipers. Martin took a piece, wonderingly, and slipped it into his mouth when I signaled him to do so. Me? Sure, I had some too. After all, it tasted good. And a man might as well check out with a clean taste on his lips.

The only man I couldn't relay a piece to at any time was Cap Hanson. Runt Hake kept an eagle eye on the skipper. As a matter of fact, Hake didn't miss many tricks, the murderous little squirt. Just before dinner was served he made my heart skip a beat when he asked, "What are you chewing, Sparks?"

"Gum," I said. Then, fearful not to ask, "You want a stick . . . sir?"

He shuddered delicately. "Barbarian custom. I do *not* want a stick."

Boy, was that a break for our side!

Well, some time later Biggs donged the dinner bell and we all trouped into the mess hall. Talk about irony; here we were, a score of honest, hard-working spacemen and an equal number of pirates, sitting down to the same table, eating the same meal. Screwy? Sure. But that was Hake for you. As Biggs had said, he was a show-off.

But don't think he took any chances. We were unarmed; his men were walking hardware stores. As for the conviviality of that banquet, that was strictly on the surface. To outward appearances we were all one big happy family at the banquet table; actually we of the *Saturn* were being fattened for the slaughter to follow.

Still, you know the old gag: "The condemned man ate a hearty meal." That's what I did. And that's what most of the others did too, because Lancelot Biggs had come up with another Q.E.D. that cooking is, after all, nothing but applied chemistry.

We had, just to make you drool a little, chilled consommé with a light sherry. Then a tempting wisp of baked whiting, served with Moselle Erdener Treppchen—and did the Old Man fume to watch *that* sliding down the hatches of an unkempt pirate crew! He'd been saving it for his golden anniversary. Then Biggs served a chicken *sauté Florentine*. These were the prelude courses. The main dish was a saddle of lamb accompanied by peas in mint and potatoes Parisienne served with Pommard, 2094. The salad was a salad Alma; the dessert was something which Biggs told me later was *plombière à l'Havane friandises*, a concoction of pineapples, bananas, frozen custard—and not a bit of tapioca in it.

This came along with the Piper Heidsieck '85. A demitasse came next, then liqueurs . . .

It was here that Runt Hake called a halt. "We'll transfer the

mister
mckee

rest of the beverages," he said, "to our own ship. We want no
drunkenness aboard while we . . . ah . . . do that which is necessary. Captain Hanson?"

He nodded significantly toward the control turret. I rose; so
did Martin. Surprisingly, Biggs joined our group as we moved
updeck. When we reached the bridge, Hake said, with a malev-
olent pseudo regret I shall never forget, "We have enjoyed our
banquet exceedingly, Captain. But you understand I can allow
nothing to stand in the way of my next . . . ah . . . duty. So . . ."

Hanson said stonily, "You'll give us a lifeskiff before scuttlin' the *Saturn,* Hake?"

Hake sighed. "Captain, I had planned to do that very thing. But it seems that my men were so careless as to blast holes in each of the skiffs. Of course, if you'd care to take your chances in the damaged craft . . ."

Oh, he was a bad one, that Hake! I glanced at Martin and saw my own thoughts mirrored in his eyes. This was our last chance. If we could capture the pirate chieftain, maybe his men would not dare do anything for fear of hurting him. And Hake, quick as he was on the trigger, might not get us both before . . .

Then Lancelot Biggs intervened. To me he barked, "No! No, Sparks!" And to Hake, quietly, almost tenderly, "Why, Mr. Hake . . . it's all a big mistake, isn't it? These nasty men think you're planning to harm them. Aren't they silly? You don't want to hurt them at all . . . do you?"

And then . . . Runt Hake's soft mouth began to twitch. Yes, twitch! It pursed up like the mouth of a scolded child; his eyes wrinkled, and he began to blubber.

"Hurt them?" he sniffled. "*Me* hurt *them?* Why, I wouldn't do a thing like that. I love them. They're my friends." And he tossed his ray-gun away, reached out—and gently patted Biggs's cheek!

Beside me Lieutenant Martin whispered hoarsely, "Great gods of Ganymede, what *is* this?" I was stunned for a moment myself. But I had sense enough to stoop and retrieve Hake's gun before his insane interlude passed.

"He's blown his fuses!" I squalled. "Grab him, Martin! Biggs, come with me. You and I will round up his crew—"

But Biggs said quietly, "Take your time, Sparks. There's no hurry. See?"

He stepped to the wall, flicked on the visiplate that showed the interior of the mess hall. There, where a moment before a grim-faced score of space pirates had maintained watch over our crew, now our lads were staring with blank, uncomprehending faces at twenty men who looked and acted for all the world like affectionate puppies.

They were hugging each other, patting each other's arms and

99

faces, murmuring soft words of endearment. It was stupefying. More than that, it was embarrassing! Off in one corner a bearded, one-eyed outlaw dandled a companion on his knee. Another burly bruiser, big enough to tear a man in half with his bare hands, was playing piggy-back with a buddy.

I choked, "But what—"

Biggs said suddenly, "Sparks! You forgot to give the skipper a piece of that pepsin!"

"I didn't get a chance. But how did *you* know?"

Then I saw. The skipper and Runt Hake were sitting in the same chair, murmuring sweet nothings to each other, stroking each other's hair fondly. Just as I looked, the Old Man leaned forward and gave the pirate a great big juicy kiss!

Then came a welcome interruption. The audio throbbed to electric life; a crisp voice called, "Ahoy, the *Saturn! Saturn,* ahoy! Space Patrol Cruiser *Iris* calling. Stand by. We'll come alongside you in twenty minutes . . ."

Later, when Runt Hake and his pirates, still babbling incoherent attestations of affection, had been removed to the patrol ship and were on their way to the Venusian prison that awaited them, we held a confab in my radio room. Martin was there, and MacDougal, and Lancelot Biggs and myself. Also a very foggy-eyed, befuddled Captain Hanson.

I asked bluntly, "What happened, Mr. Biggs? We know you put something in the food. Something from which the pepsin saved us. But what? No drug would make a man act like that!"

Biggs grinned, his Adam's apple cavorting amiably.

"Not a drug. A chemical called prolactin. If you'll remember, I started to tell you we were carrying a load of it to Earth."

"Prolactin?" said Martin. "What's that?"

"An extract that some say governs human affections. Prolactin is supposed to be the ingredient responsible for all acts of parental love. . . ."

"And we," I said, "were carrying a cargo of it. I still don't understand, though, why chewing pepsin kept us from turning into a gang of bunny-huggers like—"

100

I glanced at the Old Man, then glanced away again, embarrassed. He beamed upon me fondly.

"Well, you see," explained Biggs, "prolactin happens to be a pure protein. And pure proteins are insoluble in most things: alcohol, water, the liquids we normally take in our diet.

"I cooked Hake's banquet with liberal sprinklings of prolactin. But I had to find some way of keeping *our* men from being affected by the hormone that disrupted the pirates' morale. Pepsin was the answer. Pepsin breaks down pure proteins into soluble peptones. That is why it is commonly used as a digestive agent."

"Suiboise," mumbled the skipper, "naluvythalmuhot."

"Eh?" I started. "What's that?"

Biggs looked sheepish. "I'm not sure," he said, "but I *think* he's saying, 'You're sweet boys, and I love you with all my heart.' Sparks, maybe we'd better put him to bed until it wears off. And it might be well, gentlemen, never to—er—remind him of this episode."

So we did. And we won't. There's not much mother-love in the Old Man's right cross.

H. G. Wells

THE TRUTH ABOUT PYECRAFT

ILLUSTRATED BY *John McKee*

E SITS not a dozen yards away. If I glance over my shoulder I can see him. And if I catch his eye—and usually I catch his eye—it meets me with an expression—

It is mainly an imploring look—and yet with suspicion in it.

Confound his suspicion! If I wanted to tell on him I should have told long ago. I don't tell and I don't tell, and he ought to feel at his ease. As if anything so gross and fat as he could feel at ease! Who would believe me if I did tell?

Poor old Pyecraft! Great, uneasy jelly of substance! The fattest clubman in London.

He sits at one of the little club tables in the huge bay by the fire, stuffing. What is he stuffing? I glance judiciously and catch him biting at a round of hot buttered teacake, with his eyes on me. Confound him!—with his eyes on me!

That settles it, Pyecraft! Since you *will* be abject, since you *will* behave as though I was not a man of honor, here, right under your embedded eyes, I write the thing down—the plain truth about Pyecraft. The man I helped, the man I shielded, and who has requited me by making my club unendurable, absolutely unendurable, with his liquid appeal, with the perpetual "don't tell" of his looks.

And, besides, why does he keep on eternally eating?

Well, here goes for the truth, the whole truth, and nothing but the truth!

Pyecraft— I made the acquaintance of Pyecraft in this very smoking-room. I was a young, nervous new member, and he

102

saw it. I was sitting all alone, wishing I knew more of the members, and suddenly he came, a great rolling front of chins and abdomina, towards me, and grunted and sat down in a chair close by me and wheezed for a space, and scraped for a space with a match and lit a cigar, and then addressed me. I forget what he said—something about the matches not lighting properly, and afterwards as he talked he kept stopping the waiters one by one as they went by, and telling them about the matches in that thin, fluty voice he has. But, anyhow, it was in some such way we began our talking.

He talked about various things and came round to games. And thence to my figure and complexion. "You ought to be a good cricketer," he said. I suppose I am slender, slender to what some people would call lean, and I suppose I am rather dark, still— I am not ashamed of having a Hindu great-grandmother, but, for all that, I don't want casual strangers to see through me at a glance to *her*. So that I was set against Pyecraft from the beginning.

But he only talked about me in order to get to himself.

"I expect," he said, "you take no more exercise than I do, and probably you eat no less." (Like all excessively obese people he fancied he ate nothing.) "Yet"—and he smiled an oblique smile —"we differ."

And then he began to talk about his fatness and his fatness; all he did for his fatness and all he was going to do for his fatness; what people had advised him to do for his fatness and what he had heard of people doing for fatness similar to his. "A *priori*," he said, "one would think a question of nutrition could be answered by dietary and a question of assimilation by drugs." It was stifling. It was dumpling talk. It made me feel swelled to hear him.

One stands that sort of thing once in a way at a club, but a time came when I fancied I was standing too much. He took to me altogether too conspicuously. I could never go into the smoking-room but he would come wallowing towards me, and sometimes he came and gormandized round and about me while I had my lunch. He seemed at times almost to be clinging to me.

He was a bore . . . and from the first there was something in his manner—almost as though he knew, almost as though he penetrated to the fact that I *might*—that there was a remote, exceptional chance in me that no one else presented.

"I'd give anything to get it down," he would say—"anything," and peer at me over his vast cheeks and pant.

Poor old Pyecraft! He had just rung the bell, no doubt to order another buttered teacake!

He came to the actual thing one day. "Our Pharmacopoeia," he said, "our Western Pharmacopoeia, is anything but the last word of medical science. In the East, I've been told—"

He stopped and stared at me. It was like being at an aquarium.

I was quite suddenly angry with him. "Look here," I said, "who told you about my great-grandmother's recipes?"

"Well," he fenced.

"Every time we've met for a week," I said—"and we've met pretty often—you've given me a broad hint or so about that little secret of mine."

"Well," he said, "now the cat's out of the bag, I'll admit, yes, it is so. I had it—"

"From Pattison?"

"Indirectly," he said, which I believe was lying, "yes."

"Pattison," I said, "took that stuff at his own risk."

He pursed his mouth and bowed.

"My great-grandmother's recipes," I said, "are queer things to handle. My father was near making me promise—"

"He didn't?"

"No. But he warned me. He himself used one—once."

"Ah! . . . But do you think—? Suppose—suppose there did happen to be one—"

"The things are curious documents," I said. "Even the smell of 'em. . . . No!"

But after going so far Pyecraft was resolved I should go farther. I was always a little afraid if I tried his patience too much he would fall on me suddenly and smother me. I own I was weak. But I was also annoyed with Pyecraft. I had got to that state of feeling for him that disposed me to say, "Well, *take* the

104

risk!" The little affair of Pattison to which I have alluded was a different matter altogether. What it was doesn't concern us now, but I knew, anyhow, that the particular recipe I used then was safe. The rest I didn't know so much about and, on the whole, I was inclined to doubt their safety pretty completely.

Yet even if Pyecraft got poisoned—

I must confess the poisoning of Pyecraft struck me as an immense undertaking.

That evening I took that queer, odd-scented sandalwood box out of my safe and turned the rustling skins over. The gentleman who wrote the recipes for my great-grandmother evidently had a weakness for skins of a miscellaneous origin, and his handwriting was cramped to the last degree. Some of the things are quite unreadable to me—though my family, with its Indian Civil Service associations, has kept up a knowledge of Hindustani from generation to generation—and none are absolutely plain sailing. However, I was able to find the one that I knew was there soon enough, and sat on the floor by my safe for some time looking at it.

"Look here," said I to Pyecraft next day, and snatched the slip away from his eager grasp.

"So far as I can make it out, this is a recipe for Loss of

mister
mckee

105

Weight." ("Ah!" said Pyecraft.) "I'm not absolutely sure, but I think it's that. And if you take my advice you'll leave it alone. Because, you know—I blacken my blood in your interest, Pyecraft—my ancestors on that side were, so far as I can gather, a jolly queer lot. See?"

"Let me try it," said Pyecraft.

I leaned back in my chair. My imagination made one mighty effort and fell flat within me. "What in Heaven's name, Pyecraft," I asked, "do you think you'll look like when you get thin?"

He was impervious to reason. I made him promise never to say a word to me about his disgusting fatness again whatever happened—never, and then I handed him that little piece of skin.

"It's nasty stuff," I said.

"No matter," he said, and took it.

He goggled at it. "But—but—" he said.

He had just discovered that it wasn't English.

"To the best of my ability," I said, "I will do you a translation."

I did my best. After that we didn't speak for a fortnight. Whenever he approached me I frowned and motioned him away, and he respected our compact, but at the end of the fortnight he was as fat as ever. And then he got a word in.

"I must speak," he said. "It isn't fair. There's something wrong. It'd done me no good. You're not doing your great-grandmother justice."

"Where's the recipe?"

He produced it gingerly from his pocketbook.

I ran my eye over the items. "Was the egg addled?" I asked.

"No. Ought it to have been?"

"That," I said, "goes without saying in all my poor dear great-grandmother's recipes. When condition or quality is not specified you must get the worst. She was drastic or nothing. . . . And there's one or two possible alternatives to some of these other things. You got *fresh* rattlesnake venom?"

"I got a rattlesnake from Jamrach's. It cost—it cost—"

"That's your affair, anyhow. This last item—"

106

"I know a man who—"

"Yes. H'm. Well, I'll write the alternatives down. So far as I know the language of the Hindustani, the spelling of this recipe is particularly atrocious. By-the-bye, dog here probably means pariah dog."

For a month after that I saw Pyecraft constantly at the club and as fat and anxious as ever. He kept our treaty, but at times he broke the spirit of it by shaking his head despondently. Then one day in the cloakroom he said, "Your great-grandmother—"

"Not a word against her," I said; and he held his peace.

I could have fancied he had desisted, and I saw him one day talking to three new members about his fatness as though he was in search of other recipes. And then, quite unexpectedly his telegram came.

"Mr. Formalyn!" bawled a page-boy under my nose, and I took the telegram and opened it at once.

"For Heaven's sake come.—Pyecraft."

"H'm," said I, and to tell the truth I was so pleased at the rehabilitation of my great-grandmother's reputation this evidently promised that I made a most excellent lunch.

I got Pyecraft's address from the hall porter. Pyecraft inhabited the upper half of a house in Bloomsbury, and I went there as soon as I had done my coffee. I did not wait to finish my cigar.

"Mr. Pyecraft?" said I, at the front door.

They believed he was ill; he hadn't been out for two days.

"He expects me," said I, and they sent me up.

I rang the bell at the lattice-door upon the landing.

"He shouldn't have tried it, anyhow," I said to myself. "A man who eats like a pig ought to look like a pig."

An obviously worthy woman, with an anxious face and a carelessly placed cap, came and surveyed me through the lattice.

I gave my name and she opened his door for me in a dubious fashion.

"Well?" said I, as we stood together inside Pyecraft's piece of the landing.

" 'E said you was to come in if you came," she said, and regarded me, making no motion to show me anywhere. And then, confidentially, " 'E's locked in, sir."

"Locked in?"

"Locked himself in yesterday morning and 'asn't let anyone in since, sir. And ever and again *swearing*. Oh, my!"

I stared at the door she indicated by her glances. "In there?" I said.

"Yes, sir."

"What's up?"

She shook her head sadly. " 'E keeps on calling for vittles, sir. *'Eavy* vittles 'e wants. I get 'im what I can. Pork 'e's 'ad, sooit puddin', sossiges, noo bread. Everythink like that. Left outside, if you please, and me go away. 'E's eatin' sir, somethink *awful*."

There came a piping bawl from inside the door: "That Formalyn?"

"That you, Pyecraft?" I shouted, and went and banged the door.

"Tell her to go away."

I did.

Then I could hear a curious pattering upon the door, almost like someone feeling for the handle in the dark, and Pyecraft's familiar grunts.

"It's all right," I said, "she's gone."

But for a long time the door didn't open.

I heard the key turn. Then Pyecraft's voice said, "Come in."

I turned the handle and opened the door. Naturally I expected to see Pyecraft.

Well, you know, he wasn't there!

I never had such a shock in my life. There was his sitting-room in a state of untidy disorder, plates and dishes among the books and writing things, and several chairs overturned, but Pyecraft—

"It's all right, o' man; shut the door," he said, and then I discovered him.

There he was right up close to the cornice in the corner by the door, as though someone had glued him to the ceiling. His face was anxious and angry. He panted and gesticulated.

108

"Shut the door," he said. "If that woman gets hold of it—"

I shut the door, and went and stood away from him and stared.

"If anything gives way and you tumble down," I said, "you'll break your neck, Pyecraft."

"I wish I could," he wheezed.

"A man of your age and weight getting up to kiddish gymnastics—"

"Don't," he said, and looked agonized. "Your old great-grandmother—"

"Be careful," I warned him.

"I'll tell you," he said, and gesticulated.

"How the deuce," said I, "are you holding on up there?"

And then abruptly I realized that he was not holding on at all, that he was floating up there—just as a gas-filled bladder might have floated in the same position. He began a struggle to thrust himself away from the ceiling and to clamber down the wall to me. "It's that prescription," he panted, as he did so. "Your great-gran—"

"*No!*" I cried.

He took hold of a framed engraving rather carelessly as he spoke and it gave way, and he flew back to the ceiling again, while the picture smashed on to the sofa. Bump he went against the ceiling, and I knew then why he was all over white on the more salient curves and angles of his person. He tried again more carefully, coming down by way of the mantel.

It was really a most extraordinary spectacle, that great, fat, apoplectic-looking man upside down and trying to get from the ceiling to the floor. "That prescription," he said. "Too successful."

"How?"

"Loss of weight—almost complete."

And then, of course, I understood.

"By Jove, Pyecraft," said I, "what you wanted was a cure for fatness! But you always called it weight. You would call it weight."

Somehow I was extremely delighted. I quite liked Pyecraft

for the time. "Let me help you!" I said, and took his hand and pulled him down. He kicked about, trying to get foothold somewhere. It was very like holding a flag on a windy day.

"That table," he said, pointing, "is solid mahogany and very heavy. If you can put me under that—"

I did, and there he wallowed about like a captive balloon, while I stood on his hearthrug and talked to him.

I lit a cigar. "Tell me," I said, "what happened?"

"I took it," he said.

"How did it taste?"

"Oh, *beastly!*"

I should fancy they all did. Whether one regards the ingredients or the probable compound or the possible results, almost all my great-grandmother's remedies appear to me at least to be extraordinarily uninviting. For my own part—

"I took a little sip first."

"Yes?"

"And as I felt lighter and better after an hour, I decided to take the draught."

"My dear Pyecraft!"

"I held my nose," he explained. "And then I kept on getting lighter and lighter—and helpless, you know."

He gave way suddenly to a burst of passion. "What the goodness am I to *do?*" he said.

"There's one thing pretty evident," I said, "that you mustn't do. If you go out of doors you'll go up and up." I waved an arm upward. "They'd have to send Santos-Dumont after you to bring you down again."

"I suppose it will wear off?"

I shook my head. "I don't think you can count on that," I said.

And then there was another burst of passion, and he kicked out at adjacent chairs and banged the floor. He behaved just as I should have expected a great, fat, self-indulgent man to behave under trying circumstances—that is to say, very badly. He spoke of me and of my great-grandmother with an utter want of discretion.

"I never asked you to take the stuff," I said.

110

And generously disregarding the insults he was putting upon me, I sat down in his armchair and began to talk to him in a sober, friendly fashion.

I pointed out to him that this was a trouble he had brought upon himself, and that it had almost an air of poetic justice. He had eaten too much. This he disputed, and for a time we argued the point.

He became noisy and violent, so I desisted from this aspect of his lesson. "And then," said I, "you committed the sin of euphuism. You called it, not Fat, which is just and inglorious, but Weight. You—"

He interrupted to say that he recognized all that. What was he to *do?*

I suggested he should adapt himself to his new conditions. So we came to the really sensible part of the business. I suggested that it would not be difficult for him to learn to walk about on the ceiling with his hands—

"I can't sleep," he said.

But that was no great difficulty. It was quite possible, I pointed out, to make a shake-up under a wire mattress, fasten the under things on with tapes, and have a blanket, sheet, and coverlet to button at the side. He would have to confide in his housekeeper, I said; and after some squabbling he agreed to that. (Afterwards it was quite delightful to see the beautifully matter-of-fact way with which the good lady took all these amazing inversions.) He could have a library ladder in his room, and all his meals could be laid on the top of his bookcase. We also hit on an ingenious device by which he could get to the floor whenever he wanted, which was simply to put the *British Encyclopedia* (tenth edition) on the top of his open shelves. He just pulled out a couple of volumes and held on, and down he came. And we agreed there must be iron staples along the skirting, so that he could cling to those whenever he wanted to get about the room on the lower level.

As we got on with the thing I found myself almost keenly interested. It was I who called in the housekeeper and broke matters to her, and it was I chiefly who fixed up the inverted

112

bed. In fact, I spent two whole days at his flat. I am a handy, interfering sort of man with a screwdriver, and I made all sorts of ingenious adaptations for him—ran a wire to bring his bells within reach, turned all his electric lights up instead of down, and so on. The whole affair was extremely curious and interesting to me, and it was delightful to think of Pyecraft like some great, fat blowfly, crawling about on his ceiling and clambering round the lintel of his doors from one room to another, and never, never, never coming to the club any more. . . .

Then, you know, my fatal ingenuity got the better of me. I was sitting by his fire drinking his whisky, and he was up in his favorite corner by the cornice, tacking a Turkey carpet to the ceiling, when the idea struck me. "By Jove, Pyecraft!" I said, "all this is totally unnecessary."

And before I could calculate the complete consequences of my notion I blurted it out. "Lead underclothing," said I, and the mischief was done.

Pyecraft received the thing almost in tears. "To be right ways up again—" he said.

I gave him the whole secret before I saw where it would

113

take me. "Buy sheet lead," I said, "stamp it into discs. Sew 'em all over your underclothes until you have enough. Have lead-soled boots, carry a bag of solid lead, and the thing is done! Instead of being a prisoner here you may go abroad again, Pyecraft, you may travel—"

A still happier idea came to me. "You need never fear a shipwreck. All you need do is just slip off some or all of your clothes, take the necessary amount of luggage in your hand, and float up in the air—"

In his emotion he dropped the tack-hammer within an ace of my head. "By Jove!" he said, "I shall be able to come back to the club again."

The thing pulled me up short. "By Jove!" I said, faintly. "Yes. Of course—you will."

He did. He does. There he sits behind me now stuffing—as I live!—a third go of buttered teacake. And no one in the whole world knows—except his housekeeper and me—that he weighs practically nothing; that he is a mere boring mass of assimilatory matter, mere clouds in clothing, *niente, nefas*, the most inconsiderable of men. There he sits watching until I have done this writing. Then, if he can, he will waylay me. He will come billowing up to me. . . .

He will tell me over again all about it, how it feels, how it doesn't feel, how he sometimes hopes it is passing off a little. And always somewhere in that fat, abundant discourse he will say, "The secret's keeping, eh? If anyone knew of it—I should be so ashamed. . . . Makes a fellow look such a fool, you know. Crawling about on a ceiling and all that. . . ."

And now to elude Pyecraft, occupying, as he does, an admirable strategic position between me and the door.

Robert A. Heinlein

THE BLACK PITS
OF LUNA

ILLUSTRATED BY *Brinton Turkle*

THE morning after we got to the Moon we went over to Rutherford. Dad and Mr. Latham—Mr. Latham is the man from the Harriman Trust that Dad came to Luna City to see—Dad and Mr. Latham had to go anyhow, on business. I got Dad to promise I could go along because it looked like just about my only chance to get out on the surface of the Moon. Luna City is all right, I guess, but I defy you to tell a corridor in Luna City from the sublevels in New York—except that you're light on your feet, of course.

When Dad came into our hotel suite to say we were ready to leave, I was down on the floor, playing mumblety-peg with my kid brother. Mother was lying down and had asked me to keep the runt quiet. She had been dropsick all the way out from Earth and I guess she didn't feel very good. The runt had been fiddling with the lights, switching them from "dusk" to "desert sun-tan" and back again. I collared him and sat him down on the floor.

Of course, I don't play mumblety-peg any more, but, on the Moon, it's a right good game. The knife practically floats and you can do all kinds of things with it. We made up a lot of new rules.

Dad said, "Switch in plans, my dear. We're leaving for Rutherford right away."

Mother said, "Oh, mercy me—I don't think I'm up to it. You and Dickie run along. Baby Darling and I will just spend a quiet day right here."

Baby Darling is the runt.

115

I could have told her it was the wrong approach. He nearly put my eye out with the knife and said, "Who? What? I'm going too. Let's go!"

Mother said, "Oh, now, Baby Darling—don't cause Mother Dear any trouble. We'll go to the movies, just you and I."

The runt is seven years younger than I am, but don't call him "Baby Darling" if you want to get anything out of him. He started to bawl. "You said I could go!" he yelled.

"No, Baby Darling. I haven't mentioned it to you. I—"

"Daddy said I could go!"

"Richard, did you tell baby he could go?"

"Why, no, my dear, not that I recall. Perhaps I—"

The kid cut in fast. "You said I could go anywhere Dickie went. You promised me you promised me you promised me." Sometimes you have to hand it to the runt; he had them jawing about who told him what in nothing flat. Anyhow that is how, twenty minutes later, the four of us were up at the rocket port with Mr. Latham and climbing into the shuttle for Rutherford.

The trip only takes about ten minutes and you don't see much, just a glimpse of the Earth while the rocket is still near Luna City and then not even that, since the atom plants where we were going are all on the back side of the Moon, of course. There were maybe a dozen tourists along and most of them were dropsick as soon as we went into free flight. So was Mother. Some people never will get used to rockets.

116

But Mother was all right as soon as we grounded and were inside again. Rutherford isn't like Luna City; instead of extending a tube out to the ship, they send a pressurized car out to latch on to the airlock of the rocket, then you jeep back about a mile to the entrance to underground. I liked that and so did the runt. Dad had to go off on business with Mr. Latham, leaving Mother and me and the runt to join up with the party of tourists for the trip through the laboratories.

It was all right, but nothing to get excited about. So far as I can see, one atomic plant looks about like another; Rutherford could just as well have been the main plant outside Chicago. I mean to say everything that is anything is out of sight, covered up, shielded. All you get to see are some dials and instrument boards and people watching them. Remote-control stuff, like Oak Ridge. The guide tells you about the experiments going on and they show you some movies—that's all.

I liked our guide. He looked like Tom Jeremy in The Space Troopers. I asked him if he was a spaceman and he looked at me kind of funny and said, no, that he was just a Colonial Services ranger. Then he asked me where I went to school and if I belonged to the Scouts. He said he was scoutmaster of Troop One, Rutherford City, Moonbat Patrol.

I found out there was just the one patrol—not many scouts on the Moon, I suppose.

Dad and Mr. Latham joined us just as we finished the tour while Mr. Perrin—that's our guide—was announcing the trip outside. "The conducted tour of Rutherford," he said, talking as if it were a transcription, "includes a trip by spacesuit out on the surface of the Moon, without extra charge, to see the Devil's Graveyard and the site of the Great Disaster of 1965. The trip is optional. There is nothing particularly dangerous about it and we've never had anyone hurt, but the commission requires that you sign a separate release for your own safety if you choose to make this trip. The trip takes about one hour. Those preferring to remain behind will find movies and refreshments in the coffee shop."

Dad was rubbing his hands. "This is for me," he announced.

117

"Mr. Latham, I'm glad we got back in time. I wouldn't have missed this for the world."

"You'll enjoy it," Mr. Latham agreed, "and so will you, Mrs. Logan. I'm tempted to come along myself."

"Why don't you?" Dad asked.

"No, I want to have the papers ready for you and the director to sign when you get back and before you leave for Luna City."

"Why knock yourself out?" Dad urged him. "If a man's word is no good, his signed contract is no better. You can mail the stuff to me at New York."

Mr. Latham shook his head. "No, really—I've been out on the surface dozens of times. But I'll come along and help you into your spacesuits."

Mother said oh dear, she didn't think she'd better go; she wasn't sure she could stand the thought of being shut up in a spacesuit and, besides, glaring sunlight always gave her a headache.

Dad said, "Don't be silly, my dear; it's the chance of a lifetime," and Mr. Latham told her that the helmets' filters kept the light from being glaring.

Mother always objects and then gives in. She came along. We went into the outfitting room and I looked around while Mr. Perrin was getting them all herded in and having the releases signed. There was the door to the airlock to the surface at the far end, with a bull's-eye window in it and another one like it in the door beyond. You could peek through and see the surface of the Moon beyond, looking hot and bright and sort of improbable, in spite of the amber glass in the windows. And there was a double row of spacesuits hanging up, looking like empty men. I snooped around until Mr. Perrin finally got around to our party.

"We can arrange to leave the youngster in the care of the hostess in the coffee shop," he was telling Mother. He reached down and tousled the runt's hair. The runt tried to bite him and he snatched his hand away in a hurry.

"Thank you, Mr. Perkins," Mother said; "I suppose that's best —though perhaps I had better stay behind with him."

" 'Perrin' is the name," Mr. Perrin said mildly. "It won't be necessary. The hostess will take good care of him."

Why do adults talk in front of kids as if they couldn't understand English? They should have just shoved him into the coffee shop. By now the runt knew he was being railroaded. He looked around belligerently. "I go too," he said loudly. "You promised me."

"Now, Baby Darling," Mother tried to stop him. "Mother Dear didn't tell you—" But she was just whistling to herself; the runt turned on the sound effects.

"You said I could go where Dickie went; you promised me when I was sick. You promised me you promised me—" and on and on, his voice getting higher and louder all the time.

Mr. Perrin looked embarrassed. Mother said, "Richard, you'll just have to deal with your child. After all, you were the one who promised him."

"Me, dear?" Dad looked surprised. "Anyway, I don't see anything so complicated about it. Suppose we did promise him that he could do what Dickie does—we'll simply take him along."

Mr. Perrin cleared his throat. "I'm afraid not. I can outfit your older son with a woman's suit; he's tall for his age. But we just don't make any provision for small children."

Well, we were all tangled up in a mess in no time at all. The runt can always get Mother running in circles. Mother has the same effect on Dad. He gets red in the face and starts laying down the law to *me*. It's sort of a chain reaction, with me on the end and nobody to pass it along to. They came out with a very simple solution—I was to stay behind and take care of Baby Darling brat!

"But, Dad, you said—" I started in.

"Never mind!" he cut in. "I won't have this family disrupted in a public squabble. You heard what your mother said."

I was desperate. "Look, Dad," I said, keeping my voice low, "if I go back to Earth without once having put on a spacesuit and set foot on the surface, you'll just have to find another school to send me to. I won't go back to Lawrenceville; I'd be the joke of the whole place."

119

"We'll settle that when we get home."

"But, Dad, you promised me specifically—"

"That'll be enough out of you, young man. The matter is closed."

Mr. Latham had been standing near by, taking it in, but keeping his mouth shut. At this point he cocked an eyebrow at Dad and said very quietly, "Well, R. J.—I thought your word was your bond?"

I wasn't supposed to hear it and nobody else did—a good thing, too, for it doesn't do to let Dad know that you know that he's wrong; it just makes him worse. I changed the subject in a hurry. "Look, Dad, maybe we all can go out. How about that suit over there?" I pointed at a rack that was inside a railing with a locked gate on it. The rack had a couple of dozen suits on it and at the far end, almost out of sight, was a small suit— the boots on it hardly came down to the waist of the suit next to it.

"Huh?" Dad brightened up. "Why, just the thing! Mr. Perrin! Oh, Mr. Perrin—here a minute! I thought you didn't have any small suits, but here's one that I think will fit."

Dad was fiddling at the latch of the railing gate. Mr. Perrin stopped him. "We can't use that suit, sir."

"Uh? Why not?"

"All the suits inside the railing are private property, not for rent."

"What? Nonsense—Rutherford is a public enterprise. I want that suit for my child."

"Well, you can't have it."

"I'll speak to the director."

"I'm afraid you'll have to. That suit was specially built for his daughter."

And that's just what they did. Mr. Latham got the director on the line, Dad talked to him, then the director talked to Mr. Perrin, then he talked to Dad again. The director didn't mind lending the suit, not to Dad, anyway, but he wouldn't order Mr. Perrin to take a below-age child outside.

Mr. Perrin was feeling stubborn and I don't blame him, but

Dad soothed his feathers down and presently we were all climbing into our suits and getting pressure checks and checking our oxygen supply and switching on our walkie-talkies. Mr. Perrin was calling the roll by radio and reminding us that we were all on the same circuit, so we had better let him do most of the talking and not to make casual remarks or none of us would be able to hear. Then we were in the airlock and he was warning us to stick close together and not try to see how fast we could run or how high we could jump. My heart was knocking around in my chest.

The outer door of the lock opened and we filed out on the face of the Moon. It was just as wonderful as I dreamed it would be, I guess, but I was so excited that I hardly knew it at the time. The glare of the sun was the brightest thing I ever saw and the shadows so inky black you could hardly see into them. You couldn't hear anything but voices over your radio and you could reach down and switch off that.

The pumice was soft and kicked up around our feet like

smoke, settling slowly, falling in slow motion. Nothing else moved. It was the *deadest* place you can imagine.

We stayed on a path, keeping close together for company, except twice when I had to take out after the runt when he found out he could jump twenty feet. I wanted to smack him, but did you ever try to smack anybody wearing a spacesuit? It's no use.

Mr. Perrin told us to halt presently and started his talk. "You are now in the Devil's Graveyard. The twin spires behind you are five thousand feet above the floor of the plain and have never been scaled. The spires, or monuments, have been named for apocryphal or mythological characters because of the fancied resemblance of this fantastic scene to a giant cemetery. Beelzebub, Thor, Siva, Cain, Seth—" He pointed around us. "Lunologists are not agreed as to the origin of the strange shapes. Some claim to see indications of the action of air and water as well as volcanic action. If so, these spires must have been standing for an unthinkably long period, for today, as you see, the Moon—" It was the same sort of stuff you can read any month in Spaceways Magazine, only we were seeing it and that makes a difference, let me tell you.

The spires reminded me a bit of the rocks below the lodge in the Garden of the Gods in Colorado Springs when we went there last summer, only these spires were lots bigger and, instead of blue sky, there was just blackness and hard, sharp stars overhead. Spooky.

Another ranger had come with us, with a camera. Mr. Perrin tried to say something else, but the runt had started yapping away and I had to switch off his radio before anybody could hear anything. I kept it switched off until Mr. Perrin finished talking.

He wanted us to line up for a picture, with the spires and the black sky behind us for a background. "Push your faces forward in your helmets so that your features will show. Everybody look pretty. There!" he added as the other guy snapped the shot. "Prints will be ready at ten dollars a copy when you return."

I thought it over. I certainly needed one for my room at

school and I wanted one to give to—anyhow, I needed another one. I had eighteen bucks left from my birthday money; I could sweet-talk Mother for the balance. So I ordered two of them.

We climbed a long rise and suddenly we were staring out across the crater, the disaster crater, all that was left of the first laboratory. It stretched away from us, twenty miles across, with the floor covered with shiny, bubbly green glass instead of pumice. There was a monument. I read it:

HERE ABOUT YOU ARE THE
MORTAL REMAINS OF

KURT SCHAEFFER

MAURICE FEINSTEIN

THOMAS DOOLEY

HAZEL HAYAKAWA

G. WASHINGTON SLAPPEY

SAM HOUSTON ADAMS

WHO DIED FOR THE TRUTH
THAT MAKES MEN FREE

ON THE ELEVENTH DAY OF AUGUST 1965

I felt sort of funny and backed away and went to listen to Mr. Perrin. Dad and some of the other men were asking him questions. "They don't know exactly," he was saying. "Nothing was left. Now we telemeter all the data back to Luna City, as it comes off the instruments, but that was before the line-of-sight relays were set up."

"What would have happened," some man asked, "if this blast had gone off on Earth?"

"I'd hate to try to tell you—but that's why they put the lab here, back of the Moon." He glanced at his watch. "Time to leave, everybody." They were milling around, heading back down toward the path, when Mother screamed.

"Baby! Where's Baby Darling?"

123

I was startled, but I wasn't scared, not yet. The runt is always running around, first here and then there, but he doesn't go far away, because he always wants to have somebody to yap to.

My father had one arm around Mother; he signaled to me with the other. "Dick," he snapped, his voice sharp in my earphones, "what have you done with your brother?"

"Me?" I said. "Don't look at me—the last I saw, Mother had him by the hand, walking up the hill here."

"Don't stall around, Dick. Mother sat down to rest when we got here and sent him to you."

"Well, if she did, he never showed up." At that, Mother started to scream in earnest. Everybody had been listening, of course—they had to; there was just the one radio circuit. Mr. Perrin stepped up and switched off Mother's talkie, making a sudden silence.

"Take care of your wife, Mr. Logan," he ordered, then added, "When did you see your child last?"

Dad couldn't help him any; when they tried switching Mother back into the hookup, they switched her right off again. She couldn't help, either, and she deafened us. Mr. Perrin addressed the rest of us. "Has anyone seen the small child we had with us? Don't answer unless you have something to contribute. Did anyone see him wander away?"

Nobody had. I figured he probably ducked out when everybody was looking at the crater and had their backs to him. I told Mr. Perrin so. "Seems likely," he agreed. "Attention, everybody! I'm going to search for the child. Stay right where you are. Don't move away from this spot. I won't be gone more than ten minutes."

"Why don't we all go?" somebody wanted to know.

"Because," said Mr. Perrin, "right now I've only got one lost. I don't want to make it a dozen." Then he left, taking big easy lopes that covered fifty feet at a step.

Dad started to take out after him, then thought better of it, for Mother suddenly keeled over, collapsing at the knees and floating gently to the ground. Everybody started talking at once. Some idiot wanted to take her helmet off, but Dad isn't crazy.

124

I switched off my radio so I could hear myself think and started looking around, not leaving the crowd, but standing up on the lip of the crater and trying to see as much as I could.

I was looking back the way we had come; there was no sense in looking at the crater—if he had been in there he would have shown up like a fly on a plate.

Outside the crater was different; you could have hidden a regiment within a block of us, rocks standing up every which way, boulders big as houses with blowholes all through them, spires, gullies—it was a mess. I could see Mr. Perrin every now and then, casting around like a dog after a rabbit, and making plenty of time. He was practically flying. When he came to a big boulder he would jump right over it, leveling off face down at the top of his jump, so he could see better.

Then he was heading back toward us and I switched my radio back on. There was still a lot of talk. Somebody was saying, "We've got to find him before sundown," and somebody else answered, "Don't be silly; the sun won't be down for a week. It's his air supply, I tell you. These suits are only good for four hours." The first voice said, "Oh!" then added softly, "like a fish out of water—" It was then I got scared.

A woman's voice, sounding kind of choked, said, "The poor, poor darling! We've got to find him before he suffocates," and my father's voice cut in sharply, "Shut up talking that way!" I could hear somebody sobbing. It might have been Mother.

Mr. Perrin was almost up to us and he cut in, "Silence, everybody. I've got to call the base," and he added urgently, "Perrin, calling airlock control; Perrin, calling airlock control!"

A woman's voice answered, "Come in, Perrin." He told her what was wrong and added, "Send out Smythe to take this party back in; I'm staying. I want every ranger who's around, and get me volunteers from among any of the experienced Moon hands. Send out a radio direction-finder by the first ones to leave."

We didn't wait long, for they came swarming toward us like grasshoppers. They must have been running forty or fifty miles an hour. It would have been something to see, if I hadn't been so sick at my stomach.

Dad put up an argument about going back, but Mr. Perrin shut him up. "If you hadn't been so confounded set on having your own way, we wouldn't be in a mess. If you had kept track of your kid, he wouldn't be lost. I've got kids of my own; I don't let 'em go out on the face of the Moon when they're too young to take care of themselves. You go on back—I can't be burdened by taking care of you too."

I think Dad might even have gotten in a fight with him if Mother hadn't gotten faint again. We went on back with the party.

The next couple of hours were pretty awful. They let us sit just outside the control room where we could hear Mr. Perrin directing the search, over the loudspeaker. I thought at first that they would snag the runt as soon as they started using the radio direction-finder—pick up his power hum, maybe, even if he didn't say anything—but no such luck: they didn't get anything with it. And the searchers didn't find anything either.

A thing that made it worse was that Mother and Dad didn't even try to blame me. Mother was crying quietly and Dad was consoling her, when he looked over at me with an odd expression. I guess he didn't really see me at all, but I thought he was thinking that if I hadn't insisted on going out on the surface this wouldn't have happened. I said, "Don't go looking at me, Dad. Nobody told me to keep an eye on him. I thought he was with Mother."

Dad just shook his head without answering. He was looking tired and sort of shrunk up. But Mother, instead of laying in to me and yelling, stopped her crying and managed to smile. "Come here, Dickie," she said, and put her other arm around me. "Nobody blames you, Dickie. Whatever happens, you weren't at fault. Remember that, Dickie."

So I let her kiss me and then sat with them for awhile, but I felt worse than before. I kept thinking about the runt, somewhere out there, and his oxygen running out. Maybe it wasn't my fault, but I could have prevented it and I knew it. I shouldn't have depended on Mother to look out for him; she's no good at that sort of thing. She's the kind of person that would mislay

127

her head if it wasn't knotted on tight—the ornamental sort. Mother's good, you understand, but she's not practical.

She would take it pretty hard if the runt didn't come back. And so would Dad—and so would I. The runt is an awful nuisance, but it was going to seem strange not to have him around underfoot. I got to thinking about that remark, "Like a fish out of water." If the runt was going to die like that—

I shut myself up and decided I just had to figure out some way to help find him.

After awhile I had myself convinced that I *could* find him if they would just let me help look. But they wouldn't, of course.

Doctor Evans, the director, showed up again—he'd met us when we first came in—and asked if there was anything he could do for us and how was Mrs. Logan feeling. "You know I wouldn't have had this happen for the world," he added. "We're doing all we can. I'm having some ore detectors shot over from Luna City. We might be able to spot the child by the metal in his suit."

Mother asked how about bloodhounds and Doctor Evans didn't even laugh at her. Dad suggested helicopters, then corrected himself and made it rockets. Doctor Evans pointed out that it was almost impossible to examine the ground closely from a rocket.

I got him aside presently and braced him to let me join the hunt. He was polite but unimpressed, so I insisted. "What makes you think you can find him?" he asked me. "We've got the most experienced Moon men available out there now. I'm afraid, son, that you would get yourself lost or hurt if you tried to keep up with them. In this country, if you once lose sight of landmarks, you can get hopelessly lost."

"But look, Doctor," I told him, "I know the runt—I mean my kid brother better than anyone else in the world. I won't get lost —I mean I will get lost, but just the way he did. You can send somebody to follow me."

He thought about it. "It's worth trying," he said suddenly. "I'll go with you. Let's suit up."

We made a fast trip out, taking thirty-foot strides—the best I could manage even with Doctor Evans hanging on to my belt to keep me from stumbling. Mr. Perrin was expecting us. He seemed dubious about my scheme. "Maybe the old 'lost mule' dodge will work," he admitted, "but I'll keep the regular search going just the same. Here, Shorty, take this flashlight. You'll need it in the shadows."

I stood on the edge of the crater and tried to imagine I was the runt, feeling bored and maybe a little bit griped at the lack of attention. What would I do next?

I went skipping down the slope, not going anywhere in particular, the way the runt would have done. Then I stopped and looked back, to see if Mother and Daddy and Dickie had noticed me. I was being followed all right; Doctor Evans and Mr. Perrin were close behind me. I pretended that no one was looking and went on. I was pretty close to the first rock outcroppings by now and I ducked behind the first one I came to. It wasn't high enough to hide me, but it would have covered the runt. It felt like what he would do; he loved to play hide-and-go-seek—it made him the center of attention.

I thought about it. When the runt played that game, his notion of hiding was always to crawl under something, a bed, or a sofa, or an automobile, or even under the sink. I looked around. There were a lot of good places; the rocks were filled with blowholes and overhangs. I started working them over. It seemed hopeless; there must have been a hundred such places right around close.

Mr. Perrin came up to me as I was crawling out of the fourth tight spot. "The men have shined flashlights around in every one of these places," he told me. "I don't think it's much use, Shorty."

"Okay," I said, but I kept at it. I knew I could get at spots a grown man couldn't reach; I just hoped the runt hadn't picked a spot I couldn't reach.

It went on and on and I was getting cold and stiff and terribly tired. The direct sunlight is hot on the Moon, but the second you get in the shade, it's cold. Down inside those rocks it never got warm at all. The suits they gave us tourists are well enough insulated, but the extra insulation is in the gloves and the boots and the seats of the pants—and I had been spending most of

my time down on my stomach, wiggling into tight places.

I was so numb I could hardly move and my whole front felt icy. Besides, it gave me one more thing to worry about—how about the runt? Was he cold too?

If it hadn't been for thinking how those fish looked and how, maybe, the runt would be frozen stiff before I could get to him, I would have quit. I was about beat. Besides, it's rather scary down inside those holes—you don't know what you'll come to next.

Doctor Evans took me by the arm as I came out of one of them, and touched his helmet to mine, so that I got his voice directly. "Might as well give up, son. You're knocking yourself out and you haven't covered an acre." I pulled away from him.

The next place was a little overhang, not a foot off the ground. I flashed a light into it. It was empty and didn't seem to go anywhere. Then I saw there was a turn in it. I got down flat and wiggled in. The turn opened out a little and dropped off. I didn't think it was worthwhile to go any deeper as the runt wouldn't have crawled very far in the dark, but I scrunched ahead a little farther and flashed the light down.

I saw a boot sticking out.

That's about all there is to it. I nearly bashed in my helmet getting out of there, but I was dragging the runt after me. He was limp as a cat and his face was funny. Mr. Perrin and Doctor Evans were all over me as I came out, pounding me on the back and shouting.

"Is he *dead*, Mr. Perrin?" I asked, when I could get my breath. "He looks awful bad."

Mr. Perrin looked him over. "No . . . I can see a pulse in his throat. Shock and exposure, but this suit was specially built—we'll get him back fast." He picked the runt up in his arms and I took out after him.

Ten minutes later the runt was wrapped in blankets and drinking hot cocoa. I had some too. Everybody was talking at once and Mother was crying again, but she looked normal and Dad had filled out.

He tried to write out a check for Mr. Perrin, but he brushed it off. "I don't need any reward; your boy found him. You can do me just one favor—"

"Yes?" Dad was all honey.

"Stay off the Moon. You don't belong here; you're not the pioneer type."

Dad took it. "I've already promised my wife that," he said without batting an eye. "You needn't worry."

I followed Mr. Perrin as he left and said to him privately, "Mr. Perrin—I just wanted to tell you that I'll be back, if you don't mind."

He shook hands with me and said, "I know you will, Shorty."

H. Percy Wilkins

IS THERE
LIFE ON THE MOON?

ILLUSTRATED BY *Ann Davidow*

FROM time immemorial men have gazed and wondered at the Moon. Not until the year 1609, when Galileo directed the first telescope at the Moon, was the mystery of the dark patches solved. Poor as his telescope was, it served to reveal that the dark patches were vast plains, while the bright areas were obviously mountainous.

Thanks to careful observations in the past we now possess highly detailed maps and charts, while the face of the Moon has also been photographed with great success. Indeed, in some respects, we actually know the Moon better than we know some parts of the Earth. Being so small, a little more than a quarter the diameter of the Earth, things weigh much less on the Moon. There is no sound for there is no air to carry it, no clouds, no smell, no life.

Some people believe the Moon to be a portion of the Earth, thrown off when it was molten; others think it was a separate planet which came close to Earth and was "captured" by it.

I have observed the Moon with some of the largest and finest telescopes in the world, and on some occasions have seen what appear to be evidences of changes of some kind.

The largest crater is 180 miles in diameter, and Pluto, which is 60 miles across, has received especial attention. In April of this year, observing with the Meudon telescope, the third largest refracting telescope in the world, on a very good night, I failed to see a little crater within Pluto which had been plainly seen at other times. What is even stranger, an American observer looked at Pluto a few hours later and could see no detail on its interior, not even the four tiny craters which I saw plainly. Fortunately my friend, Mr. P. A. Moore, was with me and saw

132

exactly the same details as I did, but no trace of this particular crater. It is suggested that something like mist, or fog, or smoke was slowly drifting over the interior of Pluto.

The Moon revolves around the Earth once a month. It has no light of its own, but reflects the sun's rays and this is the reason why it seems to change its shape, according to the amount of the sunlit side we can see. It always keeps the same face turned to us, except for a slight swaying which allows us to peer a little on to the other side. The surface is covered with large dark plains, numerous ring-like objects, the so-called craters which are perhaps old volcanoes, or possibly the result of meteors hitting the Moon when the surface was still plastic. Some of the craters are larger than anything on Earth; the highest mountain is probably higher than Everest.

With good telescopes we have traced numerous cracks, some extending hundreds of miles; also strange white rays like search-light beams.

Owing to the great changes in temperatures between day and night, it is unlikely that anything like life, as we know it, exists on the Moon. It is a world of eternal silence, a still waste of rocks and craters, barren plains and mountains; but it will be the first object to be visited by man, when rocket-ships journey into space.

Science facts.

Captain Burr Leyson

TRAIL TO THE STARS

ILLUSTRATED BY *John Merryweather*

ZERO HOUR minus one! Within exactly sixty seconds a roaring inferno of flame would blast from the tailpipes of the giant and she would begin her journey into the void. Towering higher than a six-story building, she rested on her four great stabilizing fins, nose pointed into space and her metal sides gleaming in the hot New Mexican sun of the White Sands Proving Grounds.

At first glance the huge missile that dwarfed the technicians scurrying about her base on last-moment adjustments seemed odd. It differed from the usual rocket in that it had a long and pointed nose and there was a secondary and smaller set of fins at the base of the elongated nose section. Closer inspection revealed that the rocket consisted of two units. The base was the huge bulk of the familiar German V-2 rocket. The long slender "nose" with the secondary set of fins consisted of an American rocket set in the nose of the older V-2. The missile was a combination of V-2 and "WAC Corporal." The V-2 would carry the "WAC" far into the upper regions of the atmosphere and then, as its velocity became spent under the steady pull of Earth's gravity, the slender "WAC" would be fired to hurtle still farther into the void.

Now the loud-speakers blared:

"Stand clear! Prepare to fire! FIRE!"

With the command of "FIRE!" there was a muffled explosion deep within the base of the rocket. An instant later a wave of brilliant flame swept from her tailpipes, rolled across the broad cement platform upon which the rocket was poised, and licked hungrily at her broad fins. Abruptly the flame changed to an

134

almost imperceptible blue, and now waves of intense heat distorted the scene. The muted roar of the first firing became a reverberation that shook the earth. The great rocket began to rise.

For the first few feet so slow was her rise that it seemed certain she must topple and fall back to earth. But the control vanes set in the flaming geyser of her exhaust answered to the impulses of her stabilizing gyroscopes and held her steadily upright. Then, with incredible swiftness, she began to pick up speed. Within seconds she was but a minute dot against the blue vault of the sky and an instant later was gone from sight, leaving only a long tenuous trail of white condensation and the deep roar of her exhaust.

Within some seventy seconds she had burned the last of her ten tons of liquid fuel and was hurtling upward, more than one hundred miles above Earth. Now she had attained a speed of a mile a second, thirty-six hundred miles an hour. Under the urge of her tremendous energy she bored on into space until finally she was slowed, her impetus all but spent. It was at this moment that the "WAC" in her nose was fired, and now it hurtled upward, reaching for the stars.

Finally halted by Earth's gravity, the huge V-2 hung motionless for an instant, slowly turned end for end, and then began the long plunge back to Earth. Instants later, traveling at some eleven hundred miles an hour and heated to over six hundred degrees by the terrific friction of the atmosphere at that speed, she crashed into shattered fragments against the surface of Earth. Shortly after, the "WAC" followed her, smashing to pieces miles away.

This flight was merely one of the many exploring fingers we are thrusting ever deeper and deeper into the mysterious realm of space. Today we stand on the threshold of a new and utterly fantastic world—the vast reaches of outer space beyond our Earth. Here is a region where gravity is nonexistent, where water will not pour, where men can lift tons with ease, and where there is no atmosphere but a perfect vacuum, where cold reaches absolute zero of minus four hundred and sixty degrees

135

and the rays of the sun are blistering hot, where speeds of tens of thousands of miles an hour are possible. It is into this weird world that man is penetrating slowly but surely.

No less an authority than General Eisenhower has stated that "space rockets and space travel are in the immediate foreseeable future." Top-ranking officers of the Air Forces such as Doolittle, Spaatz, and Arnold all expressed similar views during their periods of command, and this has been confirmed time and again by the now heads of our military establishments who are charged with this research. Over one hundred million dollars are being spent monthly on the project. Top-flight scientists are devoting all of their time to its problems.

Within the next few years you will see space rockets constantly circling the globe, sending back a stream of scientific data as they orbit. Great metal space stations that will likewise orbit in space around Earth are even now on the drawing boards of our engineering staffs. In these huge globular satellites scientists will work and meteorologists compile accurate and elaborate weather reports. Other space stations will act as bases for exploring rockets into the vast unknown reaches of outer space. This is coldly scientific fact, not fiction. The visionary "Buck Rogers" era is all but here.

Preposterous as such developments may seem at first glance and breathtaking as they are, the problem of man's conquest of space is not as insurmountable as one would think. Physicists point to the fact that we now are possessed of the necessary knowledge and have the technical and practical means at hand. One of the essentials is a proper fuel. Rockets consume huge quantities of fuel, and there is a very definite limitation to the

amount of useful load a rocket can carry at the present, owing to the tremendous load of fuel it must take on for its flight. But scientists have developed new fuels which, although costly at the present time, are nevertheless sufficiently compact and light in weight as to augment tremendously the useful load the rocket can carry. Metal alloys which can withstand the terrific temperatures these special fuels develop are likewise being tested. The exact details of these new developments are deeply cloaked in national security and have not been released. Only the methods by which space will be conquered are clearly defined.

Scientists state that the first and all-important step is to fire a rocket to a point some two hundred miles above Earth and have it traveling at a speed of five miles a second when it arrives there. Such a rocket will never return to Earth of its own accord but will constantly circle the Earth, even without power! It will become a man-made satellite. The explanation is simple.

At a point some two hundred miles above the surface of Earth there is no atmosphere; rather, there exists a nearly perfect vacuum. Consequently there is no resistance to the passage of a rocket through this region as there is lower down where the air offers a very real resistance. The rocket will not lose the original speed with which it arrives in this region. Then, say the scientists, let's consider what would happen if we were to fire a powerful cannon at this height above the Earth.

"Suppose," they say, "that you fire the cannon so that the shot goes out parallel to the surface of the Earth. There is no atmosphere to resist its passage so it will not lose its speed. It will fly out from the cannon and continue with unabated speed. But Earth's gravity will act upon it and slowly draw it down until it eventually strikes the Earth. The result will be a long shallow curve marking the flight of the shot from the cannon's mouth to the point where it strikes the Earth. If we fire the shot with a higher speed, it will go straight out farther before gravity begins to bring it down in a curved path. This curve will be shallower than the first and slower shot. Now, it is obvious that, if we fire the shot fast enough, gravity will make it curve as before, but with sufficient speed the curve can be made to correspond with the curve of the Earth's surface. The result will be that the shot will follow the curve of the Earth and go completely around it. As there is nothing to slow it down such as an atmosphere, it will continue to follow this path forever and become a satellite like our moon!"

Calculations show that a speed of but five miles a second is required to do this. The obsolete Nazi V-2 traveled at slightly over a mile a second. That our modern rockets far surpass this speed is evident. What will happen when we reach the five-mile-a-second speed is likewise evident. The space rocket will be a fact.

From this point of establishing the space rocket that will orbit the Earth the developments are dramatic, utterly fantastic, but logical.

We know that we can send manned rockets aloft at the necessary speed once we develop the original rocket. The forces generated by the acceleration are not too severe and can be cushioned so as to be bearable. Further, once in this atmosphereless region, there is practically no limit to the speeds possible, for there is no resistance to the passage of the rockets. The rocket can be synchronized with the speed of rotation of

the Earth and so be caused to remain over a certain spot at will. The Earth and the rocket will travel at the same speed and turn together as one. This is most important, for it is the key to the establishment of the space stations of the immediate future.

Manned rockets are to carry aloft prefabricated parts for the space stations and then synchronize their speed with that of Earth so that they are over the same spot constantly. They will then unload their cargo of prefabricated parts and leave them there, poised in space! As there is no atmosphere and they have the same speed as the rocket they too will orbit the Earth. (When you ride in a car at sixty miles an hour, your body is going forward at the same speed as the car. If you were to fall out, your body would continue at sixty miles an hour unless air resistance or contact with the ground slowed it.) When sufficient material is at hand, men in space suits that contain their own atmosphere and oxygen supply will assemble the station. It will be round and hermetically sealed with an airlock entrance so that the staff and the necessary supplies can be taken in without losing the atmosphere that will be supplied from tanks of compressed gases from Earth. Here again, owing to the fact that there is no atmosphere, the men will be able to work on the structure although they are hurtling through space at five miles a second. Where there is no atmosphere there can be no wind to blow them off.

The value of rocket service stations to the future of the people of the Earth is staggering. Weather can be charted and minutely observed over the entire face of the globe from these stations. We can plan our crops ahead for weeks, know weather exactly. Because of the fact that there is a vacuum at this point in space, all of our electronic devices will operate without trouble in the open and in a far more perfect vacuum than possible here at the surface. Further, there will be no limitations as to the size of the apparatus due to the difficulty of establishing high degrees of vacuum in large containers. With no atmosphere present, observation of the distant planets is perfect, and research will be hugely augmented. The study of the different rays will likewise be made far more simple.

Of almost equal value will be the fact that these space stations will serve as bases for the rockets that will carry crews of scientists to the outer limits of space and even to the distant planets. Starting where gravity is weak and there is no atmosphere, the rockets will have infinitely longer ranges and require less speed to escape the gravitational field of the Earth. They will make distant space travel possible.

The problem of getting back to Earth or of landing on a distant planet is even now solved with the exception of a few operational details. By using auxiliary rockets set at different points in the body of the manned rocket, force can be applied to turn it in any position. If the rocket is reversed so that it approaches the Earth base first, its own power can be applied to check its fall and govern its speed. Gyroscopically controlled vanes set in the exhaust of the rocket will maintain it in any desired position. Nearing the surface of Earth or another planet, more power is applied until the speed is reduced to a safe limit. Then, nearing the actual landing, additional power will ease the rocket down gently. The start of the return journey to Earth by an orbiting rocket will be made by simply applying power in a forward direction to slow its speed so that gravity will begin to bring it down. Likewise, additional speed will permit it to go farther from the Earth and deeper into space.

This is the future, the "immediate foreseeable future" that Eisenhower spoke of and leaders of our Air Force and scientific staffs confirm. Today we are breaking the trail to the stars. It is safe to predict that before the average reader of this book attains the ripe old age of twenty, the trail will have become much clearer, thanks to the efforts of the scientists.

GLOSSARY

Airlock   The opening for entering or leaving a spaceship.

Angstrom Units   Units of measurement of electrical energy.

Asteroid and Planetoid   Identical. Small bodies traveling in the solar system between the orbits of Mars and Jupiter. Presumably the shattered residue of an ancient planet.

Bulgers   (Slang) Space-suits.

Catalyst   A reagent which assists the chemical conjoining or re-action of any two other elements.

Enzyme   A food element.

Gravs   Abbreviation of "gravities." It takes about seven gravities to liberate a spaceship from the attraction of Earth.

Heaviside Layer   An ionized layer outside Earth, otherwise known as Kennelly-Heaviside layer, after its joint discoverers.

Hypos   (Slang) Contracted from "hypatomic" motors, the engines that run future spaceships.

Isotope   A variant of a "standard" element.

Max   Abbreviation for "maximum."

Meso Lead   A stage of deterioration through which uranium passes over a period of millenia in reverting from radioactive material to inert lead.

Permalloy   A superstrong metal.

Pierce-Gun   A conceivable atomic side arm of the future.

Ray-Gun   A conceivable atomic side arm of the future.

Revs   Abbreviation for "revolutions."

Right Cross   A prizefight description of a type of blow in which, after jabbing the opponent's guard down, the fighter "crosses" his right, hoping for a K.O.

Rogue Asteroid   Asteroid with eccentric, unpredictable orbit.

Rotor-Gun   A conceivable atomic cannon of the future.

Solargram   "Solar" and "Gram." Akin to "telegram" in the solar system.

Thallium   An element in the periodic table.

Tropo   Troposphere. The layer above the stratosphere.

Visiplate   The forward viewpane of a spaceship.

Void Whacky   (Slang) "Space happy."

Pages for Parents

PAGES FOR PARENTS

Bertha E. Mahony

President,
The Horn Book Magazine

FAIRY TALES AND THE SPIRIT

I T IS said that today more people are better off than ever before. In America, if we think in terms of food and things, that is doubtless true, but if we think in terms of the spirit, it is far from true. We have widespread so-called education and with it a widespread thick layer of the commonplace. Our education fails to produce the fineness of cultivation. By cultivation is meant something which has nothing to do with colleges and universities, but a quality which unlettered people often have to a marked degree. Many early New Englanders had it; the American Indians had it; certain people the world around have it. It is the outward expression of a properly nourished inward life.

"For the soul and heart of man starves and dies" without its own food. What is the spirit's food? The answer is beauty. And for proper growth it must be had from the beginning along with milk. The first form of beauty a little child may experience is the beauty of love in human relationship. His next form is the beauty of words. And as he proceeds in life, beauty of the physical world and beauty of words will together form the richest nourishment for his spirit.

Perhaps our trouble here in America is that we no longer recognize the need for spiritual food. The savage Indian's spirit fed upon his worship of nature, and his religious ideals gave beauty and dignity to his life. It is impossible to measure the effect of the words of the Bible upon children of earlier generations where its language has been a matter of daily familiarity from earliest years. And in remote communities where few have been able to read, but the profession of story-telling has flourished, the spirit has been more fully fed than in this age of so much enlightenment.

A little child's spirit absorbs beauty of words as naturally as flowers take dew and sun and in just as intangible ways. Poetry is the essence of language, and that may be given a child as early as lullabies—not just childish poetry written for babes, but the beautiful words of the Psalms chanted and such poetry as is rhythmically strong.

At two years begins the literature which is so closely akin to poetry—the fable, the folk and the fairy tale. Truth is told as strongly in fable, legend, fairy tale, and poetry as in history, mathematics, and science. There is nothing more wonderful in the world of fairy than exists in the natural world. Many of the nursery and folk tales have come down to us from the childhood of the race. They are common to all peoples and so seem naturally the literature of childhood. Then, too, they present, if they are fables, universal truths in the form easiest for a child to absorb, and if they are fairy tales, they tell of different types of men and women—kind and unkind, honest and dishonest, simple and clever, and so prepare him for the world as it is.

Horace Scudder made one of the best collections of tales for the nursery some years ago, and today his "Book of Fables and Folk Stories" will give mothers a most satisfactory group of fables and familiar fairy tales—the best tales from Charles Perrault, the Brothers Grimm, and Madame D'Aulnoy, those early collectors of folk tales in the seventeenth and eighteenth centuries.

As a child grows a little older, in the years from five to eight, the books edited by Joseph Jacobs are among the very best. He was a folklore scholar, but the story was the important thing to him. He made one of the best collections of fables, "Fables of Aesop," and fine collections of fairy tales, English, Celtic, and Indian. In these years there are, too, American fairy tales—the Uncle Remus stories, gathered from the Negroes by Joel Chandler Harris, and the folk tales of the American Indians, of which there are many collections. Henry R. Schoolcraft was the first man to study the Indians' way of life and their stories and legends. In the early part of the nineteenth century he lived with the Indians of the West and around the Great Lakes and heard the tales told at the lodge fires. His "Indian Fairy Book" gives many of these stories.

Almost every primitive people has told many stories to explain how the earth and all the forms and ways of nature came to be—how man happened, the nature of God and man's relation to him. Men have created this literature, known as mythology, to satisfy their spiritual needs. The mythology of Greece and Rome, and to a somewhat lesser degree the mythology of the Norsemen, have come to be an essential background of our literature today. Children should have a chance at these grand tales of gods and heroes in the years from seven on. Many boys and girls between the ages of seven and ten come to know Kingsley's "Heroes," Hawthorne's "Wonder Book" and "Tanglewood Tales," Baldwin's "Golden Age," and Padraic Colum's "The Children's Homer" or "The Adventures of Odysseus," and of the Norse mythology, Abbie Farwell Brown's "In the Days of Giants," Hamilton Mabie's "Norse Stories," Colum's "Children of Odin." This order of reading the books in the case of both Greek and

145

Norse mythology is a particularly good one to follow. The first two books by Kingsley and Hawthorne present the stories of Greek mythology and religion. Mr. Baldwin wrote his "Golden Age" to prepare a boy for the great epics of Homer—"The Iliad," which tells of the last of the siege of Troy by the Greeks, and "The Odyssey," which finishes the siege of Troy and tells of the adventures of Odysseus on his long and roundabout journey home. In Colum's "Children's Homer" we have a fine retelling of these two great stories.

We have said that the spirit needs food as does the body. But the spirit needs exercise, too, as does the body. The nursery tales, the fables, the folk and the fairy tales, all bring to the child that opportunity for wonder; and wonder is an exercise of the spirit. The great stories of gods and heroes add to the element of wonder the dynamic vision of the heroes. The spirit of the listener or reader lifts, expands, grows taller and stronger. He becomes more and more of the same stuff as heroes.

And he is ready when the time comes for a new and still greater adventure in literature, the reading of a book such as Palmer's "Odyssey," or the translating of the "Odyssey" and the "Iliad" from the original. In an indescribable way these ageless stories of adventure, courage, and endurance have become a part of himself. The difference between a boy familiar with these books from early childhood and the boy who must look up in the encyclopedia every god and goddess and every hero is just the difference between cultivation and commonplace education.

These stories from the mythology and legend of Greece and the Northern countries illumine the mythology of the American Indians. Indeed, they illumine all life. And the same years to which they belong are the years to have other great hero stories, Baldwin's "Story of Roland," and "Story of Siegfried," Ella Young's "The Tangle-Coated Horse," that most beautiful telling of the boyhood and life of the great Gaelic hero, Fionn, and Howard Pyle's "Robin Hood," one of the most satisfying books we have. So many of these books should be read aloud, otherwise the child misses the emotional reaction to the beauty of the writing. This is particularly true of Howard Pyle's "Robin Hood" and of "The Tangle-Coated Horse."

"The Wonderful Adventures of Nils," that book of Swedish folk and fairy tales by Selma Lagerlof, ought always to be first read aloud. Indeed, there is so much grandeur and beauty in this book that some day it must certainly be expressed in music. There is one book which should be read aloud steadily from the earliest years on—that is the Bible. In the early years, reading should be almost entirely from the Psalms and the New Testament—but from ten on, certain beautiful sections of the Old Testament, particularly those parts which present the Hebrew feeling about God and man's own relationship to God.

146

The Bible cannot be used successfully today with young people, unless it is presented in the light of modern knowledge. Muriel Streibert's "Youth and the Bible" not only presents the modern view of the Bible by a spiritually-minded person, for many years a teacher of college students, but shows how it may be made of vital interest to young people and gives a fine descriptive reading list to parents and to children.

Hans Christian Andersen, a great modern writer of fairy tales, must have his important place in this short list of vision-building, stature-building books. There is in his wonder tales and stories almost every phase of human experience and every aspect of the physical world. A tree might well be the symbol of his work, and "the fruits from the magic tree of life" imbue it.

The "sacred Hazel Tree" drops its "starry fruitage" everywhere for the child of the listening heart. See to it that your child's world is not filled deafeningly—literally and figuratively—with "sounding brass" and "tinkling cymbal," that he has quiet, leisure time and the best works of the imagination.

Padraic Colum

Poet and Critic

POETRY AND CHILDHOOD

PLATO put music amongst the subjects that it was important to have youth trained in. Nowadays we do not look upon music as Plato looked upon it—as a foundation for knowledge; to us music is a special and separate course of study. And yet, when I think of what poetry can give to childhood, I begin to feel that I understand why Plato put music with the few important things that youth should have a training in.

I know that both poetry and music have something underlying them that holds our attention, that helps us to bring our minds to a focus. That underlying something is rhythm. The holding in our minds of certain rhythms—the rhythms of certain tunes, the rhythms of certain poems—gives us foundations for building on in our imaginative and intellectual life. Take a poem such as:

THE LAKE-ISLE OF INNISFREE

I will arise and go now, and go to Innisfree,
And a small cabin build there, of clay and wattles made;

147

Nine bean rows will I have there, a hive for the honey bee,
    And live alone in the bee-loud glade.

And I shall have some peace there, for peace comes dropping slow,
Dropping from the veils of the morning to where the cricket sings;
There midnight's all a glimmer, and noon a purple glow,
    And evening full of the linnets' wings.

I will arise and go now, for always night and day
I hear lake water lapping with low sounds by the shore;
While I stand on the roadway, or on the pavements gray,
    I hear it in the deep heart's core.

This is a piece of human speech that can be mastered, whole or in passages, and kept in the memory. Its rhythm, its rhymes, are holds that we have on it. And when we have it in our memory we have something that our thoughts can focus themselves on. The youth who has a dozen or so of poems in his or her memory has charms against straying thoughts. If he or she knows by heart Keats' "Ode to a Nightingale," or Shelley's "Ode to a Skylark" his thoughts or her thoughts can be held by a rhythm, a structure, and they will not be hopelessly scattered. And by holding our thoughts from being scattered, we win a victory for our mind.

The poems we hold in our mind are points of focus, patterns of order. Perhaps it was to give such points, such patterns, that Plato advocated a training in music as a foundation for general knowledge. Of course, there are other means than by poetry or music to get points of focus, patterns of order into our minds. A technical or professional training that would ignore music and poetry could supply them. But the patterns of order left by poetry or by music are imaginative, and, therefore, are creative. Our minds become aroused by going over them; in a poem the rhythm, the rhymes, the images, suggest other rhythms, rhymes, and images. More than this: the great thing that a poem gives us when we refer to it in memory is a sense of something begun and finished—a thing complete.

As I wandered the forest,
The green leaves among,
I heard a Wild Flower
Singing a song.

"I slept in the earth
In the silent night,
I murmured my fears
And I felt delight.

"In the morning I went,
As rosy as morn,
To seek for new joy;
But I met with scorn."

In this little poem—"The Wild Flower's Song" by Blake—there is everything that gives a pattern of order; there is a rhythm that is carried through; there is a structure—something begun and finished. And every word used in the poem can arouse us, making our own imagination creative.

There are public occasions on which we make addresses to young people, telling them that they are about to go into the world. The world that we are thinking of on those occasions is the world of business, of social relations, of mature interests. Beside it or over against it there is another world—the world that is within each of the young people that our address is being made to—the world of thought, meditation, intuition, imagination. The world of business, of social relationships, mature interests, impresses boys and girls at a certain stage in their development, and it is not difficult to prepare them to live in it. And it should not be difficult to show them—not so much as to how to enter into—but how to keep native in the other world—the world of thought, meditation, intuition, imagination.

To be popular and sought after, to make a mark at sports, to earn commendation from one's teachers, to be able to arrange a household and run everything in it smoothly and agreeably, is to do well; to be able to make combinations in business that gain the attention of one's chief and secure promotion—all that is well. But it is well, too, to have something in one that responds to the gathering of the clouds before nightfall; to have a feeling about the magnificent lines of an ocean-going ship; to be able to cherish this or that poem; to be able to read history intelligently and relate it to the events of our own time; to keep one's mind clear from the passions that take hold of crowds; to be able to communicate with the great people of the age, men and women, should we ever come near them actually. And we lose the power to feel, or to be able to do these things, if our minds are set too exclusively upon the world of practical affairs, social relationships, mature interests.

We do not enter this world—the world of imagination, thought, and intuition—at any definite time. The problem, so far as a child is concerned, is not, I repeat, the problem of entering it, but of keeping one's self native in it, of making stronger and stronger attachments to it. There is no ready way of dealing with this problem. But those who have children in their charge, whether as parents or teachers, are called upon to consider it.

149

One can only go some way towards solving this problem. One should keep open the ways that are in the children themselves, the ways into the world of imagination, thought and intuition. The faculty of reverie should not be destroyed by dragging children out of it and by insisting upon their becoming too active in their practical tasks. There should be times and places where and when the children might turn towards meditation. In some religious schools it is part of their training—and a good part, too— that they be led to a deliberate meditation. I have been in Quaker schools where they had arranged for what might be called indeliberate meditation. It was a room derived from the Friend's Meeting House where all could sit silently for half or three quarters of an hour; no doubt some of the children who sit there feel thoughts stir in them, have intuitions wake in them.

There are no rules for getting on in the world that is alongside of or over against our practical world; that world is in ourselves, and we can only get on in it by individual impulse, individual seeking, individual enlightenment. A little can be done to strengthen the impulse, to prevent the enlightenment from going out. To learn poetry is to find one way. Children should be taught, not merely to read and to know poetry, but to possess some part of the heritage of poetry. They should know poems by heart—a dozen, twenty, forty, fifty poems. These poems should be there so that at any time they might well up within their minds. Through this possession they can enter the world that has been spoken about—the world of imagination, thought, and intuition. It would be well if they could receive this poetry orally and from someone who had regard for the rhythm of verse, and was able to impart a delight in the rhythm and in the structure of verse. This possession of poetry is a possession that lasts, a possession that no one can take away from whoever has it; it is a talisman that gives an entrance into that world that we may not be separated from without loss to our humanity. For without some ability for making themselves at home in the world of thought, imagination, meditation, intuition, a boy or girl will never be able to understand all that is summed up in art and philosophy, will never have any deep feeling for religion, and will not be able to get anything out of the reading of history; in short, unless they are somewhat at home in that world, they will live without any fineness in their lives.

Marchette Chute

Author of "Shakespeare of London,"
"Ben Jonson of Westminster," etc.

BIOGRAPHIES BRING NEW COMPANIONS

THERE are many ways of enjoying ourselves, and one of the pleasantest is to meet interesting people.

The world is full of remarkable men and women, but even if we had time to go all over the earth to visit them and carried a suitcase stuffed with letters of introduction, we should still not be able to encounter more than a small fraction of the people we admire. Soldiers, statesmen, writers, scientists, inventors, actors, painters—most of them we shall never meet. But there is one easy way to get to know them all, and that is in the biographies that are written about them.

A biography is the life story of a real person. If it is a good biography it brings its hero as vividly to life as if he were standing in the same room. If you met him in person you would probably not get more than a polite handshake and a "How do you do?"; but in a biography you can find out all about him—what he did when he was a small boy, the way he went about his work, the friends he made, even his taste in neckties. It is not surprising that so many people like to read biographies, for they are a kind of window into a man's life; the better the biography the larger and clearer the window.

Moreover, anyone who reads biographies meets not only the people who are alive today but those who lived in all the past centuries. The men and women whose lives are worth remembering stretch over the whole of history, like a great, lighted procession, and we could never make their acquaintance if it were not for biographies.

It is true that a biographer has an easier time of it if the man he is writing about is still alive. James Boswell, for instance, could sit in the same room with Dr. Johnson, with his eyes and ears open like a good reporter's, listening delightedly and remembering what he heard, so that when he came to write his book he could transfer Johnson's bossy, magnificent self to paper and catch the very sound of his voice. If the hero is no longer living and his life has to be reconstructed from documents, the biographer has a more difficult time of it. But everyone leaves records of himself, and it is the biographer's task to put them together and bring back a living man.

This sense of reality, of showing great people as they really were, is one of the best things about biography. A non-reader, for instance,

151

might think of George Washington as being the way he is shown on dollar bills. He looks strong-minded and dignified in a stuffed kind of way, what with his unyielding mouth and glassy eyes, but he does not look as if he had ever really been alive. But a good biography shows the real man, the Washington who took such enormous risks and who knew that he would be hanged for treason if he failed in what he was trying to do. Washington was not a great man because he somehow soared above the troubles of ordinary people—confusion and discouragement and a sense of defeat; he was a great man because he never gave in to them.

A good portrait can sometimes bring a man back to life, but even then it fixes him at just one moment of time. The pictures of Longfellow, for instance, show him with a beard, and it is hard to remember that he was once a small boy going to school, or a young man trying to work out his first rhymes. Cicero is a marble figure in a toga, and no one would guess what a complex, sensitive, brilliant, and irritating man he was in real life. A biography of Cicero brings him back as his friends in politics knew him, and a schoolroom bust turns into an interesting person to know.

A good biography takes away the sense of "costume" that often blocks our imagination when we think about the past. Because Napoleon wore a cocked hat and Queen Elizabeth a starched ruff and Richard the Lion-Hearted armor instead of khaki, we forget that these were just their ordinary clothes, and we think of them as being remote, unfamiliar, and just a little odd. This is hardly fair, because if you look at old photographs of your friends, the clothes of ten or twenty years ago will look just as odd. It is time that turns clothes into costume, and a good biography can destroy time. What happened to Abraham Lincoln or Joan of Arc becomes "now" as long as you are reading about them, and no one who reads a good biography of Leonardo da Vinci could ever again think that Renaissance Italy was peopled by remote figures in improbable costumes. Biography brings the times to life again, just as it brings the people; and it makes the world a more spacious and interesting place to live in.

Another advantage of reading biography is that it widens your sense of enjoyment over things that have nothing to do with books. Even the pasteurizing of milk is more interesting if you know something about that stubborn man, Louis Pasteur. Brooklyn Bridge is twice as impressive if you know about the father and son who gave their lives to bring it into being, and traveling in the Far West becomes a special adventure to anyone who has read about Lewis and Clark. Radium becomes an even more awe-inspiring discovery if you know how a small woman in black named Madame Curie struggled with fierce patience to find it; and even a new type of wheat becomes more important if you know about the man who brought it into being.

152

So many things that now seem like fixed stars were born of fierce struggle and apparent defeat. Lincoln believed that he had done a poor job after he delivered the Gettysburg Address, and Keats died believing that his name would not be remembered. Beethoven wrote his greatest music after he became deaf, and Milton his greatest poetry after he became blind. The people who are worth knowing are the people who never gave up, and a good biography illuminates the springs of their heroism. From the outside, to their own friends, many of them seemed ordinary enough people; but each of them held a kind of special light inside himself, and a good biography shows why.

Even in the case of Shakespeare, whose life has nothing to do with the delight that any reader can get from his plays, it gives an added interest to know something about him as a man. It is interesting to know he worked in the theater all his adult life; he himself was an actor. Other playwrights of the time usually entered the theater only for conferences. He helped build the finest theater in London and owned part of it, and a little of the greatness of his plays comes from his thorough understanding of stagecraft and the needs of an audience. Many people in his own day did not think Shakespeare's plays were very good, since they pleased ordinary people and it was felt that really good work ought to please only a chosen few; but everyone liked him as a man and two of his fellow actors loved him so much that they saved all his plays in the special collection that is now known as the First Folio.

Good biography brings the past near and makes it real. It gives us a more spacious world to live in and heroes for our companions, and it pushes back the horizon so that we can make friends not only with the people around us but with all the people in history who have made the world a place worth living in.

Bess Porter Adams

Author of "About Books and Children"

THE CHILD'S PERSONAL LIBRARY

WHETHER the city library is five hundred miles away or right next door, every child should have a library of his own. Books owned are among the most satisfactory friends we know: they are always available, always the same (yet with the subtle differences good books and good friends both reveal as we live with them), always ready to take us out of the present moment and set us down in a satisfying new one. They are inexpensive, offering enduring pleasure in exchange for a very modest amount of money.

Each book the child owns is important and should be thoughtfully selected. It is important, first, just because it is *his,* and children have a keen sense of pride in personal belongings. It is important, secondly, because, either for better or worse, it is a factor in the development of his literary taste. A child's book should be beautiful: it should have fine illustrations, clear print, uncluttered pages, sturdy cover, and firm binding. It should be worthy of its owner's respect and affection, and it should receive good care from him. If there is more than one child in the family, certain "family book policies" should be developed. They should encourage sharing while helping to insure that an older child's treasured books are not mutilated by the youngest.

The parent, interested in building a library for his children, is confronted by so many books that he often buys haphazardly, failing to get the best return on his investment. The stories which are interesting for one reading only, had best be left for library reading; the child's own bookshelves should contain the books he returns to with continuing delight. A few enduring favorites, thoroughly tested by several generations of child readers, should form the nucleus of the personal library, to be added to as other books demonstrate lasting value.

A good edition of Mother Goose is generally one of the child's first important books. . . . Other books which will give continued pleasure to the small child are Beatrix Potter's *The Tale of Peter Rabbit* and *The Tale of Jemima Puddleduck,* and Margaret Wise Brown's *The Golden Egg Book,* the appealing story of a little rabbit who finds an egg and wonders what could be inside. He wonders if it contains a little boy, or an elephant, or some other creature. Unable to open it, though he tries in various ways, he goes to sleep beside it; and while he is sleeping, the egg hatches. The small yellow duck which emerges takes his turn wondering about the furry little animal beside him. The illustrations by Leonard Weisgard are delightful.

Make Way for Ducklings, by Robert McCloskey, is the story of a Mallard family; the plot is simple, the pictures exceptionally fine. Children and their parents will find this a book to read and re-read. Small children never seem to weary of *The Story About Ping,* by Marjorie Flack, or *Millions of Cats,* by Wanda Gág. *White Snow, Bright Snow,* by Alvin Tresselt and Roger Duvoisin, is an appealing picture book about the snowfall and what it means to different people. *The Big Snow,* by Berta and Elmer Hader, pictures the little animals in their struggle to prepare for winter and their difficulties when the food supply is not sufficient. They are helped by kindly people, so the story has a happy ending. The pictures are excellent.

154

The Rooster Crows, by Maud and Miska Petersham, contains a very interesting collection of American rhymes and jingles. It makes a fine companion piece for the Mother Goose book. There are so many satisfying picture-books for young children that parents will enjoy browsing and making selections.

The child's own bookshelf should contain some of the best of the religious books on his development level. Most of the modern books which are designed to help children understand something of God, and prayer, and faith in a power beyond the strength of men, are non-sectarian. Any reader of the Bible, regardless of his interpretation of the Book, should feel free to place in his child's hands such books as *Small Rain,* a selection of simple Bible verses beautifully illustrated by Elizabeth Orton Jones, or *Prayer for a Child,* by Rachel Field, also illustrated by Jones, an appealing little volume picturing a child's gratitude for the everyday comforts and small possessions which make his world bright and secure.

A Prayer for Little Things, by Eleanor Farjeon, is a beautiful book with a special appeal for the appreciation of little birds, colts, children, and so forth. This book, also, was illustrated by Miss Jones. Dorothy Lathrop's *Animals of the Bible* is a little more difficult, but it has lovely drawings of animals famous in Biblical history, and accompanying Bible verses. Small children will enjoy the pictures; as they grow a little older they will read the texts and grow in familiarity with the Bible stories. Maud and Miska Petersham's *The Christ Child* is designed for the youngest children; the pictures are excellent. . . .

Quite aside from its religious value, the Bible is important as literature. Along with a background in the classics of Greece and Rome, any student of English and American literature finds a knowledge of the Bible essential if he is to understand fully what he reads in the works of most of the enduring authors. The Bible helps the young reader develop literary taste, for in most versions the language is rhythmical, clear, and beautiful; and, lastly, the Bible contains some of the world's finest stories —stories with characters, plots, and exciting action. The greatest book of all is not dull reading!

Until a child is a very proficient reader he wants someone to read stories to him. He maintains his interest in the picture-books, but as he goes through his first two or three years at school his interests broaden, and he is ready for longer, more imaginative stories. Kipling's *Jungle Book* and *Just So Stories;* a good collection of the simpler folk tales, containing such stories as "The Gingerbread Man," "The Three Bears," "Little Red Riding Hood," "The Bremen Town Musicians," "Cinderella," "Snow White and the Seven Dwarfs"; A. A. Milne's *Winnie the Pooh* and *House at Pooh Corner;* Clare Newberry's *Mittens* or *April's Kittens;* and Joel Chandler Harris's *Nights With Uncle Remus* all deserve a permanent place in the child's library. He enjoys hearing them, and will go back to read them many times for himself when he has acquired sufficient skill.

A fine edition of *Aesop's Fables,* augmented with a book or two of fables from other sources, and a selection of Grimm's fairy tales furnish important traditional material, which will be read with delight by the third or fourth-grade child and enjoyed by the whole family when the stories are read aloud.

Every child's library should contain one of the better editions of the stories of Hans Christian Andersen, the greatest of the modern writers of fairy tales for young and old. His stories will entertain the entire family and should be read aloud. An outstanding edition is the translation of Jean Hersholt, published by the Heritage Press. For children who love fairy tales there are many collections of tales from other lands; the *Arabian Nights* series is the best known of these, and deserves a place on every ten to twelve-year-old child's bookshelf.

Alice's Adventures in Wonderland was a landmark in children's literature. It has never grown old, and has never ceased to appeal to adults as well as younger readers. Its gay nonsense is meant to be shared, and the book gains immeasurably when it is read aloud by someone who has long cherished it. Young people meeting Alice for the first time will enjoy any of the well-illustrated editions, but parents will probably prefer the original drawings of John Tenniel, whose interpretations of the characters in Lewis Carroll's story have never been surpassed. Though no child should miss this delightful book, experience has shown that the age at which a child will enjoy Alice varies tremendously. If a youngster does not like it at first, it is well to wait a year or two before trying it again.

When the interest in fairy tales begins to lag, the young reader is ready for the traditional hero tales, myths, and legends which form an important part of our literature. King Arthur, Robin Hood, Paul Bunyan, Roland, Siegfried, Jupiter, Odin, Lancelot, Sigurd, Thor, Apollo, and dozens of other exciting characters, real or imaginary, should be familiar to all young people in the upper grades and high school. The stories are excellent reading; they abound with adventure and interesting personalities; and familiarity with them provides the necessary background for later appreciation of much of the finest literature for adults. Many excellent editions of these stories are available. In choosing the books, the parent should consider illustrations, size of type, quality of paper and binding, and, most important, good literary style.

Children should not confine their reading of hero stories to those woven around imaginary characters only. There are now available numerous well written biographies, which will provide real characters for the young readers to think about. From the true life story of Buffalo Bill, to sensitive presentations of the lives of artists, dancers, and musicians, there is a world of excellent biographical material on the library shelves. From the stories of Benjamin Franklin, Abraham Lincoln, Anna Pavlova, Florence Nightingale, Theodore Roosevelt, Queen Elizabeth, Daniel Boone, Kit Carson, Franz Schubert, and many others, the parent can select those which will appeal to his children as they develop different interests.

From the third or fourth grade on, children are ready to enjoy the selected Newbery Award books. The parent can select each book as his child is ready for it; many of them deserve a permanent place in the young person's own library.

With all the wealth of current literature, Tom Sawyer is still a favorite with children in the upper grades; *The Adventures of Tom Sawyer* and *Huckleberry Finn* are as popular now as they have ever been. Probably no one else has captured the spirit of boyhood as Mark Twain did in those stories. *Heidi,* by Johanna Spyri, and *Little Women,* by Louisa M. Alcott, belong in every girl's library. Though somewhat old-fashioned in style, modern children enjoy them as their mothers did, for the characters are real and the concepts true.

By the time a child is in the third or fourth grade he has begun to develop special interests and talents. He may like animals, flowers, birds, woodcraft, leather work, modeling, drawing, music, gardening, or sports. Whatever his interests, he can be encouraged in them through books dealing with those particular hobbies.

Many parents stock their children's library with a good set of encyclopedias. If one can afford the expense this is desirable. . . .

Dictionaries are now available for very young children. They are not expensive and can be replaced easily as the child's vocabulary grows. *The Golden Dictionary* contains over fifteen hundred words, all illustrated by colored pictures; it is a very appealing book for the five to eight-year-old. *The Rainbow Dictionary* is another excellent book for the primary grades. It is beautifully illustrated, has good type, clear explanations and examples, and about twenty-three hundred word entries. *The Thorndike Century Beginning Dictionary* is designed for the children in the fourth, fifth, and sixth grades. It has clear type, many illustrations, and some very good exercise and study material. *The New Winston Dictionary for Children* is an excellent book for children from the fourth grade through the junior high school. It is well illustrated, and it defines around thirty-three thousand terms. Unsurpassed, for children of this same age range, is *Webster's Elementary Dictionary: a Dictionary for Boys and Girls.* A Merriam-Webster book, it contains thirty-eight thousand entries, has very clear type, and is profusely illustrated. Children gain a wide knowledge and an enduring interest in language through the daily use of these books. They are worth many times the price paid for them.

157

No young person's library would be complete without several volumes of poetry. The nursery rhymes first introduce the child to the wonderful world of rhythm and rhyme, and before he is ready for school he should have heard many of the poems of Robert Louis Stevenson, Eleanor Farjeon, James Tippett, Rose Fyleman, Elizabeth M. Roberts, Rachel Field, Christopher Morley, Elizabeth Coatsworth, Annette Wynne, Kate Greenaway, Edward Lear, A. A. Milne, and other poets to be found in any well-edited anthology. These poets will continue to delight him as he goes through the grades, and he will gradually come to know and respond to the poetry of Lewis Carroll, Eugene Field, Henry W. Longfellow, Vachel Lindsay, Carl Sandburg, Emily Dickinson, Sara Teasdale, Robert Frost, John Masefield, Christina Rossetti, William Shakespeare, and the other poets who have enriched our culture, and who have written poetry which can be understood and appreciated by youthful readers. Parents should select several books by the poets their children enjoy most and at least one good anthology to assure variety in the family reading, and they should find time frequently to read aloud and enjoy the poems with their children.

A carefully selected, well-balanced library of their own is one of the greatest contributions parents can make to the intellectual, emotional, and spiritual welfare of their children. Worthy books, shared, pay big dividends in enriched family living and in the establishment of a true sense of ethical, moral, and aesthetic values. The child who has acquired the habit of going to good books for pleasure and information has an inestimable advantage over the child who rarely gets beyond the weekly comic books and the television or radio programs.

When one realizes that he may find, printed in books, the entire history of man's accomplishments, all his knowledge, his speculations, philosophies, theories, convictions, ideals and inspirations, it is scarcely possible to overestimate the importance of reading. Knowledge is pleasure as well as power, and one can begin in the nursery to instill in his child a respect for learning, and a love of books, which will prove a constant source of enjoyment and intellectual progress.

Agatha L. Shea

Director of Children's Work
Chicago Public Library

YOUR CHILD AND WORLD NEIGHBORLINESS

B OOKS for the World of Tomorrow"—this was the slogan of
National Book Week a few years ago and its underlying theme
was preparation of our children for that different world which
they would find awaiting them at maturity. It was to be a new and chal-
lenging world with new frontiers in science and far reaching changes in
our lives as a result of them. It promised to be a stimulating world and
we hoped that our children would find their places in it and fare well.
But it was the "world of tomorrow" in our thinking and we went on living
pretty much as usual in the world we knew.

Time has passed and we suddenly find ourselves aware that many of
the problems which we were expecting in the future are confronting us
now and that our children's world is, like our own, not of Tomorrow but
of Today. Modern science with its superhighways, its planes, and its
strat-o-liners is carrying us rapidly into new lands and across national
borders which we never thought to cross. Continents are now but a few
hours flying time away, and a two weeks' vacation may be spent in almost
any land one chooses. For our children and grandchildren globe-trotting
will be a very casual adventure.

What does all this mean to the boy and girl of today? One must pay a
price for all progress and with the broadened horizon and the mobility
which makes possible their entry through many gates, comes a heightened
responsibility of conduct and a need for deeper understanding of those
peoples with whom they are to share these new adventures, and who are
to be, in truth, their neighbors.

There is perhaps no better way of preparing them for this understanding of others than through children's books. Through them young Americans become acquainted not only with the story of their own country,
but also with the many peoples of many backgrounds whose customs and
cultures are very different from their own. Young readers follow the
fortunes and misfortunes of their book friends with sympathy and understanding and many a cherished book hero or heroine has become an ideal
for real living to the boy or girl. Yes, and not infrequently, an ideal which
is followed through the years. In this writer's opinion, children's books
are playing an important part in preparing youth to meet this New World,
and their authors, editors, and publishers are making no small contribu-

159

tion to that goal of world understanding which we are all seeking.

America is made up of many diverse peoples, and stories of these various national groups, their problems and accomplishments are perhaps the first step to understanding by children of people whose habits, language, or appearance may be unlike their own. Our children's literature is rich in fine stories of this type, helping to break down prejudices and misunderstandings.

Regional stories, picturing life as it is lived in various regions of our country, carry young readers far beyond the narrow boundaries of their own settled lives and show them other children with hopes and desires like their own, yet leading very different lives.

A story which leaves its impress upon young readers is Eleanor Estes' *The Hundred Dresses*. This is an excellent story for younger children who are inclined to be snobbish or unkind in their dealings with others less fortunate than themselves. The heroine is a gentle little girl of foreign parentage who is alone in a school in which the children have not been used to having pupils outside their own neighborhood. Little Wanda is shy, but she has her two idols in the class of unfriendly girls, and the fact that they are the unkindest of all to her does not destroy her admiration for them. The child reader, closing the book, will remember for a long time the story of that last morning and Wanda's gift. He will not forget the sorrow of the realistic ending. He will remember that there is not always time to make amends for wrongdoing after one understands. Here is a lesson in kindliness which points no moral, as such, and yet a lesson whose message is clear for all to read. Such a book as this, read in early childhood does its part, perhaps years later, in creating the atmosphere in which good neighbors can live, even though they come from far distant points on the earth's surface.

Stories of yesterday, too, bring to Young America the picture of children not unlike themselves finding their pleasures in a simpler way of life, and doing their part in the building of their own homes, and bearing their share of the family load. Louisa M. Alcott's beloved *Little Women*, with a message and the same appeal as it had in 1868, Ruth Sawyer's *Roller Skates*, Carol Brink's *Caddie Woodlawn*, and Mark Twain's *Tom Sawyer* are but a few of the background stories of an earlier America which was quite different from the America in which today's children are growing up. They are invaluable in aiding young readers to realize that America was not always rich and great in the way she is today. Her treasure in her growing years lay rather in the spirit, courage, integrity and hard work of her people. With children having this in mind (as part of their own antecedents) there will be less tendency to look down upon a more humble and simple pattern of living, or to think less of peoples who are still striving to reach a higher and better plane of life.

Before children can be at home with world neighbors they must know something too of those other Americans whose racial backgrounds may be different from their own. Minority groups must work together in the building and safeguarding of America, and success can come only if they respect each other's differences and join forces for the common good. The Negro, the Indian, the Chinese or Japanese, the immigrant recently come from his European homeland, all of these are world neighbors at home and our children should have the good fortune of meeting them in children's books.

Many of these people have a rich heritage which will do much to offset the differences which are too often emphasized. Florence Crannell Means, a woman of many friendships with many types of Americans, has done an outstanding job in picturing for young people her pleasure in these associations. Her acquaintance at first hand with the Indians of the Southwest, the Hopi and Navajo Indians, resulted in two very fine books dealing with the modern life of these nations, *Tangled Waters*, a story of the Navajos, and *Whispering Girl*, a tale of the Hopis. Both have values of importance in building a world outlook as well as a friendly neighbor situation at home. In them we see the impact of the white man's ideas and modern living on the old Indian beliefs and tribal customs, and discover, as Mrs. Means did, that there is a dignity and kindliness among them of which the outsider is often unaware.

That is one side of the picture which our children must know, the origins of our own great nation, the understanding of its many racial groups, their customs, their problems, and their contributions to the development of the whole. Aware of these things, they will be ready to profit by the other side of the picture portraying for them the peoples of older lands with perhaps different ways of thought, of living, and of expression.

Monica Shannon's *Dobry*, set in Bulgaria, is outstanding as a sympathetic presentation of people in other lands whom young readers may have thought of as queer. *Call It Courage*, by Armstrong Sperry, is a story of a Polynesian boy who, even as many American boys have had to do, proved himself a leader by overcoming his own fears. Alice Geer Kelsey's *Racing the Red Sail*, showing the brave children of Greece, and the beautifully written story of the old Hungary which Kate Seredy gave us in *The Good Master*, leave pictures of other lands and other peoples which prepare young readers for the new world facing them, and do much to offset misconceptions and misjudgments.

These are but a few of the many excellent books for young readers which will serve as an introduction to the world's people who are increasingly becoming their close neighbors. They offer good reading to child and parent alike and will stand well at the top of contributing factors if our dream of world friendship becomes a reality, for it is to the children we must look for that realization. An evening reading hour in the home with all the family sharing it would perhaps hasten its dawning.

At the American Library Association Convention in Chicago in 1951, the Newbery Medal for the most distinguished children's book of the year was awarded to *Amos Fortune, Free Man,* by Elizabeth Yates. Miss Yates, as a guest speaker, told the actual story behind the book. As she unveiled the picture of those long-ago happenings in the little New England village, the stature of the one-time African slave grew before us, until we saw him, through force of character and innate nobility, stand forth as an example of the higher democratic ideal.

The great audience sat enthralled, and one could not help but feel, as the moving story reached its conclusion, that friendship of man for man throughout the world would not be a distant hope if only we could all know each other as Miss Yates had helped us to know Amos Fortune that evening. The Negro spirituals which followed the talk seemed the only fitting end. My own personal regret was that the audience was adult rather than juvenile, but on second thought, I realized it was perhaps just as well.

Such books as this and others like it will help give our children, and in translations, the world's children, the vision which they need. Truly, as the old legend runs, "Without a vision the people perish."

Herman Schneider

Science Supervisor,
New York City Elementary Schools

WHAT IS A GOOD SCIENCE BOOK?

EVERY YEAR, some two or three dozen science juveniles are published. Review copies are duly sent off to book reviewers, library committees, school officials, and other evaluating groups. And then the trouble begins. Those reviewers who happen not to have majored in science glance warily at "The Boy's Own Book of Home Experiments in Nuclear Fission" and wonder—how does one go about judging a children's science book? In my work as a school science supervisor, I ask that question frequently, and occasionally find a fragment of an answer. Pieced together, these fragments turn out to be certain criteria that by and large are the same criteria we apply to any children's book. Some of them may seem fairly obvious, yet they deserve mention. Let us first consider these:

162

Does the author write clearly and lucidly? This criterion refers to more than the mere absence of over-long sentences, multi-syllabular words, and a tendency to grammatical inversions. I mean—can the reader understand it? For example, let us examine this statement: "When metallic sodium is placed on water, small flashes of light and puffs of steam are emitted, because that is the nature of sodium." The book from which this meaningless quotation was taken contains several hundred more gems of this type, and it can be found in the juvenile science section of most libraries.

Clarity and lucidity can be boiled down to a very simple question: Do *You* really understand what the author is saying? Please observe that I say you, not the child reader. Children often find difficulty in admitting that they do not understand a statement, especially when they really do understand each separate word in that statement. But you will not be deceived by spurious simplicity.

Is the book clearly illustrated? Again, it is you who are asked to be the judge. If the illustrations confuse you, they will certainly confuse the children. A child should be able to follow the steps in a project or experiment without difficulty. The details should be clearly visible, with no extraneous matter to confuse the main point. I offer no culprits for your judgment, but I have in mind the books in which a chart or diagram has been supplied gratis by a manufacturer, and then reduced to one-tenth its size.

In an experiment or project book, are the activities safe? This, you would say, goes without question. Surely the publishers have done a careful job of checking and double-checking. In the great majority of cases they have, but nevertheless it is highly desirable that you submit the book to a local science teacher, just to be sure. A scientist-turned-author may consider certain precautions as too obvious to be worth mention, because they have become second nature to him. To the child experimenter, they may be anything but obvious. I have on my desk a recently published book in the "ten-and-up" range, in which one project calls for the use of ether "which a grownup can buy for you at any drugstore." No mention is made of the fact that ether is highly inflammable, that its fumes are toxic; and that a pilot light in the kitchen gas range can set off a serious explosion. Please bear in mind that although this example is definitely an exception, still we cannot be too careful.

Are the projects and experiments satisfying and workable? To achieve the finished product, a child must pay a certain price in terms of materials gathered or purchased and a certain inevitable minimum of drudgery. Will the airplane model, chemical experiment, or steam engine be worth it? Here again the science teacher should be consulted, or the scout leader, and several children as well, to protect the young tinkerer against frustration. As a case in point, I call to your attention several home-experiment books giving detailed directions for the construction of a

163

chemical barometer out of several hard-to-get chemicals, distilled water, and a test tube. When completed, the gadget presumably forecasts weather by the appearance of the chemicals dissolved in the water—clear in advance of clear weather, a hazy layer before cloudiness, bright crystals before a snowfall, etc. A lovely idea, except that you can make the instrument go through its entire repertoire by simply moving it from a warm place to a cooler place. The chemicals dissolve thoroughly when warm, less thoroughly when cool. The basic fallacy has been known and explained for years, but the project keeps popping up. The child who assembles it and finds that it doesn't work blames himself and not the author.

Is the book accurate? Accuracy is not a simple thing to define. Essentially, no science book is entirely accurate in the light of possible future discoveries, nor can a children's book give every possible facet of a science concept. Nevertheless, such a book must be as accurate as possible in the light of the child's experience. For example, I would accept as accurate the statement that a stone dropped into water will sink, although I know that certain volcanic stones of foamy structure will float. On the other hand, I would not accept an anthropomorphic explanation such as the following: "When the water vapor reaches cool air, the tiny drops of which they are made come closer together; they huddle together to keep warm." An author who needs to endow water drops with human desires is usually shaky about his facts or his ability to explain them. The book in which the tiny drops are discovered huddling contains also several dozen errors of fact, not tiny.

Lucid, accurate writing, clear illustrations, safe, satisfying projects— these are obvious but important requirements in any science book. Were they the only requirements, we could be content with the scores of well-written, clearly illustrated books on butterfly collecting, chemical experimenting, and rocket-ship building that offer safe, satisfying projects for children interested in butterflies, chemicals, and rocket ships. But our concern goes beyond the needs of the hobbyist and experimenter, to the needs of other children, even the least science-minded. These are the children we must try to reach.

For these are the children who will grow up saying, "It's Greek to me," who will feel alien to science in a world that grows increasingly science-minded. They will become the mass market that switches to Cigarette Brand A because "Scientific Tests Prove That . . ." and they will stand by, bewildered and humble, while H-bombs and germ warfare are concocted in glittering laboratories. For such children, we need books that say, "Science is *your* business."

How does one recognize such a book? It is not a set of preachments on science's responsibility to society, nor does it preach at all. It may deal with any one of a wide variety of subjects, from the pipes under the street to the pipes in the human circulatory system. But certain basic values shine through:

The total impact of the book is reassuring. If it is a book on astronomy, the child is not left with a feeling of tininess and insignificance in the presence of vast time and space, but rather with a feeling of the strength, reliability and orderliness of celestial motions. If it is a book of physiology, it imparts a sense of confidence in the superb functioning of his body, and not a sense of uneasiness or fear over the perils of vitamin-deficient diets or unbrushed teeth.

The book permits the child to achieve a sense of participation. We do not merely read a good book, we partake of it. In a science book, the child will partake when the examples, activities and relationships are all derived from the child's experience, so that he can participate in the development of a concept, rather than sit back and be dazzled by the author's superior wisdom.

The book has a sense of human importance and dignity. Its approach is not one of science for science's sake, but for people's sake. The author who lovingly describes the exquisite mechanism of a guided missile as if it were a pedigreed race horse is contributing his little bit to the devaluation of the human spirit. In glamorizing an instrument of destruction, we cheapen ourselves. Let the author's writing skill be used in helping the child to see the wonder in the everyday things about him.

It is a book that stays with reality. The real fact is breath-taking and thrilling. It needs no window dressing in terms of ancient myths, Martian men or animals with human speech and emotions. The configuration of the Milky Way is beautiful in itself. The facts about our neighboring planets are fascinating without conjectures about imaginary inhabitants. A robin's nest-building and child-rearing instincts are absorbing facets of nature without the mother robin's being dressed in a bonnet and apron, busily sweeping her little nest with a little broom.

It is a book that enlarges a child's understanding of the world. It does not clutter his mind with unrelated facts. When he has finished this book, he is better able to see orderliness and relationships in that area. From its experiments he has achieved an understanding of basic principles, rather than performed science magic. Its facts are those that provide pattern and relationship rather than statistics.

It is a literary book. There is no excuse for dull, unimaginative writing in a children's book. The information that children need does not require the unique services of some learned specialists—the only scholar capable of giving the definitive statement on a specific area of learning—but who is, alas, a dreary writer. A science book for children should be written with grace, ease and imagination.

These are exacting criteria and I would be hard put to it to name half a dozen books that fulfill every one of them. But if we—parents, librarians, teachers and editors—keep these criteria in mind, the books will come.

BIBLIOGRAPHY

Editor's Note: The Horn Book asked Mr. Schneider to make a list of science books he would recommend even if they do not fulfill all the requirements. The list, he says, "is by no means definitive—just some books that I like and that I have found children enjoy. I have grouped the books at the lowest age level at which they can be used successfully, but many of them will prove of interest to much older children and even to adults." Mr. and Mrs. Schneider's own books are, of course, outstanding in the field and we have added all of them to the list.

FOR THE VERY YOUNG

(These are not science books in the strict sense of the word, but rather "awareness" books, to help the child as he sniffs and touches the physical and social world around him.)

Mary McBurney Green   *Everybody Eats*   Illustrated by Edward Glannon. Scott, 1946.

——   *Everybody Has a House*   Illustrated by Jeanne Bendick. Scott, 1944.

Ruth Krauss   *The Happy Day*   Illustrated by Marc Simont. Harper, 1949. Animals in the winter woods.

——   *The Growing Story*   Illustrated by Phyllis Rowand. Harper, 1947.

——   *I Can Fly*   Illustrated by Mary Blair. Simon, 1950. A child imitates birds and animals. A Little Golden Book.

Margaret Rey   *Spotty*   Illustrated by H. A. Rey. Harper, 1945. Problems of the only spotted rabbit in a family of white ones.

Miriam Schlein   *Fast Is Not a Ladybug*   Illustrated by Leonard Kessler. Scott, 1953.

Nina Schneider   *While Susie Sleeps*   Illustrated by Dagmar Wilson. Scott, 1948. About the people who are working and the things that are happening at night.

Louise Woodcock   *This Is the Way the Animals Walk*   Illustrated by Ida Binney. Scott, 1946.

FOR SIX AND UP

Jeanne Bendick, Author-Illustrator   *All Around You; a First Look at the World.*   Whittlesey, 1951.

Ruth Benedict and Gene Weltfish, Author-Illustrators   *In Henry's Backyard; the Races of Mankind.*   Schuman, 1948.

Milton I. Levine and Jean H. Seligmann   *A Baby Is Born; the Story of How Life Begins*   Illustrated by Eloise Wilkin. Simon, 1949.

Herman and Nina Schneider   *Follow the Sunset*   Illustrated by Lucille Corcos. Doubleday, 1952.

——   *How Big Is Big? From Stars to Atoms*   Illustrated by Symeon Shimin. Scott, 1951.

——   *Let's Find Out; a Picture Science Book*   Illustrated by Jeanne Bendick. Scott, 1951.

——   *Let's Look Under the City; Water, Gas, Waste, Electricity, Telephone*   Illustrated by Bill Ballantine. Scott, 1954.

Millicent E. Selsam   *All About Eggs and How They Change Into Animals*   Illustrated by Helen Ludwig. Scott, 1952.

Campbell Tatham   *The First Book of Automobiles*   Illustrated by Jeanne Bendick. Watts, 1949.

Irma E. Webber, Author-Illustrator   *Travelers All; the Story of How Plants Go Places.*   Scott, 1944.

——   *Up Above and Down Below.*   Scott, 1943. Parts of plants above and below ground.

FOR EIGHT AND UP

Benjamin Brewster   *The First Book of Eskimos*   Illustrated by Ursula Koering. Watts, 1952.

Wilfrid S. Bronson, Author-Illustrator   *The Grasshopper Book.*   Harcourt, 1943.

——   *Starlings.*   Harcourt, 1948.

Mary Elting and Margaret Gossett   *The Lollypop Factory—and Lots of Others*   Illustrated by Jeanne Bendick. Doubleday, 1946.

Eva Knox Evans   *All About Us*   Illustrated by Vana Earle. Capitol, 1947. The story of people told with a view to breaking down prejudice.

Harriet E. Huntington   *Let's Go Outdoors*   Illustrated by Preston Duncan. Frogs, turtles, insects and other little creatures.

——   *Let's Go to the Seashore*   Illustrated with photographs by the author. Doubleday, 1941.

Herman and Nina Schneider   *How Your Body Works*   Illustrated by Barbara Ivins. Scott, 1949.

——   *Let's Look Inside Your House*   Illustrated by Barbara Ivins. Scott, 1948. Water, heat and lights.

——   *Now Try This*   Illustrated by Bill Ballantine. Scott, 1947. Inclined planes, leverage, wheels and friction.

——   *Plants in the City*   Illustrated by Cynthia Koehler. Day, 1951.

——   *You Among the Stars*   Illustrated by Symeon Shimin. Scott, 1951. A first book about the universe.

167

Irma E. Webber   *Bits That Grow Big; Where Plants Come From.*
Scott, 1949.

Margaret Williamson, Author-Illustrator   *The First Book of Bugs.*
Watts, 1949.

Herbert S. Zim   *Golden Hamsters*   Illustrated by Herschel Wartik.
Morrow, 1951.

——   *Goldfish*   Illustrated by Joy Buba. Morrow, 1947.

——   *The Great Whales*   Illustrated by James Gordon Irving. Morrow, 1951.

——   *Rabbits*   Illustrated by Joy Buba. Morrow, 1948.

FOR TEN AND UP

Jeanne Bendick, Author-Illustrator   *The First Book of Space Travel.*
Watts, 1953.

Ruth Brindze   *Gulf Stream*   Illustrated by Helene Carter. Vanguard,
1945.

Jeanette Eaton   *That Lively Man, Ben Franklin*   Illustrated by
Henry C. Pitz. Morrow, 1948.

Mae B. and Ira M. Freeman   *Fun with Astronomy*   Illustrated with
photographs. Random, 1953.

——   *Fun with Chemistry*   Illustrated with photographs. Random,
1944.

——   *Fun with Science*   Illustrated with photographs. Random, 1943.

Herman Schneider   *Everyday Machines and How They Work*   Illustrated by Jeanne Bendick. Whittlesey, 1950.

——   *Everyday Weather and How It Works*   Illustrated by Jeanne
Bendick. Whittlesey, 1951.

Herman and Nina Schneider   *More Power to You*   Illustrated by
Bill Ballantine. Scott, 1953.

——   *Rocks, Rivers and the Changing Earth*   Illustrated by Edwin
Herron. Scott, 1952.

——   *Science Fun with Milk Cartons*   Illustrated by Jeanne Bendick.
Whittlesey, 1953.

Millicent E. Selsam   *Microbes at Work*   Illustrated by Helen Ludwig. Morrow, 1953.

——   *Play with Leaves and Flowers*   Illustrated by Fred F. Scherer.
Morrow, 1953.

——   *Play with Plants*   Illustrated by James MacDonald. Morrow,
1949.

——   *Play with Trees*   Illustrated by Fred F. Scherer. Morrow, 1950.

Irma E. Webber, Author-Illustrator   *Thanks to Trees—Their Use and
Conservation.*   Scott, 1952.

168

Nelson F. Beeler and Franklyn M. Branley *Experiments in Science* Illustrated by Ruth Beck. Crowell, 1947.

—— *Experiments with Airplane Instruments* Illustrated by Leopold London. Crowell, 1953.

Jeanne Bendick, Author-Illustrator *Electronics for Young People.* Whittlesey, 1947.

Jeanne and Robert Bendick *Television Works Like This.* Whittlesey, 1954.

George P. Bischof *Atoms at Work* Illustrated by Jere Donovan. Harcourt, 1951.

William Harry Crouse *Understanding Science* Illustrated by Jeanne Bendick. Whittlesey, 1948.

Mary Elting *Machines at Work* Illustrated by Lazlo Roth. Garden City, 1953.

James Gray *How Animals Move* Illustrated by Edward Bawden. Cambridge University Press, 1953.

Dorothy C. Hogner *The Animal Book; American Mammals North of Mexico* Illustrated by Nils Hogner. Oxford, 1942.

James Geralton *The Story of Sound* Illustrated by Joe Krush. Harcourt, 1948.

Alfred Morgan *First Chemistry Book for Boys and Girls* Illustrated by Bradford Babbit and Terry Smith. Scribner, 1950.

Clifford H. Pope *Snakes Alive and How They Live* Illustrated with photographs. Viking, 1937.

William Maxwell Reed *The Stars for Sam* Illustrated with photographs. Harcourt, 1931.

Herman and Nina Schneider *Your Telephone and How It Works* Illustrated by Jeanne Bendick. Whittlesey, 1952.

Julius Schwartz *It's Fun to Know Why* Illustrated by Edwin Herron. Whittlesey, 1952.

Katherine B. Shippen *The Bright Design* Illustrated by Charles M. Daugherty. Viking, 1949. Electrical energy and the men who have harnessed it.

William R. Van Dersal and Edward H. Graham *The Land Renewed; the Story of Soil Conservation* Illustrated with photographs. Oxford, 1946.

Henry L. Williams, Author-Illustrator *Stories in Rocks.* Holt, 1948.

Herbert S. Zim, and others. "The Golden Nature Guides" (Several volumes including *Flowers; Trees; Birds; Insects; Stars.*) Simon.

This list Mr. Schneider brought up-to-date in February, 1954.

Rachel Field

Newbery Award Author

MY FIRST BOOK FRIENDS

SOMETHING had gone wrong. At this late date I forget the reason, and it probably was a good one, but at all events I was *not* going to the theater with the rest. I must have been eleven or a little older at the time and it mattered terribly. Theaters were few and far between and movies practically unknown, so I hoped up to the last minute that a miracle would happen. Sometimes they did, and you found yourself let in at the last, just when you were most despairing. I reminded myself of Cinderella and the ball, an encouraging story to recall on almost any occasion. But on this particular one, it did me no good and I saw the lucky ones setting off. The last minute had come and gone and Fate had done nothing about it. I remember as if it were yesterday the sound of that door closing and of how I went listlessly into my room and over to the bookshelves. It was *Heidi* that I reached for and took down. Although I had read it many times before, it took only a few minutes of turning the printed pages and I was on the steep mountainside with Heidi and the Blind Grandmother, with Peter and all the goats. As I read I knew that the end of the world had not come. No matter what happened, I told myself, there would always be books. They would never change. You could depend upon them in a world that I was beginning to realize often held disappointments and regrets.

It has been a good while now since I lost myself in *Heidi,* but I still feel so about books. I am sure I always shall.

There were several other volumes on those shelves that I might as easily have reached for and that would, I know, have given me the same comfort. To this day I still read and re-read Hans Andersen, turning first, as I did then, to "The Little Mermaid." Of all fairy tales I put this first as the most beautiful, the most sad, and the most altogether satisfying. Just to read the opening paragraph is a never-to-be-forgotten experience:

170

"Far out in the wide sea, where the water is blue as the loveliest corn-flower, and clear as the purest crystal, where it is so deep that very many church towers must be heaped one upon another in order to reach from the lowest depth to the surface above, dwell the Mer-people."

That is sheer magic and after that I gave myself up completely to the little mermaid and her mer-sisters, and the sad but beautiful story of her love for the prince and her sacrifice for his sake. I still shiver over the part where she visits the sea-witch to procure the potion which shall turn her green tail into a pair of legs and feet that shall be as light as gossamer, although at each step it must seem they are treading on sword points. I read her story first on a rainy spring day with drippings on a tin roof and wet New England lilacs just outside the window; and it was more real to me than the rain, than the purple spikes of bloom, even than the voices of children across the street calling me to come over and play. It still is, no matter when or where I read it.

"The Wild Swans" and "The Snow Queen" were almost as great favor-ites, especially the account in the latter of the two children in that old-world city who lived in adjoining houses and played among flowering rose trees in pots on their roofs. Perhaps because I was a girl I liked best the part where Gerda gets in the boat to search for Kay and is carried down the river till she reaches the house of the old witch. How clever of the old witch to send all the roses in her garden back into the earth lest they remind Gerda of Kay and send her forth again! How right and proper that the same roses should spring up once more when the little girl's tears fell on the ground above them! Yes, you could trust Hans Andersen to know what to do. Even the splinter of glass in Kay's eye that made him cold and hard and forgetful of his friends melted at last. How good to leave them together on the final page: "grown up, yet children in heart, while all around them flowed summer—warm, glorious summer."

No less dear to me, but in quite another mood and manner were *My Wonderful Visit* and *Rebecca of Sunnybrook Farm*. By a curious coin-cidence they appeared the same year and were both about little girls in the state of Maine of another generation. At that time I had never been in Maine, though not long after I read these two stories I was to spend a summer on one of its islands, and to lose my heart forever to "the coun-try of the pointed firs."

Rebecca has been read and loved by so many, old and young, and made so many friends via the stage and screen, that I have almost come to believe she was a real person who lived in the state where I am writ-ing at this moment. It seems impossible to believe that she is only a made-up character. She was as real as the next-door neighbors to me when I was ten and one of the great experiences of that time was a dramatization we gave of the book in our country school. I shall never

171

forget the preparations for that production or the awe that filled me when I was chosen to play Rebecca. It was a great responsibility, the more so because I knew I must act it very well to make the audience forget that I looked more like the descriptions of Emma Jane Perkins! We were very ambitious, the twelve of us in that little school, and although a covered porch was our only stage and a clothes horse, ill disguised, had to do duty for the stagecoach, yet so earnest were we and so thoroughly in the spirit of the book, that people in the audience still speak of it as a happy memory. I remember it vividly, too, but more perhaps for the black and blue bruises with which I was covered from my efforts at perfecting my fall into the lilac bushes after Mr. Alladin, as you remember, made his spectacular purchase of the three hundred cakes of soap.

Although I have lost the picture of myself in the button-up-the-front checked gingham dress and the pink parasol, I cherish a letter which Kate Douglas Wiggin wrote to my mother in answer to an account of the performance. Her interest and enthusiasm are still alive in the pages. It was a pity she was in Europe and so unable to be present. Several years later I was to meet and know her, and she was to say encouraging words about some early writing attempts of mine.

My Wonderful Visit, by Elizabeth Hill of Portland, Maine, was never so widely known as *Rebecca,* but it was none the less genuine, being an authentic account of the author's visit to a Maine farm and of all the thrilling adventures which befell her and her young cousin Rosalie. I got my copy of it out only a short while ago, to find it falling from its covers, worn out with years of devoted thumbing. It was more simple than most stories, but every smallest doing seemed of the most vital importance, and there was a last chapter about the two little girls running away to go to an old-fashioned country raspberrying that stays in my mind as clearly as the first time I read it. The book has long been out of print. I wish someone would revive it with the same charming small black-and-white pictures that came at the head of each chapter.

But perhaps *Sara Crewe* by Frances Hodgson Burnett has more of the elements that children, especially little girls, loved and still love. To have a heroine first an heiress and then a poor, ill-treated little drudge living in the attic of a girls' boarding school in London is an almost irresistible plot to begin with, and then Mrs. Burnett packed it full of so much besides. She made you feel the cold and wet of the London streets as Sara Crewe trudged through them on her errands; she made you thrill to the secret parties in Sara's attic when Lottie and Ermingarde sneaked up to visit their old friend; she made you curious about the Indian gentleman next door with his turbaned servant and the shivering monkey. How you hated Miss Minchin with her pride and her thin lips, and how you rejoiced to have Sara safe out of her clutches at the end! So many people think of *Little Lord Fauntleroy* whenever Frances Hodgson Burnett's name is mentioned, but as for me, *Sara Crewe* will always come first.

There are a score of other books I could mention, all well battered from those days, and all loved and lent clear around the neighborhood, but the most beloved of all I kept to myself. It was not considered a juvenile; indeed it is not so listed today, except for much older boys and girls, and yet at seven I was held spellbound by its pages. *Lorna Doone* did not seem at all out of place to me as a companion to *Rebecca* and *Sara Crewe* and "The Little Mermaid." This may have been because I was fortunate enough to hear it being read aloud and to absorb many chapters of it before anyone noticed an unseen listener, busily cutting paper dolls behind the sofa. So Lorna and John Ridd and Lizzie and Ruth and all the rest became part and parcel of everyday life. My mind was full of them as I walked to school in the morning and a certain swift brown brook will always seem more like Bagworthy Water to me than when I saw the true stream flowing between the banks of the Doone valley. My favorite dolls were always christened Lorna as a matter of course and to this day I prefer brunettes to blondes because of the likeness. I doubt very much if Mr. R. Blackmore ever had a greater tribute than this.

After one reaches the teens one reads so many books, they all begin to run together. There is less time to mull over each page and to read and reread as one can earlier on long summer holidays or when one happens to be laid up with a cold at home. That is why I am glad that some of the books I write happen to be on the shelves for younger readers. It isn't that I don't want readers of all ages, for I do, but I know only too well that the younger you catch your audience, the better chance you stand of having your books look thumbed and falling out of their covers. And that after all is what every writer hopes for when all is said and done!

•

Padraic Colum

Poet and Critic

IMAGINATION AND CHILDREN'S LITERATURE

THERE is no time in one's life when right reading is so important as in one's childhood. One has good instincts then; later on they become corrupted by continuous reading of that which is just current and just topical. The good instincts that the child has, and the taste that goes with them, should be kept right. But we do spoil them. We spoil them by giving children snippets out of newspapers and stories which, because the writers have to follow a certain vein year in, year out, are trite—trite in invention and trite in expression.

When I say that children have good instincts in reading I mean that they respond to real imagination when it is shown in a story. Now what is imagination? It is not merely a faculty for stringing improbabilities together and making up a world that is wholly unreal. Imagination is the faculty of revealing things freshly and surprisingly.

Sometime, perhaps very soon, it will come to be recognized that it is as important to cultivate the imagination as it is to cultivate the will or the intelligence. At present our systems of education are directed towards training the will or training the intelligence, but perhaps the time is at hand when we will have an education that will be directed towards training the intelligence and the will through the imagination. For imagination is one of our great faculties. It is the one quality common to all great men—to soldiers and statesmen, to saints and artists, to scientists, philosophers and great businessmen. Says the Serpent to Eve in *Back to Methuselah*, "She told it to me as a marvelous story of something that never happened to a Lillith that never was. She did not know that imagination is the beginning of creation. You imagine what you desire; you will what you imagine; and at last you create what you will." The time may come when that sentence will be written above all places of education: "Imagination is the beginning of creation. . . . You imagine what you desire; you will what you imagine; and at last you create what you will." If children are to will out of their imagination and create out of their will, we must see to it that their imaginations are not clipped and made trivial.

A great writer, Sir Walter Scott, has written down all that is to be said as to the way stories for children should be told. "A good thought has come into my head," he writes in his *Journal* for 1827, "to write stories for little Johnnie Lockhart from the *History of Scotland,* like those taken from the *History of England.* I will not write mine quite as simply as Croker has done. I am persuaded both children and the lower class of readers hate books which are written down to their capacity, and love those that are more composed for their elders and betters. I will make, if possible, a book that a child will understand, yet a man will feel some temptation to peruse should he chance to take it up. It will require, however, a simplicity of style not quite my own. The grand and interesting consists in ideas, not words."

Scott, I am certain, was right in what he puts down here. Children are quick to feel patronage. The storyteller must have a respect for the child's mind and the child's conception of the world, knowing it for a complete mind and a complete conception. Scott had that kind of a respect; Hans Andersen, Stevenson, Kipling had it, and their ever memorable stories are grounded on it.

174

It is more important, I believe, to let the child's imagination develop than it is to labor to inculcate in him or her some correct ethical point of view. If a child has in his or her mind the images that imaginative literature can communicate—the heroic, sweet or loving types that are in the world's great stories—it is much more likely that he or she will grow up into a fine human being than if some austere mentor spoke to them out of every page of their reading. I think the mood of a child's story should be one of kindliness. I do not mean that the characters in a story should be always kind to each other. I mean that the auditor or the reader should be assured that the teller is inspired with a mood of kindliness for his conspicuous character. "Now you must know that the King had no horse to give Boots but an old broken-down jade," says the Norse story, "for his six other sons had carried off all the horses; but Boots did not care a pin for that; he sprang up on his sorry old steed. 'Farewell, father,' said he, 'I'll come back, never fear, and like enough I shall bring my six brothers with me,' and with that he rode off." When we hear this we know that the teller of the tale has the right feeling for his hero.

With the mood of kindliness there should be the mood of adventure. The hero should be one who is willing to take strange paths in the morning and lie down under the giant's roof when the darkness falls. "After that they went around the castle, and at last they came to a great hall where the Trolls' two great swords hung high up on the wall. 'I wonder if you are man enough to wield one of these,' said the Princess. 'Who? I?' said the lad, ' 'Twould be a pretty thing indeed if I couldn't wield one of these.' With that he put two or three chairs one a-top of the other, jumped up, and touched the biggest sword with his fingertips, tossed it up in the air, and caught it again by the hilt; leapt down, and at the same time dealt such a blow with it on the floor that the whole hall shook." That is the humor proper to a hero.

Then there should be happenings in a child's story, many happenings, even the same happenings over again. The good characters should undoubtedly be fine and upright, but we should not insist upon their being always good boys at school. If they are heroic and adventurous and have a simple-minded goodness it is enough; the stories they figure in need not bristle with moralities and recommendations to good conduct. And the old figures of romance should be left to the children; when Kings and Queens and Princes have taken their leave of the political world they should still be left to flourish in the world of the child's romance. Witches, giants, dwarfs, gnomes, and trolls should be left to them, too.

I think the ideal children's book should be . . . a continuous narrative with the same characters living through many varied incidents. Things need not be too simplified in that world. It will do no harm if things are left mysterious there—such mysterious things are "magic," and "magic" is an element that is not only accepted but is looked for. And it flatters a child to be able to read a long story that has mysteries in it. The probabilities that we know of from experience have no place in the world we make for a child. A tree may talk; a swan may change into a king's daughter; a castle may be built in an instant. We know tree, swan, and castle by their limitations, but a child knows them in their boundless possibilities. To a child each thing mentioned is distinct, unique, a thing in itself, having all the possibilities of things in Eden. Did we know, in the time that we flew kites, that there was a space in the atmosphere that no kite ever flew before and that our kite might enter it? That sense of boundless possibility should belong to everything in a child's story.

The delight in things, the sense of the uniqueness of things, is in every story that children delight in. An old lamp may be Aladdin's. A key may open the door to mystery. A dish may be the supreme possession of a king. For children feel, as people with few possessions feel, the adventure and the enchantment that are in things.

Miriam Blanton Huber

Author of "Story and Verse for Children"

CHILDREN'S INTERESTS IN READING

ONE of the most profitable experiences a prospective teacher can have is to spend an afternoon in the children's room of a busy public library. She will note with pleasure the physical arrangements for the comfort of children—the low tables and chairs and the bookshelves that children can reach. She will notice the attractive bulletin boards, the posters announcing new books, and special exhibits of interest to children. Perhaps the library she is visiting has a fireplace or other favored spot where the librarian holds story hours for children at convenient times.

We will assume that our observer is familiar with the classification system in use and the position of the shelves containing the different types of books. By looking at the appearance of books she can learn much that is enlightening in regard to children's interests in reading. The books they love are worn and soiled and require frequent rebinding. There are several duplicate copies of the books most in demand. A book that has been in the library for some time and has its original covers fresh and unsoiled has failed to attract children. It is interesting to speculate why.

When the children arrive for their daily selection of books, the unobtrusive observer can learn a great deal. She will probably be astonished at the businesslike way in which children choose their books. There is much less indecision in their actions than in those of a group of adults. As a rule children know what they want and where to find it. When they consult a librarian, their explanations are clear and to the point. They may be uncertain as to exact titles of books, but they are certain in their likes and dislikes among books.

When the children's room closes for the day, perhaps our observer may borrow duplicate copies of some of the books that have been in demand. Perhaps she may take some of them home with her and attempt to discover what it is that makes them satisfying to children.

Observations such as we have described are helpful in understanding children's interests in reading. In working with children, however, we learn to study the interests of each group and each child and make the best provision we can to satisfy them. Needs and interests vary, but the wider one's observation, the more sensitive one becomes to the variations in groups and in individuals.

There is no doubt that children are discriminating in their choices and that they recognize good books. A number of careful experimental studies of children's reading interests have been made and they show that children, at all levels of intelligence, are appreciative of the quality of the materials they read. They really do discriminate and express consistent preferences.

Jordan [1] reports a carefully conducted investigation of children's reading based upon library withdrawals and upon questionnaires to children. After an interval of five years he gave the same questionnaire to other children and found a striking similarity in the returns of the investigations. The boys and girls he studied ranged in age from 9 to 18 years. He found marked differences in the interests of boys and of girls, with the greatest difference in interests at the ages of 12 and 13 years. The major interest of the boys at all ages was adventure. The literature most popular with them pictured strenuous adventure, mastery, love of sensory life, loyalty, and self-control. The major interests of the girls were home life and stories that pictured kindliness, attention to others, and response to approval and to scornful behavior. *The Call of the Wild, Treasure Island,* Boy Scout books, and books by Joseph Altsheler stood high in boys' choices; the most popular book among girls was *Little Women.*

---

[1] Arthur M. Jordan, *Children's Interests in Reading.* University of North Carolina Press.

From the Stanford research on gifted children in California, Terman and Lima [1] report on the reading of 1,000 children of very high intelligence compared with 1,000 unselected children, the ages ranging from 6 to 16 years. The types of material standing highest in the regard of both the gifted boys and the boys of the unselected group were adventure and informational fiction, but the reading of the gifted boys showed a much larger proportion of books of science, history, and biography than that of the boys of the unselected group. The books best liked by both groups of girls were stories of home and school life and of adventure, but the girls of the unselected group revealed a greater liking for emotional fiction than the gifted girls. The children of all four groups showed an interest in fairy tales and animal stories. The books reported by the children in this investigation were uniformly books of value and literary merit, due, the investigators believe, to the fact that the children had access to good books.

An extensive investigation of children's reading was made by Washburne and Vogel [2] assisted by committees of the American Library Association. In thirty-four cities, 36,750 children furnished reports giving their opinions of all the books they read during a school year. Over 9,000 different books were reported. Librarians rated the literary merit of the 800 books most frequently reported and considered 100 of them low in quality. The books high in children's choices, however, were in the main considered acceptable by the librarians. Among the books given high rank by children were the following: Grade IV—*Grimms' Fairy Tales, Peter Pan, Fairies and Chimneys*, and *The Story of Mrs. Tubbs;* Grade V—*Black Beauty, Pinocchio, The Story of Dr. Dolittle*, and *Alice's Adventures in Wonderland;* Grade VI—*Heidi, Hans Brinker, Toby Tyler*, and *The Peterkin Papers;* Grade VII—*Tom Sawyer, Little Women, Huckleberry Finn*, and *Treasure Island;* Grade VIII—*The Call of the Wild, Kidnapped, Penrod*, and *The Dark Frigate;* Grade IX—*Jim Davis, Sherlock Holmes, Lorna Doone*, and *A Tale of Two Cities.*

Seegers [3] reports an analysis of the undirected, uncontrolled reading of books done outside school hours by 924 pupils in a large city. These children read a wide variety of books, many of good quality and others of doubtful value. He believes that most of the selections were due to availability. He found that many of the children were susceptible to suggestion and read and enjoyed a great number of desirable books recom-

[1] Lewis M. Terman and Margaret Lima, *Children's Reading.* D. Appleton-Century Company.

[2] Carleton Washburne and Mabel Vogel, *Winnetka Graded Book List,* American Library Association; *The Right Book for the Right Child,* The John Day Company.

[3] J. C. Seegers, "A Study of Children's Reading," *Elementary English Review,* XIII: 251.

mended by their teachers. *Tom Sawyer* was read by a larger number of boys than any other book, and *Little Women* by a larger number of girls. Seegers reports also that among the most frequently read books were many that the children had recently seen produced as motion pictures. This was true not only of the classics, but of less desirable books. Librarians from various parts of the United States have reported the same result from books pictured upon the screen, and this seems to indicate that motion pictures may be a means of stimulating reading instead of supplanting it. It has been observed, too, that children express pleasure when they find a screen version faithful to the original book.

Huber, Bruner, and Curry [1] conducted an experiment involving 50,000 children and 1,500 teachers geographically distributed over the United States, to determine the poetry most suitable for children in the elementary and junior high schools. From the opinion of teachers and writers and from courses of study, 100 poems for each school grade were chosen and published in experimental booklets which were put into the hands of children taking part in the experiment. The procedure was so worked out that each booklet was used over a range of five grades. During a period of a year each child came in contact with at least 60 poems. The reactions of each child were recorded and studied, and the findings have had a marked influence upon the selection and grade placement of poetry for children.

In the Huber-Bruner-Curry experiment it was found that children at all age levels have decided preferences and that these preferences differ at different age levels. Exception to this was found in the case of 59 poems which were high in children's choices over a range of three or more grades; these poems appear to contain elements of compelling interest for children of various ages. This situation seems to suggest that certain literature for children belongs in any grade—that certain poems, and probably stories also, hold the interest of readers of all ages, perhaps from "seven to seventy." Other materials, in themselves good but lacking the qualities of universal appeal, need to be considered more carefully and offered to children of the particular ages to which they are suited.

In this experiment, "The Raggedy Man," [2] by James Whitcomb Riley, was used in the first five grades and called out a reaction of preference far exceeding any other poem. In the first, second, and fourth grades it ranked first in children's choices; in the third, second; and in the fifth grade, fifth. It, however, held in the second grade a weighted score that indicated its greatest interest there. Why do children like "The Raggedy

[1] Miriam Blanton Huber, Herbert B. Bruner, and Charles M. Curry, *Children's Interests in Poetry*. Rand McNally and Company.
[2] "The Raggedy Man," by James Whitcomb Riley, may be found in Volume 5:311.

Man" so much? Is it the dialect or the social situation? Or is it one of the following: animals, play, outdoor activities, fairies, magic, humor, surprise, choosing a life career, kindness, or a vivid lovable character? Or do all of these combine in the poem to give satisfaction to children?

In reading the poems arranged for each grade according to children's choices as shown by this experiment, it seems possible to detect a growing maturity in taste; there appears to be some unity of interest in a grade, but each grade shows a variety of interests. In Grade I the greatest interests appear to be animals and play; in Grade II many lullabies and poems about children are liked; in Grade III many fairy poems are found to be of interest as are poems of the outdoors; in Grade IV humor and nonsense make a high appeal, as do poems of patriotism; in Grade V many ballads and poems of heroes are liked; in Grade VI interest divides between home and danger, but poems of romance also receive recognition; in Grade VII humor continues to rank high, but the humorous situations become more complex, there are fewer hero poems although many bloody encounters, and there is an increased love of romance; in Grade VIII romance, tragedy, and retribution hold the stage; in Grade IX the poems high in regard are more reflective and thoughtful, as if the readers are seeking the causes of things. A surprisingly large number of the poems strongly preferred by boys and girls in this experiment are written in dialect. Children unhesitatingly delight in the human quality and homely artistry of dialect in literature. Their choices throughout show the satisfaction children find in verse that pictures action and the vivid quality of living.

Workers in children's literature are indebted to Dunn [1] for a study of the factors in stories that hold the greatest interest for children in the primary grades. Her study reports stories that children like and, by a process of analysis, the qualities in them that are believed to appeal most highly to young children. Thirty-one samples of primary reading material were arranged in forty pairs and read to 195 different classes in Grades I, II, and III. After each pair was read, the children expressed their preference. Among the stories that stood high in children's choices were "One Eye, Two Eyes, and Three Eyes," "The Wolf and the Seven Kids," "Epaminondas," "Boots and His Brothers," and "A Story of Washington's Boyhood." The thirty-one stories were analyzed by adult judges for the presence of one or more of twenty characteristics previously selected as significant in interest to children. The data statistically treated led to the following conclusions: The interests of boys and girls of these ages are very similar. The characteristics of greatest interest are *surprise* and *plot*

[1] Fannie Wyche Dunn, *Interest Factors in Primary Reading*. Teachers College Bureau of Publications.

for both boys and girls; *animalness* (presence of animals in the story) for boys; *childness* (presence of child characters in the story), *familiar experience,* and to a lesser extent *repetition* and *conversation* for girls.

It is interesting to find that in this experiment *liveliness* had an unfavorable effect upon children's choices. Children are quick to detect artificial sprightliness and reject it in favor of genuine plot in which things really happen. The fact that *surprise* outranks *plot* leads to some interesting speculations also. Factual material in nature study and science may be made very attractive to children if unexpected phenomena are presented simply enough for them to understand.

Many questions have arisen in regard to the reading interests of dull children and superior children. Do dull and superior children wish to read about the same things? Do children of average intelligence have the same reading interests as children of more intelligence or less intelligence? To find an answer to these questions, Huber [1] presented selections from children's literature to groups of children of different levels of intelligence under experimental conditions and made comparisons of their reactions and preferences.

Thirty poems and stories were selected as representative of the following types of material: *familiar experience, unusual experience, humor, fancy, information,* and *heroism and service.* Groups of expert judges rated each selection for literary quality, for suitability, and for difficulty. The selections were arranged in pairs so that each type of material might be presented in comparison with all the other types.

The subjects of the experiment were 408 children in fifteen classes in five typical good public schools. Six of the fifteen classes were considered in their schools as dull, five as average, and four as superior. The dull groups were organized in "special" or ungraded classes, and the average and superior groups were taken from Grades I, II, III, IV, and V. An intelligence rating was secured for each child from an individual Stanford-Binet Intelligence Test. The experiment was conducted with each class separately in its individual classroom, but for greater accuracy the pupils were re-sorted into three groups before the results were tabulated. These groups were arranged so that they were approximately equal in average chronological age, about nine years, and in number of years in school; and the children of the average and bright groups were approximately equal in grade status. The one marked difference in the groups was intelligence.

The stories and poems in pairs were read to the children under pleasant and enjoyable conditions. Each child indicated a preference in each pair.

[1] Miriam Blanton Huber, *The Influence of Intelligence upon Children's Reading Interests.* Teachers College Bureau of Publications.

The resulting data were treated by statistical methods which made provision for the relation between children's preferences and the judges' ratings of quality and difficulty. The results showed clearly that the reading interests of children at different levels of intelligence, as measured by the materials used in this experiment, are strikingly similar. The material liked best by the dull, the average, and the bright children was unmistakably that of the fourth type, *fancy*. The stories and poems of that type used were: "The Gingerbread Boy," "A Visit from St. Nicholas," "The Tinder Box," "A Story of the Springtime," and "The Selfish Giant."

The order of preference of the other five types of material was the same for the average and the superior children as were the choices of the dull, except that the dull children placed *humor* lower than did the average and bright children. The dull children liked the selections of *familiar experience* better than did the average and bright children, but they liked them least, as did all the children, though the adult judges rated those selections less difficult than the others. The order of preference of the average and bright children in the types of material was as follows: (1) *fancy*, (2) *humor*, (3) *unusual experience*, (4) *heroism and service*, (5) *information*, and (6) *familiar experience*. The choices of the dull children were in the same order, except that *humor* fell to fourth place, with *unusual experience* second and *heroism and service* third. The humorous selections used were: "Frogs at School," "The Baby Elephant and the Red Cap," "The Tar Baby," "The Elephant's Child," and "The Walrus and the Carpenter."

The results of this experiment indicate that the reading interests of dull children are strikingly similar to the reading interests of average and superior children. Dull children, however, are more influenced by difficulty and complexity than are more intelligent children. It follows, then, that dull children, attempting to read for themselves, find difficulty of language and complexity of ideas serious handicaps. To provide satisfying books that dull children can read is an opportunity for service that no teacher or librarian should overlook. Many dull children have special abilities, and many have integrity and strength of character that enable them to become useful members of society. Provision for enjoyment in reading is as necessary for them as for children more fortunately endowed in intelligence. Often the problem is met by offering the dull child a book written for younger children because it is easy reading. The dull boy, however, wants to read about the same things that other boys of his age like to read about, and a "babyish" book not only fails to interest him but disgusts him. An over-age girl also cannot be satisfied by literary fare suitable for younger children; she would like to read about the things that interest girls of her own age *if she could read the books*. Struggles with difficult words, involved sentence structure, and abstract ideas soon lead

182

to discouragement and reading is abandoned. The reading needs of dull children have not received sufficient attention and the supply of suitable books is limited.

Experimental studies of children's interests in reading have resulted in a wholesome respect for children's tastes. Today a child's book is judged not only by literary standards but in the light of whether children will like it or not. Regard for children's preferences has not lowered literary standards, for children prove themselves excellent judges of literary quality. When they choose books of little merit, it is largely because that is the kind of books available to them. When they are given access to good books, they develop an appreciation of them. This is a different situation from one in which adults make the choices for children, and this changed emphasis is the very heart of providing successful experiences in literature.

In the studies of children's interests, the conditions of the experiments were purposely arranged to discover the reactions of children to the literature itself, with as little influence of other factors as possible. In ordinary situations, many factors peculiar to the situation are present, and the alert teacher or parent takes advantage of them. Groups of children, and individual children, have special interests that may be capitalized. A stamp collection may lead to absorbed reading of history and travel. The natural environment or industrial environment in which children live may be the starting point for wide reading. The activities and experiences of the school offer rich opportunities for exploration in books. With these special incentives and purposes, children will find satisfaction in books that under other conditions they might consider uninteresting. Even difficulties in language and style may sometimes be surmounted by the drive of real purposes. The teacher who is sensitive to all such possibilities modifies what she knows of children's interests in general to suit the needs and desires of the children about her.

Who's Who

IN THE CHILDREN'S HOUR

WHO'S WHO IN THE CHILDREN'S HOUR

BESS PORTER ADAMS, now on the faculty of the University of Redlands in California, has taught in elementary schools and has lectured widely on reading for young people. She has had an opportunity, by following the changing and expanding reading interests of her own two children, to study her subject both as a teacher and as a parent. Her book, *About Books and Children* (Holt), is a history of children's literature.

LOUISA MAY ALCOTT (1832–1888) began to write at the age of eight, and at sixteen sold her first story. From that time on her life was devoted to writing and teaching. Her best-loved story, *Little Women* (Little), reflects her experiences as a girl (she was Jo), and many of her other books did, too. During the Civil War she served as an army nurse. An interesting account of her life is given by Cornelia Meigs in *Invincible Louisa* (Little). Two episodes from *Little Women* will be found in Volume 3:113 and Volume 3:138, but you will surely want to read the whole book.

DOROTHY ALDIS'S verses are usually for smaller boys and girls, written about everyday subjects (see *All Together*, Putnam). She was born in Chicago. Both parents were newspaper people, and when she left college it was to take a series of jobs on newspapers. After her marriage to Graham Aldis, she began writing and raising a family of four at about the same time. She lives in Lake Forest, Illinois, where she writes stories and delightful poetry. Sometimes she does this after driving her car into a meadow. She writes then with her portable typewriter in her lap!

CECIL FRANCES ALEXANDER (1818–1895) wrote childlike verses many years ago that still often appear in collections of poems for children. She is also remembered for her many hymns, among which "There Is a Green Hill Far Away" is perhaps best known.

MARGARET FORD ALLEN, formerly an assistant editor of *Child Life,* is a Chicago writer and artist. She is living now in New Orleans.

JESS DOBSON ALT has written a great many funny rhymes for *Child Life* and other magazines. She was born in a Methodist minister's family, a girl among four inspired "minister's sons," in the Black Hills of South Dakota. She says of this, "Life was never dull, a little short on luxuries but always stimulating."

JOSEPH ALTSHELER is one of the most popular boys' writers in America. He has a natural gift for writing vivid, adventurous tales. A reporter, Joseph Altsheler wrote his first stories for boys when he became editor of the *New York World's* tri-weekly magazine edition. *The Forest Runners* (Appleton) is a part of The Young Trailers Series. The other four famous series are: The Civil War Series, The Great West Series, The Texas Series, and The First World War Series. An episode from *Forest Runners* (Volume 11:295) will make you want to read the whole book.

Louisa May Alcott

Dorothy Aldis

Jess Dobson Alt

186

Edith Mason Armstrong   Mildred Bowers Armstrong   Montgomery Atwater

HANS CHRISTIAN ANDERSEN (1805–1875), the son of a Danish shoemaker, wanted to be an actor. He was educated by generous patrons and made several continental tours. He wrote some brilliant travel books. The first of the immortal *Fairy Tales* was published in 1835. They continued to appear until 1872. Andersen considered his tales to be of secondary importance, but they remain as enthralling to children today as they were a century ago.

C. W. ANDERSON's usual subjects for his stories, drawings, and sketches are horses. He has done three books about a little boy named Billy and his horse Blaze. One of these appears in *The Children's Hour*. His *Sketchbook* (Macmillan) will help young artists to draw horses, too. He and his wife spend most of their time in their New Hampshire home.

MARJORIE ALLEN ANDERSON is a contemporary writer for children, who lives in Arkansas.

MILDRED LEIGH ANDERSON is a contemporary writer for children, who lives in Rhode Island.

EDITH MASON ARMSTRONG, who has written several books, is a Chicagoan by birth, the daughter of Edward G. Mason, a president of The Chicago Historical Society. She writes about the amusing and lively adventures of her twelve brothers and sisters and herself, as children, at their summer home. Mrs. Armstrong's grandfather, Roswell B. Mason, was mayor of Chicago at the time of the Fire.

MILDRED BOWERS ARMSTRONG's many activities have served as an inspiration for her poems, many of them written for children. Among other things she has been an English teacher and a welfare worker in New York (where she claims she runs a "kitten underground" for the Animal League on Long Island). Her interest in animals stems from childhood days in West Virginia, where her pets included a duck, an owl, and a possum. She married a naval officer, lives in New York, and is the mother of two talented daughters.

HERBERT ASQUITH, in addition to being a poet, is known for his novels. He was born in England where he practiced law and served as a captain in World War I. In 1940 he again returned to the army. He is the author of *Pillicock Hill* (Macmillan), *The Volunteers* (Sidgwick) and several other books.

MONTGOMERY ATWATER, the son of a mining engineer, has spent most of his life in the mountains, which provide the setting for all of his fine books for boys. He has been successively trapper, guide, logger, rancher, and head of the avalanche research unit of the U. S. Forest Service. During World War II he instructed ski troops and became leader of a reconnaissance unit in the Ardennes Forest. *Avalanche Patrol* (Random), *Rustlers on the High Range* (Random), and *Smoke Patrol* (Random) reflect the outdoor life which he has led.

187

Salcia Bahnc   Carolyn Sherwin Bailey   Margaret Baker   Margaret J. Baker

RICHARD ATWATER was born and educated in Chicago where he at first taught Greek at the University of Chicago and later was the famous Riq, a humorous columnist on the old *Evening Post*. He married Florence Carroll with whom he collaborated in writing *Mr. Popper's Penguins* (Little). His other books were *Doris and the Trolls* (Rand), a fanciful story about his own two daughters, and *Rickity Rhymes of Riq* (Covici). "Mr. Popper and Captain Cook" (Volume 4:30) will make you want to read the whole book, *Mr. Popper's Penguins*.

MARY AUSTIN lived for sixteen years, in the manner of an Indian woman, on the edge of the Mohave Desert. Here she studied Indian lore. She wrote of her experiences in many of her verses which portray phases of western life. *Children Sing in the Far West* (Houghton) is one of her best known collections.

MARGARET AYER, a well-known contemporary illustrator, lives in New York City. Among the many books containing her authentic illustrations and cover designs are Bose's *Totaram* (Macmillan), Sowers' *The Lotus Mark* (Macmillan), Landon's *Anna and the King of Siam* (Day), and Bailey's *Tell Me a Birthday Story* (Lippincott).

C. H. BACHARACH was a fine illustrator of an earlier day.

RHODA W. BACMEISTER is a contemporary writer of delightful juvenile verse which appears in many children's magazines. A collection of her work is found in *Stories to Begin On* (Dutton).

SALCIA BAHNC was for many years located in Chicago but is now living in New York. She was born in the Carpathians but came to America when she was a child and studied at the Chicago Art Institute. She has illustrated a number of books and has found much of her material during her travels in France. She has had a number of one-man shows and has taught at the Chicago Art Institute and at the Parsons School of Design. Her son is a student at Johns Hopkins University in Baltimore.

CAROLYN SHERWIN BAILEY began her career at the age of five when she won first prize in a writing contest. Even before this, however, she liked to make up stories which she would dictate to her mother. At nineteen her first verses and stories were published, and she is now the author of more than thirty-five children's books, one of which, *Miss Hickory* (Viking), was awarded the Newbery Medal. Her childhood, spent near the Hudson River, furnishes the material for many of her stories. She has been a teacher and a magazine editor and has traveled extensively. Today, she and her husband live in New Hampshire six months of the year, in a hundred-and-fifty-year-old house surrounded by forests and orchards. In the winter their home is in New York City.

MARGARET BAKER, author of *The Lost Merbaby* (Dodd) and *Patsy and the Leprechaun* (Dodd), lives in a village on the edge of the Cotswolds in England. Her only visit to America was when she was five. She began to write when she was about seven

Janet Norris Bangs   Ralph Henry Barbour   Sir James Barrie

years old, and edited and largely wrote a family magazine in her teens. However, she was twenty-one before any work was accepted for publication. She specializes in folk tales. Her hobbies are motoring, gardening, climbing, and field botany.

MARGARET J. BAKER's home is a tiny cottage in Somerset, England, which she shares with Candy Buffalo, a small but very determined Pekinese. Her time is spent in motoring, walking, gardening, swimming, home decorating, reading, watching television, and, of course, writing. As a child she wanted to be a painter, but she has found herself writing for children, whom she delights with such fine stories as: *Four Farthings and a Thimble* (Longmans), *A Castle and Sixpence* (Longmans), *Benbow and the Angels* (Longmans), and *The Family That Grew and Grew* (Whittlesey).

FAITH BALDWIN has written popular novels for adults for many years. Her novel, *The Juniper Tree* (Rinehart), is her sixty-second book. She has also written some excellent short stories for boys and girls. In addition to her writing she has raised four children. She is devoted to her home in Norfolk, Connecticut, and only with reluctance makes the short trip to New York.

JANET NORRIS BANGS' book of verse *Cornstalk Fiddle* (Decker) is full of midwestern scenes that she portrays so well. Mrs. Bangs was born on a farm near La Moille, Illinois, and is of pioneer stock. She received her early education in Princeton, Illinois, and was graduated from Wellesley College. After teaching for a while, she married Edward H. Bangs. Besides writing verse, Mrs. Bangs is interested in club work and conservation. The late Margaret Norris was her sister.

JOHN KENDRICK BANGS (1862–1922) was an editor of *Harper's Weekly, Harper's Magazine, Life,* and *Puck.* He published thirty volumes of humor and verse, the best known of which is *The Houseboat on the Styx* (Harper).

RALPH HENRY BARBOUR (1870–1944) has been called "the dean of sport story writers for boys." Over one hundred and forty of his books have been enjoyed through the years by countless children. He started on a journalistic career before turning to children's stories. His first book, *The Half-Back* (Appleton), written in 1899, is still selling. For some time he lived in Florida with his wife where his leisure time was spent in playing tennis and in gardening.

KATHERINE ELLIS BARRETT is a contemporary writer of verse for children.

SIR JAMES BARRIE (1860–1937) was born in Scotland of humble parents. While in school he wrote his first play, in which he appeared as an actor. His professional life began as a journalist, and he soon achieved a reputation for his character sketches. *The Little Minister* (Scribner) established him as a novelist but his most lasting fame was to come from his plays. His whimsey and his sincerity endeared him to all. *Peter Pan* (Scribner) is loved by young and old alike. When you read "Peter Pan and Captain Hook" (Volume 2:225) you are sure to read the rest of his adventures.

189

Marjorie Barrows   **Walter Ransom Barrows**   **Audrey Baxendale**   **Edna Becker**

MARJORIE BARROWS, editor of *The Children's Hour,* has written for children ever since she was a little girl of ten. At that time she wanted to be like Jo in *Little Women* and enthusiastically drilled neighborhood children in wildly dramatic plays of her own making. When she was twelve she edited a school paper at Chicago's Ascham Hall and, as she blushingly admits, wrote most of it herself. She continued editing publications in college (at Northwestern and at the University of Chicago) and then she became a writer for *Compton's Pictured Encyclopedia.* A children's play she wrote in college brought her to the attention of Rand McNally's new magazine, *Child Life,* and she joined its staff, becoming assistant editor, and in time associate editor, and editor in chief. While editor, she made a special study of children's tastes in reading and talked on this subject at schools and colleges throughout the country. After a number of years at *Child Life* she resigned in order to have time to write her own books. She has written a number, and among her own favorites are *Muggins Mouse* (Reilly and Lee), *Fraidy Cat* (Rand), and *Two Hundred Best Poems* (Grosset). This poetry anthology, endorsed by literary critics, was high on the list of the fifty best-selling books of the past fifty years. Later she joined the staff of the Spencer Press, compiled *1000 Beautiful Things* (Consolidated), and other adult anthologies, and is now working happily on *The Children's Hour* and on *Treasure Trails,* the magazine of *The Children's Hour.* "There couldn't be more rewarding work than giving boys and girls a love of good reading," she says.

WALTER RANSOM BARROWS is a Chicago teacher and mathematician. He was graduated from Oberlin College and received his M.A. at Yale University where he also taught. His favorite hobby is golf.

KATHARINE LEE BATES (1859–1929), American poet and educator, wrote the stirring words for "America the Beautiful." Although chiefly remembered for this, she also wrote several volumes of poetry: *America the Beautiful and Other Poems* (Crowell), *America the Dream* (Crowell), and *Fairy Gold* (Dutton), which is especially for children. For many years, at Wellesley, she was an inspiring teacher of English.

AUDREY BAXENDALE was born in London. Soon afterwards, her father's ship disappeared at sea. Audrey and her mother went to live on a farm in the bush country of Australia. "The Secret of Rainbow Ridge" depicts life on just such a farm. Audrey's first story appeared on her fourteenth birthday. At eighteen she married and went to live in Canada. She has traveled a great deal. She has revisited England and Australia, and has been all over the United States, in Honolulu, New Zealand, Fiji, Norfolk Island, and Scotland. Audrey Baxendale is greatly interested in directing plays, especially with children's groups. Her daughter Diana has also written stories for publication.

EDNA BECKER's first ambition was to study medicine, but after being left badly handicapped by a serious illness she turned to writing. Since then she has written not only poems and stories for magazines and school readers but numerous books, operettas, and plays for children. Her *Nine Hundred Buckets of Paint* (Abingdon) is particularly well liked. She is active in many clubs and is a member of the Poetry Society of Kansas, the Kansas Author's Club, and the National League of American Pen Women. She enjoys her brother's family next door and is now building a new home.

MARY BEIMFOHR is an Evanston, Illinois, writer who has lectured much on the subject of juvenile literature. She has a delightful sense of humor and lends a helping hand to many a young writer.

HILAIRE BELLOC (1870–1953) was not only a writer of excellent nonsense rhymes, such as are found in *Cautionary Verses* (Knopf), but was a novelist, journalist, essayist, and a fine historian as well. He was considered one of the most prolific of English writers. He was active in politics for a short time and served in the French Army. He had two sons and two daughters.

STEVE BENEDICT was brought up in New York City where illness forced him to leave school after the third grade. As a young man he hoboed his way across the United States engaging in many different professions. These experiences later provided unlimited material for his writing. His adventure story, *Gabee of the Delta* (Abingdon), is a book boys like. In addition to his novels he has contributed to many magazines, and two of his stories are included in university textbooks. He makes his home in Oakland, California.

LAURA BENÉT's long residence in New York has given her the requisite knowledge of the Revolutionary War background which we find so aptly portrayed in her stirring story, "Horseshoe Nails." The daughter of an army officer, and sister of two famous poets, William Rose Benét and Stephen Vincent Benét, her early life was subject to frequent upheaval. After attending the Emma Willard School and Vassar, she joined her parents in California, but soon was drawn back to the East. Social work in New York was followed by a career on the *New York Evening Post* and the *New York Sun*, where she assisted in the book department and ran a poetry column. She also is the author of sixteen books, among them *The Hidden Valley* (Dodd), *Young Edgar Allan Poe* (Dodd), and *Enchanting Jenny Lind* (Dodd), and has written numerous short stories and poems.

STEPHEN VINCENT BENÉT (1898–1943), American storyteller and poet, had his first book published while he was a freshman at Yale University. After graduating he tried advertising but did not like it. Later he spent some time in France where he met and married Rosemary Carr. There, too, he wrote his famous *John Brown's Body* (Rinehart) which won the Pulitzer Prize and the Roosevelt Medal. He and his wife collaborated on *A Book of Americans* (Rinehart) and several other books dedicated to their three children.

JOHN BENNETT always wanted to be an artist, but even as a boy he was the official storyteller of the neighborhood. He was a journalist in early life, but with the publication of *Master Skylark* (Appleton), which is now a classic, his writing talent was firmly established. He is married and lives in South Carolina. In addition to his writ-

Mary Beimfohr **Laura Benét** **Stephen Vincent Benét**

191

ing and illustrating, he is interested in repairing old furniture, cabinetmaking, and tree culture. "A Gift from the Queen" (Volume 12:69) is just one of Master Skylark's interesting adventures.

JUANITA BENNETT was born in Indiana, but studied at the Chicago Art Institute and did fashion drawings in both Chicago and New York. When her own children were little she began drawing babies and has been drawing them ever since. She now lives on a farm near Dundee, Illinois, and, among other things, gives lectures on ceramics.

ROWENA BENNETT is both author and poet. Her first writing was done at the age of nine. She attended the University of Michigan and a private school in Berlin, Germany, before entering on her career as lecturer and free-lance author. She lives in Warrenville, Illinois, with her husband and three children. Among her books is a collection of poetry, *Around a Toadstool Table* (Follett), and *Story-Teller Poems* (Winston). In 1941 and 1942 she was a member of the faculty of the Northwestern University Writers' Conference.

BIANCA (Heilborn), though born in Chicago, now resides in California. She studied art and sculpture at the Leonardo Da Vinci School and the Art Students' League in New York. Her art studies completed, she made an extended stay in Europe where she visited the various art centers. In 1935 she went to Los Angeles where she worked on story development and illustrating at the Walt Disney studios. At present she is teaching ceramic sculpture and assisting her artist husband, Carl Heilborn, in the Gallery of Fine Arts.

MARGERY WILLIAMS BIANCO (1881–1944) was born in London but lived most of her life in the United States. She began to write while still a young girl and had her first novel published at twenty-one. It was not until her children were born that she directed her writing to stories for them. In 1922 *The Velveteen Rabbit* (Doubleday) launched her successful career in this field. *The Little Wooden Doll* (Macmillan) and *The Skin Horse* (Doran) were illustrated by her daughter Pamela. Margery Bianco was very fond of dogs and cats and other pets which figured in many of her sensitive, imaginative stories as well as in her realistic books about animals. "A Winterbound Adventure" (Volume 6:327) is taken from her book *Winterbound* (Viking), which has been called "the *Little Women* of the twentieth century."

CLARENCE BIERS lives in a cottage near the ocean in Florida. Here he does much of his illustrating. For many years his home was near Chicago where he went to the Chicago Art Institute, and where he did many illustrations for Rand McNally, Whitman, and *Child Life Magazine*. He illustrated many of Rand McNally's Glowing Eye books and *Cocky* (Rand). He has also written books for children and drawn many paint books for them. When he was only sixteen years old he conducted the children's page for a national magazine. One of the more recent books he has illustrated is *Tut-Tut Tales* (Garden City). Mr. Biers, who has a fine sense of humor, has also done a number of clever cartoons for the *Chicago Tribune* and for Consolidated Book Publishers.

| Juanita Bennett | Rowena Bennett | Bianca | Margery Williams Bianco |

REGINALD BIRCH (1856–1943), when he was a little boy in London, wanted to be a sailor or an actor. He lived on the island of Jersey with his grandfather who looked just like the old earl in *Little Lord Fauntleroy*. When he was fifteen he traveled to San Francisco with his family, and the clever woodblocks and posters which he helped his father make started his art career. He studied painting at the Royal Academy in Munich. When he came back to the United States in the 1880's his humorous, charming drawings began to appear in *St. Nicholas* and in many other magazines. He is remembered particularly for his drawings for the stories by Frances Hodgson Burnett and John Bennett's *Master Skylark* in *St. Nicholas*. In later years he illustrated *The Last Pirate* and stories for *Child Life Magazine*. He loved New York and for a long time was one of its most distinguished figures, witty, courteous, and charming. In his earlier days Reginald Birch was a contemporary of Joaquin Miller, Mark Twain, and Bret Harte.

LORENCE BJORKLUND was born in Minnesota and went to school there, but by the time he was eighteen he had traveled the length of the Mississippi in a rowboat and had seen nearly all the states. After being awarded an art scholarship he went to the Pratt Institute in Brooklyn. He has specialized in drawing or painting geographical and historical subjects. He is fond of doing Indians, pioneers, and animals. He now lives in Westchester County in New York with his wife, his daughter, his dogs, cats, and rabbits.

WILLIAM BLAKE'S (1757–1827) poetry has a quality of beauty and simplicity which makes children enjoy it despite its symbolism and mysticism. He is known, too, for his mystical painting and design, and today his copper engraving is considered very fine.

RALPH STEELE BOGGS is the joint author of *Three Golden Oranges* (Longmans) and has studied throughout Puerto Rico, Spain, and North Carolina. He not only teaches and prepares courses on folklore but is a councilor of the American Folklore Society and a chairman of the Folklore Section of the Modern Language Association of America.

IVY BOLTON writes historical stories and books for teen-agers, and thus follows in the footsteps of her great-uncle and her father, who were both historians. Her early childhood was spent in Kent, England, and she came to the United States as a schoolgirl. She graduated from St. Mary's School, Peekskill, New York, where she is now teacher and librarian. Her first biography, *Father Junipero Serra* (Messner), a pioneer of California, was published in 1952. She is also the author of three plays for amateurs. Her hobbies are gardening and stamp-collecting.

NELSON BOND is a contemporary writer who writes fantastic stories that appear in anthologies and on television. *Mr. Mergenthwirker's Lobblies and Other Fantastic Tales* (Coward) came out in book form. "Lancelot Biggs on the Saturn" (Volume 16:70) is one of the adventures you will find Lancelot getting into in *Lancelot Biggs: Spaceman* (Doubleday).

Clarence Biers

Reginald Birch

Lorence Bjorklund

193

Mary Hastings Bradley   Vivian Breck   Matilda Breuer

LYSBETH BOYD BORIE wrote *Poems for Peter* (Lippincott) and other verse for children and adults. She is also active in civic work. Her free time is spent with her husband and two grown sons as well as with her hobbies—Japanese prints and modern decoration.

BEE BOWERS writes many poems for children from her home near Chicago. Some of them have been set to music and are on records.

MARY HASTINGS BRADLEY's stories about big game hunting come from personal experience. She has made trips with her husband into the Belgian Congo hunting gorillas, and into Sumatra and Indo-China for tigers. She also made an expedition with her husband and small daughter to study the Pygmies in Africa. She lives in Chicago where she does much of her writing. Among her many books is *On the Gorilla Trail* (Appleton). One of the adventures in that book is "Gorillas and Lions" (Volume 13:158).

BERTON BRALEY writes funny verses and stories for children and for grownups. He has published more than fourteen hundred of them in newspapers and magazines. Some have also appeared in book form. His work as a reporter, special correspondent, and free-lance writer has taken him all over the world. Some of his best-known books are *A Banjo at Armageddon* (Doran), *Songs of the Workaday World* (Doran), and *Things as They Are* (Doran).

VIVIAN BRECK lives in Berkeley, California. She is the author of two books for young people, *High Trail* (Doubleday) and *Hoof Beats on the Trail* (Doubleday). Both are stories of the Sierra Nevada mountains, where she has spent many summers with her husband and her two sons.

MATILDA BREUER went to Chicago from Oklahoma to study at the Art Institute. She had been painting since childhood, and had spent three summers in Colorado studying outdoor sketching. She once spent three years as a commercial artist in New York, before she settled near Chicago's Lincoln Park, where she has enjoyed doing children's illustrations ever since.

HOWARD MAXWELL BRIER is the author of *Skycruiser* (Random) and *Smoke Eater* (Random) and many other popular sports and adventure stories. His great interest in boys and girls and the use of his boyhood experiences combine to make his stories vivid and full of authentic detail. He is married and has two children. At the present time he is teaching journalism at the University of Washington and acting as director of the Pacific Slope School Press.

CAROL RYRIE BRINK, who is a consultant editor of *The Children's Hour*, began writing stories for her two children when they were young and later these stories grew into books. Two of them, *Anything Can Happen on the River* (Macmillan) and *Lad with a Whistle* (Macmillan), were inspired while living in France and Scotland. One of

194

her most famous books, *Caddie Woodlawn* (Macmillan), which won a Newbery award, is based on stories of her grandmother's childhood. She and her family live in Minnesota where her husband is a professor at the University. Her *Family Grandstand* (Viking) depicts just such a family. "Caddie's Silver Dollar" (Volume 11:127) is one adventure you will find in *Caddie Woodlawn,* and "The Willow Basket" (Volume 11:93) comes from her book *Magical Melons.* These are both fine books you will want to read.

JOYCE L. BRISLEY is a contemporary writer of delightful juvenile verse.

C. E. BROCK (1870–1938) and H. M. BROCK were well-known English artists who illustrated many old classics, particularly books that boys and girls like.

EMMA L. BROCK is a distinguished artist-author. She finds most of her material while traveling and visiting throughout the world. Especially loved are her stories and illustrations for *Drusilla* (Macmillan), *The Greedy Goat* (Knopf), and *Here Comes Kristie* (Knopf). "In a Covered Wagon" (Volume 11:72) tells about one adventure you will find in the book *Drusilla.*

WALTER BROOKS has lived most of his life in New York state, but it was when he was in Washington, D. C., one summer, that he wrote his first children's book, *To and Again* (Knopf). Freddy, the pig, was an unimportant character in that book, but he soon became the leader of the barnyard, and hero of the books that bear his name. Mr. Brooks has written about one hundred fifty short stories, and fourteen children's books, including *Freddy the Detective* (Knopf), *Freddy Goes Camping* (Knopf), and *Freddy and the Space Ship* (Knopf). "Freddy the Detective Solves a Mystery" (Volume 4:71) tells of one of Freddy's adventures.

PATRICIA BROUGHAM was born and educated in London, England. She has worked in a film studio, in an advertising agency, on a daily newspaper, and in the Public Information Office of the United States Navy in Europe during World War II. She now works on *Collins Young Elizabethan Magazine* along with her husband. "Cuckoo in the Nest" was written because Shakespeare is her favorite writer and because the Elizabethan stage is such a fascinating subject. She likes cats, but does not have one because she would have to leave it alone all day. She writes stories for both children and adults, but likes writing plays better than anything else.

BEATRICE CURTIS BROWN, made famous by her *Jonathan Bing and Other Verses* (Oxford), has lived in England all of her life although she does visit the United States often. The first "Jonathan Bing" was scribbled on an envelope to take to a brother convalescing from wounds received in World War I. She has written nearly a dozen Jonathan Bing poems since, as well as novels, biographies, and other poems. Along with writing, Beatrice Brown has been a social service worker, assistant editor, freelance journalist, film critic, civil servant, and producer on B. B. C. From her home in Chelsea she can hear the boats on the Thames, and it is here that she writes.

| Howard Maxwell Brier | Carol Ryrie Brink | Walter Brooks | Beatrice Curtis Brown |

Bill Brown   Robert Browning   Dorothy Bryan   Fannie Buchanan

BILL BROWN is a writer of teen-age adventure and science fiction. He worked for several years as a newspaper reporter, and during World War II he served as a photographer in the Air Force, stationed in the jungles of India and Burma. He is married to Rosalie Moore, the poet, and they have three children. One of his books is *Roaring River* (Coward).

ROBERT BROWNING (1812–1889) was a great poet who is considered one of the most interesting personalities in English letters. "The Pied Piper of Hamelin" and "How They Brought the Good News from Ghent to Aix" are among the few simple poems children enjoy. His *Complete Poems* (Macmillan) is for older readers.

DOROTHY BRYAN, editor and author, attended convent schools in New Orleans and New York, and later went to Barnard College. She wanted to work in a publishing house and was pleased when she was given a chance to read juvenile manuscripts, as a volunteer. Later she became assistant to the head of Doubleday's Junior Books. Miss Bryan guided this department until she went to Dodd, Mead & Company, where she edits books for children. With her sister Marguerite she has written *Johnny Penguin* (Doubleday), and *Fun with Michael* (Doubleday), to mention only two of her own fine juveniles.

MARGUERITE BRYAN was a talented artist who illustrated many of the books of her sister, Dorothy Bryan. These included *Johnny Penguin* (Doubleday), *Michael Who Missed His Train* (Dodd), *There Was Tammy* (Dodd), and *Friendly Little Jonathan* (Dodd). Michael and Patsy were their own Sealyham terriers who posed for many of her amusing pictures.

FANNIE BUCHANAN gives her address as the Wee Hoose, Grinnell, Iowa, and her occupation as writing for children, specializing in poems and songs. Her writing began as an avocation during her extensive travels, and was done in depots, on trains, and wherever she might be. Among her many activities, Miss Buchanan conducted a private music school, organized music and recreation service during World War I, was Rural Specialist for the RCA-Victor Company, and served with the Extension Service of Iowa State College. In 1941 she was the recipient of a citation for distinguished contribution to rural culture, and in 1944 received a presentation from the 4-H Club members of the United States.

PEARL BUCK, American novelist and winner of the Nobel Prize for Literature, has spent much of her life in China, teaching, writing, and doing missionary work. Many of her children's books, among them *Chinese Children Next Door* (Day), *Dragon Fish* (Day), and *Water Buffalo Children* (Day), are about China. She is married and now lives on a farm in Pennsylvania with her husband and six children.

ROSEMARY BUEHRIG is married and lives in Greenwich, Connecticut, with her doctor husband and baby daughter. For a number of years she lived in Chicago and did illustrations for advertisers as well as for various Chicago publishers.

196

| Harry H. A. Burne | Constance Burnett | Rafaello Busoni | George Gordon, Lord Byron |

HARRY H. A. BURNE was born in Australia and when he was sixteen years old went to sea in a square-rigged ship. After four years of visiting strange ports in many parts of the world he came to the United States. Here he worked in a lumber camp in Arizona and later sold bonds on Wall Street. In World War I he was a major in the artillery. During one of the bombardments he was buried alive when a trench collapsed. Fortunately, however, his life was saved. He had always wanted to be an artist but his efforts to get started were so discouraging that he almost went back to sea. However, a poster firm had him design theater displays, and with a regular salary he was able to attend art school and improve his drawing technique. His drawings began to appear in *Collier's, Boys' Life, The Ladies Home Journal,* and in other magazines. In World War II he was engaged in governmental security work. He has taught at the Whitney School of Art in New Haven, and his work is well-liked because of its authenticity.

CONSTANCE BURNETT loved books as a child and grew up wanting to write, although her start did not come until middle life. Her first effort, a short story, was published in a girls' magazine. From then on she turned to biography. Several articles and books followed. Among her books are *The Shoemaker's Son* (Random) and *Five for Freedom* (Abelard).

FRANCES HODGSON BURNETT (1849–1912) was an English-American author, beloved by three generations of children. Her first book, *That Lass O' Lowrie's,* came out in 1877. This famous novelist, who lived many years abroad, wrote a number of famous children's books such as *Little Lord Fauntleroy, Sara Crewe,* and *The Secret Garden,* which first appeared in *St. Nicholas.*

ROBERT BURNS (1759–1796), Scotland's great lyric poet, wrote most often of the common man and of humble life such as he knew. Although not famous before his death, his poems are now loved by all the world.

RAFAELLO BUSONI was born in Berlin of a Swedish mother and an Italian father. His father was a famous pianist and made friends all over the world, and these friends came to see him. Rafaello remembers those early days when the conversation was carried on in five or six different languages. He traveled with his family in the United States and Europe. When he was fifteen years old he left school in order to paint, and two years later had his first show in Zurich. He studied in Paris and exhibited his work in Germany, Sweden, Spain, and Switzerland. He reached the United States in 1939 and since coming here has illustrated many juveniles and has written some himself. As a little boy he liked to collect stamps. Today his special interest is in geography, though he also is interested in the theater and the dance.

GEORGE GORDON, LORD BYRON (1788–1824), one of England's renowned poets, had a life filled with sorrow and misfortune. He was lame and brooded over it. His first volume of poems, published when he was nineteen, was cruelly criticized by a reviewer. Byron attacked him in a scathing satire. When the first part of his "Childe

| Dorothy Canfield | Pearl B. Carley | Frances Carpenter | Mary Jane Carr |

Harold's Pilgrimage" was published, he "awoke one morning to find himself famous." He was hero-worshipped for awhile and people wore open collars and flowing ties like his. Later, when he became unpopular, he left England. He died of a fever when serving in a war against Turkey, a war for Greek independence.

DOROTHY CANFIELD (Fisher) was educated both here and in France. After her marriage to John Fisher she made her home in Arlington, Vermont. Her first novel, *The Squirrel Cage* (Holt), was published in 1912 and was followed by *The Bent Twig* (Grosset). During World War I she did relief work in France and then returned to writing. Her book *Four-Square* (Harcourt) was published in 1949. Her most famous book for children is *Understood Betsy* (Holt). "Down in the Wolf Pit" (Volume 13:38) is one of the episodes of this book.

ELEANOR CAMPBELL is a contemporary illustrator whose delightful pictures of children are to be found in many textbooks. She lives in Philadelphia.

PEARL B. CARLEY was a well-loved teacher in the famous Frances Parker School of Chicago. She has had some interesting experiences taming hummingbirds.

FRANCES CARPENTER, daughter of Frank G. Carpenter who was famous for his geographical series for children, is the author of several books in collaboration with her father, editor of several distinguished collections of fairy tales, and author of legends of her own. Among these are: *Tales of a Korean Grandmother* (Doubleday), *Tales of a Chinese Grandmother* (Doubleday), and *Wonder Tales of Horses and Heroes* (Doubleday), a Junior Literary Guild Selection. She started writing at the age of ten and was editor of *Smith College Literary Magazine* in her senior year. In private life she is Mrs. Huntington. She has two married daughters and three grandchildren and lives in Washington, D. C.

RUSSELL CARPENTER is a contemporary writer whose stories appear in children's magazines.

MARY JANE CARR was born and educated in Portland, Oregon, where she became a free-lance journalist and then assistant editor of the *Catholic Sentinel*. Her first book, *Children of the Covered Wagon* (Crowell), a choice of the Junior Literary Guild, has been published in French, and she has a contract for a motion picture version with Walt Disney. Her anthologies of poetry and regional stories have proved very popular. *Young Mac of Fort Vancouver* (Crowell) was the choice of two book clubs. Miss Carr is a member of an honorary professional journalistic fraternity and the Gallery of Living Catholic Authors.

BETTY CARROLL is an "ambidextrous" person, for on the one hand she practices the role of busy wife and mother of two fine boys, and on the other she indulges in her favorite pastime, painting and drawing. A graduate of the University of Illinois School of Fine Arts, she had additional training at the American Academy of Art and the Institute of Design in Chicago. Two years were spent in the Art Department of Consolidated Book Publishers gaining invaluable experience in book designing and in the knowledge of printing processes. It was here that she became fired with enthusiasm for the fascinating field of illustration for children. Since that time she has been a regular contributor to leading children's magazines. At present she is making drawings for a series of educational film strips for children, edited by the Society for Visual Education, Inc., in Chicago. A member of the National League of American Pen Women, she sandwiches in bits of commercial art work now and then, and sometimes makes very clever puppets, but always returns to her first love, drawing for children. She now lives in Springfield, Illinois.

LEWIS CARROLL (1832–1898) was the pen name used by Charles L. Dodgson, a mathematics professor. Although a bachelor, he had many young people among his friends. Two of his world-famous classics, *Alice's Adventures in Wonderland* and *Through the Looking Glass,* were developed from a tale he told to amuse Alice Liddell and her sister while boating on the Thames. *The Hunting of the Snark* and *Sylvie and Bruno* were also amusing nonsense—some of the best ever written.

CHARLES EDWARD CARRYL (1841–1920) was born in New York City where he was a member of The New York Stock Exchange. He wrote to please his own son and daughter, and as a result, produced two whimsical and imaginative classics: *Davy and the Goblin* (Houghton) and *The Admiral's Caravan* (Houghton). These were first published long ago in *St. Nicholas* and the nonsense verses they contain are still loved by children everywhere.

JULIA M. H. CARSON, who is a consultant editor for *The Children's Hour,* is a writer of outstanding biographies. She was admitted to the Connecticut bar and to the United States Supreme Court bar shortly after graduating from Yale. She has always been interested in government functions on both the local and national levels, and has worked closely with the League of Women Voters. She chose Patrick Henry to write about (Volume 15:337) as he was one of the brilliant leaders when our government was being organized. Her book about him is called *Son of Thunder* (Longmans).

RUSSELL GORDON CARTER is the author of thirty-five books. Most of them are for young people and many of them are historical. Quite a few have received prizes and special awards. After serving in World War I, Mr. Carter was a member of the editorial staff of the *Youth's Companion* for six years. Since 1925 he has been a freelance writer. His latest book is *Teen-Age Animal Stories* (Grosset), and he has also contributed many nonsense verses to anthologies. He is married and has two children.

ANN CHALMERS is a contemporary poet whose work appears in leading juvenile magazines.

FREDERICK T. CHAPMAN was born in California. He studied at the Art Students League. Throughout his life he has illustrated many books and his outstanding pic-

| Betty Carroll | Lewis Carroll | Julia M. H. Carson | Russell Gordon Carter |

tures have been found in most of the national magazines. "I have always enjoyed my work," he writes, "but I consider it lucky that I was born with what little talent I have. Otherwise I should have starved long ago, having brains for little else!" During World War II he served as an ambulance driver with the British Armies overseas in Italy, Holland, and Germany. "A much more useful job than any I ever performed in the practice of my so-called profession," he says.

POLLY CHASE began writing poetry for magazines shortly after her marriage to Preston Boyden. Her selections appearing in *The Children's Hour* are representative of her delightful poetry for children. In 1930 she published a book of adult poetry which was awarded the Midland Author's Prize. This was followed in 1942 by a fantasy in which all the characters appear as birds.

FLORENCE CHOATE, who has an early New England background, came upon the material for "Adventure in a Chimney" while doing research in the Essex Museum at Salem for the first of three historical books. The last of these, *Lisbet*, is a story of old New York, where Miss Choate now lives. Another of her many books is *The Crimson Shawl* (Stokes). The recent books of this excellent author and illustrator have modern settings though she confesses to a greater interest in the more romantic olden time.

ARTHUR BOWIE CHRISMAN was born on a farm near White Post, Virginia. His father and mother were descended from the early colonial settlers. He was educated in the schools of Virginia and Maryland, and at Virginia Polytechnic Institute. He is the author of *Shen of the Sea* (Dutton), which won the Newbery Award in 1925, and *Treasures Long Hidden* (Dutton). Mr. Chrisman now lives in Arkansas. "Capture of the Shen" (Volume 8:300) comes from *Shen of the Sea*.

B. J. CHUTE (Beatrice Joy) grew up in Minneapolis and sold her first story in 1931. Since going to New York in 1941, she has written several hundred fine boys' stories, five outstanding books for boys, two adult novels, and numerous adult short stories. She writes under her initials because nearly all her juvenile work, including *Shift to the Right* (Macmillan) and *Teen-Age Sports Parade* (Grosset), has been written from the masculine point of view.

MARCHETTE CHUTE grew up in a large country home at Hazelwood, Minnesota. This later furnished the inspiration for her first delightful book of verses, *Rhymes about Ourselves* (Macmillan), which she also illustrated. This was followed by *Rhymes about the Country* (Macmillan) and *Rhymes about the City* (Macmillan), the last written after she moved to New York. The best-known of her adult books are her scholarly biographies: *Shakespeare of London* (Dutton), *Geoffrey Chaucer of England* (Dutton), and *Ben Jonson of Westminster* (Dutton). Her *An Introduction to Shakespeare* (Dutton) was written for younger readers. Her sister is the talented writer, B. J. Chute. "A Life of William Shakespeare" (Volume 15:222) was written especially for *The Children's Hour*. Older readers will enjoy her article, "Biographies Bring New Companions" (Volume 16:149).

Frederick T. Chapman   Polly Chase   Arthur Bowie Chrisman   B. J. Chute

MARGERY CLARK is a pen name for two collaborators, Mary Elizabeth Clark and Margery Closely Quigley. Miss Clark is a native of New York and a graduate of Columbia University. Miss Quigley was born in Los Angeles and attended Vassar. Both received library training and are experienced librarians, as well as writers of stories for children. For some time they resided together in Montcalm, New Jersey, where they wrote *Poppy Seed Cakes* (Doubleday). "The Picnic Basket" (Volume 1:158) is taken from this book.

BEVERLY CLEARY, author of the humorous *Henry Huggins* (Morrow) and *Ellen Tebbits* (Morrow), specializes in library work with children. She lives with her husband in Berkeley, California. "Gallons of Guppies" (Volume 6:17) and "Ellen's Secret" (Volume 6:177) are two of the very funny happenings taken from these two books that every boy and girl will want to read.

SAMUEL L. CLEMENS (1835–1910) spent his boyhood in Hannibal, Missouri, where he liked to play on the Mississippi River. These experiences later led to writing, under the pen name of Mark Twain, *The Adventures of Tom Sawyer* (Harper) and *The Adventures of Huckleberry Finn* (Harper), dearly-loved classics that never grow old. Before settling down to a literary career which was to make him famous the world over, this great American humorist was a reporter, river pilot, and miner. "The Glorious Whitewasher and His Friends" (Volume 3:1) and "Tom and Becky in the Cave" (Volume 3:308) come from *The Adventures of Tom Sawyer*. "Cub Pilot on the River" (Volume 11:321) tells about his early adventures on the Mississippi. For more information about Samuel Clemens see Volume 15:43.

NANCY CLINTON is a contemporary Chicago writer who has written a great deal for *Child Life* and for numerous anthologies.

ARTHUR HUGH CLOUGH (1819–1861) was an English poet of the nineteenth century, whose most famous poem is "Say Not the Struggle Naught Availeth."

ELIZABETH COATSWORTH has the distinction of having had printed in current magazines more poetry than any other living poet. She is the mother of two daughters and lives now on Chimney Farm in Maine with her husband, Henry Beston, who also writes for children. Many of her lovely poems have been inspired by her leisurely travels abroad. She is the author of such juvenile books as *The Cat and the Captain* (Macmillan), *House-Boat Summer* (Macmillan), and *The Cat Who Went to Heaven* (Macmillan), which won the Newbery Medal. She also writes reviews of children's books for leading magazines.

ROBERT P. TRISTRAM COFFIN, teacher, lecturer, and writer, "is married, has four children, three grandsons, two farms, and lives in Brunswick, Maine." He was educated at Bowdoin College, Princeton, and Oxford, where he was a Rhodes Scholar. He saw service in World War I. Since his return to America he has held professorships at Wells College and Bowdoin. "Any man who has a pair of good eyes and ears and a

Marchette Chute   **Beverly Cleary**   **Samuel L. Clemens**   **Elizabeth Coatsworth**

201

Robert P. Tristram Coffin   Padraic Colum   Fleur Conkling

residence in the State of Maine," says Robert P. Tristram Coffin, "has a pretty fair equipment for setting up housekeeping as a poet." Mr. Coffin has this equipment. He has won, for his *Strange Holiness* (Macmillan), the Pulitzer Prize in Poetry. His *Apples by Ocean* (Macmillan), *Yankee Coast* (Macmillan), and *Primer for America* (Macmillan) also contain his heart-warming poems of New England.

Ruth H. Colby is a contemporary writer whose work appears in a number of juvenile magazines.

Samuel Taylor Coleridge (1772–1834) was a daydreamer all his life. Some of his finest imaginative poems are "The Rime of the Ancient Mariner," "Christabel," and "Kubla Khan." He was a close friend of Wordsworth and Southey, and was one of England's great poets.

Padraic Colum, steeped in the folklore and culture of his native Ireland, has been a writer from youth. His plays were among the first to be produced by the Irish Theater, and his early lyrics marked a new departure in Irish poetry. Soon after his marriage, Mr. Colum came to America, where he has contributed travel volumes and folk legends to our literature. *The King of Ireland's Son* (Macmillan), *The Big Tree of Bunlahy* (Macmillan), and *The Island of the Mighty* (Macmillan) reveal the whimsey and the spell of Ireland. Colum has also retold many of the Greek legends especially for children. A member of the Academy of Irish Letters, in 1947 he was awarded the medal of The American Irish Historical Society for literary eminence, and in 1952, the Fellowship of the Academy of American Poets.

Fleur Conkling, wife of William Heyliger, has been teacher, writer, poet, critic, and lecturer. Trained to be a kindergarten and primary teacher, she has always been interested in children. She served as educational director of *Cue Magazine* in New York and has been on the staffs of Silver Burdett & Co., Dell Publishing Co., and Walt Disney Publications. A frequent contributor to children's magazines, her poetry has also appeared in the *Saturday Evening Post, Saturday Review of Literature,* and other publications. Among her children's books are: *The Bingity Bang School Bus* (Westminster), *The Brave Little Duck* (Westminster), *Billy Between* (Westminster), and *Mr. Grumpy and the Kitten* (Winston), a Junior Literary Guild selection. Fleur Conkling greatly helped her husband with his work as consultant editor of *The Children's Hour.*

Hilda Conkling's mother, a poet and professor at Smith College, wrote down the first poems which Hilda composed about the events of the day and published them as *Poems by a Little Girl* (Lippincott) when Hilda was only eight years old. When Grace Hazard Conkling saw that boys and girls liked these poems she encouraged her daughter to write more, but asked grownups not to discuss poetry with her, so that the verses might remain natural. A second volume, *Shoes of the Wind* (Lippincott), published before Hilda was ten, was the result. Hilda, now grown up, lives in Northampton, Massachusetts.

202

CHARLES COOMBS, a writer of action stories for young readers, has done many books about sports for the Young Readers Bookshelf (Lantern Press). *Indoor Sports Stories, Baseball Stories, Stories of the Diamond,* and *Football Stories* are in this series.

JOSEPH COTTLER is co-author with Haym Jaffe of *Heroes of Civilization* (Little), a collection of outstanding biographies.

HAROLD COURLANDER is well-known as a novelist and student of folklore. His book on folk customs and music of Haiti is considered one of the best in its field. Especially appealing to children are *Uncle Bouqui of Haiti* (Morrow), and *The Cow-Tail Switch* (Holt). At present he is political analyst for "Voice of America" and editor of the Ethnic Folkways Library of music around the world.

G. W. COX, well-known writer, has retold many legends.

WILLIS G. CRAIG is a contemporary writer whose work appears in children's magazines.

DONN P. CRANE (1878–1944) was born in Springfield, Missouri, but moved to Illinois when he was very young. He lived in Chicago most of his life, and in his early years was an actor, a playwright, a stage designer, and an artist at one and the same time. Although entirely self-taught, his pen-and-inks and etchings have been exhibited at the Chicago Art Institute. Later he wrote and illustrated children's books which were popular. His drawing is noteworthy for its painstaking detail, it's free-flowing action.

RUTH CRARY was born in Boone, Iowa, and attended Grinnell and Cornell colleges. She was married and now has one son and two daughters that are grown up. She herself lives in Chicago during the winter months and goes to the MacDowell Colony in Peterborough, New Hampshire, during the summer. She is closely associated with a number of clubs and is the president of the Chicago Center of the Poetry Society of London. She has won many awards for her poetry and has contributed to many national magazines. Aside from her serious verse she writes outstanding humorous light verse under many pen names. Among her books are *Forty Shillings* (Decker) and *Legends from Ancient China* (Wings Press).

ELLIS CREDLE's classic, *Down Down the Mountain* (Nelson), brought her success overnight. The book grew out of her experiences as a teacher in the Blue Ridge Mountains of her native state of North Carolina. In 1925 she went to New York to study interior decorating, but attained such success as a mural painter that in 1931 she received the commission to paint the murals for the Brooklyn Children's Museum. For the past few years she has lived in Mexico with her husband and son. Some of her other books which she illustrated herself are: *Flop-Eared Hound* (Oxford), *Johnny and His Mule* (Harper), and *Little Jeemes Henry* (Nelson).

FLEMING CREW, brother and collaborator of Alice Crew Gall, grew up in Ohio, where much of his time was spent on hiking trips, exploring the surrounding regions. It was

Harold Courlander   Donn P. Crane   Ruth Crary   Ellis Credle

203

here that he and his sister grew to love the small wild creatures they later wrote about in such books as *Ringtail* (Oxford), *Bushy Tail* (Oxford), and *Flat Tail* (Oxford).

HELEN COALE CREW (1866-1941) wrote first for adults but soon found that it was children she knew and loved best. She wrote many favorite books for teen-agers, including *Saturday's Children* (Little), *Laughing Lad* (Appleton), *The Singing Seamen* (Appleton), and *The Lost King* (Appleton). She lived in Evanston, Illinois, with her husband, a Northwestern University professor, and three children.

IRVING CRUMP, a well-loved editor of *Boys' Life,* and consultant editor for *The Children's Hour,* learned to like the out-of-doors as a child. It was at this time, too, that he first decided to write stories for boys when he grew up. Before he was able to do this, however, he worked as a reporter for six years and then wrote several adult tales. In addition to his magazine work he has done many books, some of which are: *Boys' Book of Cowboys* (Dodd), *Our Firemen* (Dodd), and *Our Airliners* (Dodd). He has also written radio shows and motion pictures, and has been associated with both the Local and National Council of the Boy Scouts of America.

ALLAN CUNNINGHAM (1784-1842) spent most of his life in London where he held a clerkship. It was only as a side line that he wrote poetry and essays. Some of his fine poems, such as "My Ain Countree," "A Sea Song," and "The Skylark," are still well known. He was the father of five sons.

ALICE DALGLIESH was born in Trinidad, B. W. I., and was educated in England and at Columbia University. After teaching school, she began writing for the children she had taught, but since then she has published both fiction and non-fiction for many different age groups. She is now the well-known editor of children's books for Charles Scribner's Sons. Her *Wings around South America* (Scribner) was preceded by a trip around that continent by plane. Her autobiographical *Silver Pencil* (Scribner) and her two books about the Davenport family are very popular with children. *The Bears on Hemlock Mountain* (Scribner) was selected as one of the "distinguished books of 1952." When you read "Rusty—Movie Star" (Volume 6:87) you will be glad to know that Rusty has more adventures in the book *The Smiths and Rusty* (Scribner).

LOUIS DARLING was born in Stamford, Connecticut, and has lived in New England most of his life. He studied at the Grand Central School of Art, and then worked privately with Frank Dumond and Frank Riley. He was a photographer in the Air Force during World War II. Now he is married, lives in Westport, Connecticut, and spends his summers on a Maine farm. Mr. Darling used to hunt and fish, but now his hobby is biology. He has done a good deal of work in landscape, animal, and bird painting. He has illustrated several children's books very humorously, including Beverly Cleary's *Ellen Tebbits* (Morrow) and *Henry Huggins* (Morrow).

GEORGE WEBBE DASENT (1817-1896) became interested in Scandinavian folklore at the suggestion of Jacob Grimm. He translated many classic Norse legends into English

Irving Crump   Alice Dalgliesh   Louis Darling   James Daugherty

to give children the pleasure of reading such tales as "Boots" and "East of the Sun and West of the Moon." Among his books are *Norse Fairy Tales* (Lippincott) and *Tales from the Fjeld* (Putnam). He was knighted in 1876 for his service to literature.

JAMES DAUGHERTY, although generally known for his illustrations, turned to writing, too. *Andy and the Lion* (Viking), which he wrote and illustrated delightfully, was followed by *Daniel Boone* (Viking) which was awarded the Newbery Medal as the year's most distinguished children's book. "The Saving of Boonesborough" (Volume 11:181) is from this book.

SONIA DAUGHERTY, the wife of James Daugherty, is also well known as a children's author. Her husband has illustrated most of her books, some of which are: *Marshink's Secret* (Stokes), *Vanka's Donkey* (Lippincott), and *Way of an Eagle* (Oxford). The Daughertys live in Connecticut with their son.

ANN DAVIDOW has been interested in horses since she was a little girl, and has done some very fine sketches of them. When she was thirteen years old she illustrated "Horace," a horse story by Mathilda Schirmer that was published by Consolidated Book Publishers. When she grew up and went to college she took her own horse with her. She was born in Pennsylvania but has lived most of her life in Highland Park, a suburb of Chicago. The young artist has studied at the Chicago Art Institute and is now attending the University of Chicago.

MARY CAROLYN DAVIES is a New York writer whose delightful poems have appeared in many juvenile magazines.

JULIA DAVIS, who is now Mrs. Paul West in private life, spent some years in Copenhagen gathering material for her first book, *Swords of the Vikings* (Dutton). *Vaino* (Dutton), a story of Finland, soon followed. She has written many books of a historical nature, dealing with great American tales. Perhaps one of her most distinguished books is *Stonewall* (Dutton), the only life history of Stonewall Jackson for older boys and girls.

LAVINIA R. DAVIS' childhood playhouse is now her studio where she creates such intriguing stories as *Hobby Horse Hill* (Doubleday), *Roger and the Fox* (Doubleday), and *The Wild Birthday Cake* (Doubleday). Several of her mystery stories for adults have been published by the Crime Club and six of her children's stories have been selections of the Junior Literary Guild. She began her professional career the year of her marriage to Wendell Davis by working as research assistant on *Fortune Magazine*. She lives at Still Farm, Brookfield Centre, Connecticut, with her lawyer husband and her six children. Her hobbies are gardening and riding.

MARGUERITE DAVIS has done some of her best illustration in the field of children's books, published by Little Brown, Macmillan, and Houghton Mifflin. She was born in Massachusetts, graduated from Vassar, attended the Boston Museum of Fine Arts, and

| Sonia Daugherty | Ann Davidow | Julia Davis | Lavinia R. Davis |

Marguerite Davis   Marguerite De Angeli   Walter De La Mare

for many years worked in her studio in Boston. She has traveled and worked in Europe and in England. For her *Heidi* pictures, she spent a month in Switzerland making sketches for them. In recent years her summers are spent in New England, but her winters are spent in Tucson, Arizona, enlivened by painting jaunts to Mexico with the Gerry Pierce Water Color School.

MARY GOULD DAVIS' interest in children developed through her daily contact with them while doing library work in New York. For many years she was supervisor of storytelling in the New York Public Library. She had always loved folk tales and soon acquired a desire to trace them back to their source. Two of her books are *The Truce of the Wolf* (Harcourt) and *The Handsome Donkey* (Harcourt). In 1945 she became editor of Books for Young People, a department of the *Saturday Review of Literature*.

MARGUERITE DE ANGELI's longing to draw and her longing as a child to put things down in words was not realized until after her marriage. When her first three children were small she began to study drawing with her neighbor, M. L. Bower, a well-known illustrator. In 1934 she began writing her own books, and soon wove stories about children in Pennsylvania Dutch communities, depicting the quaint speech, customs, and dress of Amish and Mennonites. The illustrator of "The Wastwych Secret" has written *Yonie Wondernose* (Doubleday), *Thee Hannah!* (Doubleday), *Elin's Amerika* (Doubleday), *Jared's Island* (Doubleday), and other fine books. Her *Door in the Wall* (Doubleday) won the Newbery Award. "Robin Finds a Way" (Volume 12:26) is part of this book.

JEAN DE BRUNHOFF (1899–1937), creator of the lovable little elephant *Babar* (Random), lived in France and studied painting there. Every night he lulled his three sons to sleep with delightful stories about Babar. Soon the storyteller had to illustrate his tales with his witty and alert pencil, and thus came into existence Babar, Celeste, the Little Old Lady, Zephir the monkey, and many others, who have since enchanted children and grown-ups all over the world. When he died his eldest son, Laurent, continued the series.

WALTER DE LA MARE, one of the greatest of modern poets for children, is also the author of *Collected Stories for Children* (Faber), which won the Carnegie Medal in 1948. This is the British equivalent of the Newbery Medal. The writer was born in Kent, England. Forced to leave school at an early age, he worked as a bookkeeper for Standard Oil until a small pension permitted him to retire and devote himself to writing. *Peacock Pie* (Holt), filled with enchanting verses, first brought him fame as a poet. This was followed by *Down-Adown-Derry* (Holt), *Poems for Children* (Holt), and *Bells and Grass* (Viking), as well as much lovely poetry for adult readers. Of his stories, adults in particular enjoy his *The Three Mulla-Mulgars* (Knopf), while *Mr. Bumps and His Monkey* (Winston) is liked by boys and girls.

JEANNE DE LAMARTER, daughter of a famous orchestra leader, is a Chicago writer who tries out her delightful verse on her own children.

206

Louise De La Ramée (1839–1908) grew up in Paris but returned to England, her birthplace, to start her literary career. She was a sensational overnight success as a writer but died in poverty. Always eccentric, she lived in a bizarre house in Italy most of her later life. She wrote dog stories including her famous book, *A Dog of Flanders*.

Johanna De Witt is the author of *The Littlest Reindeer* (Childrens Press).

Agnes Louise Dean wrote many delightful poems for children, some of which have appeared in her book *Let Us Be Merry* (Knopf).

Geoffrey Dearmer, an English poet, grew up in London. His father was an author and professor of art, and his mother was a novelist and dramatist. He served in the British army during World War I and did not resign until 1927. Many of his whimsical poems about animals are in his book, *Poems* (McBride).

Duane Decker is a graduate of Colgate and served in the Marine Corps during World War II as a combat correspondent for *Leatherneck*, the official Marine Corps publication. He has contributed stories and articles to many magazines and is the author of *Hit and Run* (Morrow), *The Catcher from Double-A* (Morrow), and *Starting Pitcher* (Morrow). "Marshall at Bat" (Volume 10:314) is from this book.

Daniel Defoe (1660–1731) was born in London and died there. His life was filled with adventure. Once he was imprisoned for political reasons. Once his ship was almost captured by pirates. He wrote extensively, but is best remembered for his greatest work, *Robinson Crusoe*.

Wesley Dennis was born on Cape Cod. He felt he should be a clam digger, and his mother wanted him to be a postmaster, but he became an artist instead because "it was the best-paying job I could get." He loves horses and has four of his own. His first important book was his own *Flip* (Viking), the popular story of an engaging colt. He has illustrated almost fifty books by other authors but calls Marguerite Henry's *King of the Wind* (Rand) his own favorite horse story. He does all his writing and drawing in his home on a Virginia mountaintop. He loves children and is always making horse drawings for them for their scrapbooks. He has two boys of his own and he knows just the sort of pictures boys and girls like.

Beatrice Derwinski is a contemporary artist who lives in Rockport, Massachusetts. She has illustrated many children's stories.

Edward Wade Devlin is a Canadian writer of some excellent juvenile stories.

Charles Dickens (1812–1870), the great English novelist, portrayed lives of the poor and the oppressed in many of his books. Through his writing he was able to break the moralistic writing style of that period and directly influence the development of children's literature. Although many of his stories were not intended for

Daniel Defoe

Wesley Dennis

Charles Dickens

children, *Cricket on the Hearth* and *A Christmas Carol* are loved by all ages. So is *The Magic Fishbone*.

EMILY DICKINSON (1830–1886) is sometimes called America's finest poet. She was born in Amherst, Massachusetts, where she lived a quiet, sheltered life, rarely going out. Her first volume of delicate and thoughtful lyrics was published after her death, and the second, four years later.

RUTH DIXON is the Chicago author of *Yip and Yap* (Rand), *Scallywag* (Rand), and many other books for children. Her gay verses are found in many poetry anthologies.

PELAGIE DOANE could not help liking to draw and to write. Her grandfather was a sculptor, her mother an interior decorator, and her father a writer and editor. She, herself, after leaving art school has settled in Belmar, New Jersey, and has illustrated over sixty books for children, including many old favorites. Among her best-known books are *A Small Child's Bible* (Oxford) and *A Small Child's Book of Verse* (Oxford).

MARY MAPES DODGE (1831–1905), founder and editor of the famous old juvenile magazine, *St. Nicholas*, wrote many stories and poems which appeared in it. Her well-loved *Hans Brinker* (Appleton) won a prize many years ago from the French Academy. It was first told to her two sons. Today it is still considered a classic juvenile of Dutch life. "Mystery—and the Race" (Volume 3:261) is part of this book.

MARY DICKERSON DONAHEY was born in New York City and later moved to Ohio. As a child she began selling verses, articles, and short stories. Her first adult venture was in the field of journalism, as she was a reporter on the *New York Journal* and later worked on the *Cleveland Plain Dealer*. After her marriage to William Donahey, she moved to Chicago and began to contribute to *Child Life* and other juvenile magazines and wrote *Marty Lu* (Doubleday), *Mysterious Mansions* (Doubleday), *The Spanish McQuades* (Doubleday), *Apple Pie Inn* (Crowell), and *The Castle of Grumpy Grouch* (Random). In fifty-eight years of writing she has produced over twenty-two books. The Chicago Women's Advertising Club named her the Chicago Woman of Distinction for 1953. "Mr. Dooley Disgraces His Family" (Volume 6:202) is just one of the interesting chapters in *Marty Lu*.

WILLIAM DONAHEY was not allowed to read fairy tales as a child. They were not true! When he was a little boy and had to behave at long dull dinners he was very, very bored. So he pretended he saw little people playing tag among the spoons and falling into the gravy. He laughed aloud, but would not explain why he laughed. That is undoubtedly when his famous Teenie Weenies were really born. Mr. Donahey was born in Ohio, and went to the Cleveland School of Art. He has done newspaper work, especially his Teenie Weenie features, for many years. His books are *Teenie Weenie Town* (Whittlesey), *Teenie Weenie Days* (Whittlesey), and *Teenie Weenie Neighbors* (Whittlesey). Mr. Donahey loves the wild life of the North Woods and spends long summers with his wife near Lake Superior. At one time the Donahey's summer home

Ruth Dixon

Pelagie Doane

Mary Dickerson Donahey

William Donahey

208

A. Conan Doyle   Glenn Ward Dresbach   John Drinkwater   William Pené Du Bois

was in the shape of a huge barrel—just like their Teenie Weenies' house. "The Teenie Weenie Picnic" (Volume 1:132) is one of the stories found in *Teenie Weenie Days,* and "Uppity Orioles" (Volume 1:137) is from *Teenie Weenie Neighbors.*

MALCOLM DOUGLAS wrote some fine story poems and excellent nonsense verse for the old *St. Nicholas Magazine.*

(ARTHUR) CONAN DOYLE (1859–1930), famous for his detective stories, was born in Scotland. The need of money to supplement a starving medical practice brought forth the stories of Sherlock Holmes, the best-known and best-loved detective in literature. His first story using Sherlock and his admiring friend, Dr. Watson, was *A Study in Scarlet,* published in 1887. From then on many Sherlock mysteries appeared both in England and America. Older boys and girls enjoy them just as much as do their parents. Because of his professional services in the Boer War, he was knighted in 1902.

GLENN WARD DRESBACH, poet, was born in Lanark, Illinois. He received his education at the University of Wisconsin, where he was also active in athletics. During World War I he was a captain in the Army and received three citations. He is the author of eleven books of poetry and is represented in many textbooks and anthologies. His *Complete Poems* (Caxton) is his most recent collection. His home is now in Arkansas, where he lives with his wife, Beverley Githens, who is also a poet.

JOHN DRINKWATER (1882–1937), English playwright and poet, attended Oxford High School. Then for twelve years he worked in an insurance office, though he wanted to go on the stage. He published his first book of poetry at the age of twenty-one, but called it "unbelievably bad verse." He became manager of the Birmingham Repertory Theatre, for which in 1918 he wrote the play that made him famous, *Abraham Lincoln.* This was followed by other historical plays. He wrote lyric poetry, too, and, for children, *All about Me* (Houghton) and *More about Me* (Houghton).

WILLIAM PENÉ DU BOIS, author and illustrator of *Otto at Sea* (Viking), was born in New Jersey of a distinguished family of artists, but he was educated in France. He had written and illustrated four books by the time he was twenty-three, all of them for children. *The Great Geppy* (Viking) became very popular. *Peter Graves* (Viking), *Squirrel Hotel* (Viking), and *Three Policemen* (Viking) were followed by *Twenty-One Balloons* (Viking), for which he received the Newbery Award.

ALEXANDER DUMAS (1802–1870), clever French novelist, had his first success as a playwright. In 1844 his first historical novel was published and he wrote many others that are still remembered. The best of his sixty plays and two hundred novels are probably: *The Count of Monte Cristo, The Three Musketeers,* and the two sequels *Twenty Years After* and *The Vicomte de Bragelonne.*

DEE DUNSING combines a career as a newspaper woman with writing short stories for boys and girls. One story for boys, *Swamp Shadows* (Longmans), deals with the his-

Alexander Dumas   Dee Dunsing   Roger Duvoisin

tory of Florida where she now lives with her mother, her thirteen-year-old daughter, and a black cocker spaniel. "Tooth of the Great One" is one of the most outstanding of the hundred short stories she has written.

ROGER DUVOISIN began to draw at an early age and studied at the Ecole des Arts et Métiers, where he specialized in murals and stage scenery. He became manager of a French pottery works, then a designer of textiles. An American firm brought him to the United States, where he soon published a book written for his young son. He became a U. S. citizen in 1938, and lives in New Jersey, where he writes and illustrates such delightfully humorous stories as *The Christmas Whale* (Knopf), and *The Four Corners of the World* (Knopf).

ELEANOR OSBORNE EADIE is an artist who lives in New York and has illustrated many books. Her realistic drawings of children can also be found in many school readers.

MAX EASTMAN, American poet and essayist, considers his first book, *The Enjoyment of Poetry* (Scribners), to be his best, and it is still used today as a textbook in many schools. The same year, 1913, he brought out a volume of adult poems, *Child of the Amazons* (Kennerley). His home is on the Hudson River in New York where he is working on his autobiography.

IVY O. EASTWICK lives in South Africa where she writes beautiful poems for children. A number of these are collected in her book *Fairies and Suchlike* (Dutton), illustrated by her friend Decie Merwin. Some of her other lovely verse has appeared in English magazines as well as American ones.

IRMENGARDE EBERLE began her career as an author soon after her graduation from college in Texas. She now lives in New York with her family, devoting all her time to writing. Her first poem was published in *The American Mercury*. She continued to write stories, articles, and verse. At twenty-four she became editor of a woman's magazine and since then has held other editorial positions. *The Visiting Jimpsons* (Reynal), *Wide Fields* (Crowell), *Hop, Skip, and Fly* (Holiday), and *The Very Good Neighbors* (Lippincott) are among her books for boys and girls.

FRANCES ECKART's childhood was spent on a large ranch in North Dakota and later on another in the state of Washington. Thus she studied and knew horses and other animals firsthand. Her first art training was through a correspondence school. Then she attended the Chinard School of Fine Arts in Seattle and the Art Center School in Hollywood, California. She has done some outstanding jackets and endsheets for Russell Janney's *The Miracle of the Bells* (Peoples), Mary O'Hara's *My Friend Flicka* (Peoples), and *Thunderhead* (Peoples), and a book about horses for the Domesday Press. She is married to Walter Eckart and draws pictures for her own little boys. Among the ten books she has illustrated are *Cookie the Rabbit* (Garden City) and *The Little Bear Who Wanted Friends* (Garden City). She lives in Chicago, and has illustrated many stories for children's magazines and *The Children's Hour*.

210

Irmengarde Eberle   Frances Eckart   Walter Eckart   Clara Edmunds-Hemingway

WALTER ECKART was born in Chicago and has lived there all his life. During World War II he served in the Military Intelligence in the Army and received the Army Commendation Medal. After this, he worked as an industrial designer and then turned to book design. An expert typographer, he has supervised the typography of *The Children's Hour.* His hobby is photography.

CLARA EDMUNDS-HEMINGWAY is a person of many talents and at one time or another has been a Chicago poet, artist, singer, composer, playwright, and critic. She and her husband make their home now in southern Michigan.

RICHARD M. ELAM, JR., interested in science fiction since he was a boy, has written hundreds of stories and articles about this fascinating subject. He uses established scientific fact as a basis for his imaginative tales. A good collection of his stories is found in *Teen-Age Science Fiction Stories* (Lantern) and *Young Visitor to Mars* (Lantern).

JILL ELGIN enjoys people, books, and dogs. She was brought up in Baltimore and studied at the Maryland Institute of Art and at the Grand Central School of Art in New York City. She has done a number of portraits and has illustrated several children's books. She likes to travel throughout the United States, especially in the West.

RUDOLPH ELSTAD spent one year drawing the mother deer in *Bambi* for Walt Disney. He did many drawings for Disney's *Fantasia,* too. After graduating from St. Olaf College in Northfield, Minnesota, he graduated from the Minneapolis School of Art. Then came ten years of hard work in Minneapolis. He was an art director, an instructor in evening classes at the Minneapolis School of Art, and a teacher in the University of Minnesota extension division. Afterwards, he went to Hollywood. He now lives in Park Forest, Illinois, and is busy illustrating stories. He particularly likes to draw animals.

RALPH WALDO EMERSON (1803–1882), one of America's most influential essayists and poets, was of a retiring nature. He spent a quiet life in Concord writing great philo-

Richard M. Elam, Jr.   Jill Elgin   Rudolph Elstad   Ralph Waldo Emerson

| Elizabeth Enright | Eleanor Estes | Hubert Evans | Alf Evers |

sophical essays and occasionally lecturing and preaching. He was a wonderful friend to Louisa Alcott and her family and to his many other friends.

ELIZABETH ENRIGHT, writer and illustrator of many children's books, comes from an artistic family. Her mother is a well-known illustrator, her father, a political cartoonist, and her uncle, Frank Lloyd Wright, the great architect. Her own love for children led her to write her first book, *Kintu* (Rinehart). *Thimble Summer* (Rinehart) won her the Newbery Medal in 1939. She lives in New York City with her three sons. Her many books, full of high spirits, fun, and pleasant pictures of the very real and very lovable Melendy family include *Spiderweb for Two* (Rinehart), *The Saturdays* (Rinehart), *Then There Were Five* (Rinehart), and *The Four-Story Mistake* (Rinehart). Three of the adventures of the Melendy family found in two of these books are: "Randy at the Art Gallery" (Volume 6:211), "Clarinda, 1869" (Volume 6:297), and "Oliver at the Circus" (Volume 13:26).

CLARA ERNST is a New York artist who is well known for her delightful drawings of children.

RAGNA ESKIL, a free-lance writer of plays and articles, lives in Flint, Michigan.

ELEANOR ESTES, winner of the Newbery Award for *Ginger Pye* (Harcourt), has spent many years of her life as a children's librarian. She grew up in West Haven, Connecticut. Her mother's gift as a storyteller and her parent's love of books were the two influences which led her into library work. *The Moffats* (Harcourt), *The Middle Moffat* (Harcourt), and *Rufus M* (Harcourt) have become classics. Her sympathy, humor, and understanding assure her books of a lasting place in the affections of children. Stories from three of the Moffat books are: "The First Day of School" (Volume 4:146), "Ginger on the Fire Escape" (Volume 10:1), and "The Middle Bear" (Volume 6:144).

HUBERT EVANS, lay missionary and free-lance writer, has lived for the past eight years in Indian villages of the British Columbia mountains and in the country east of the Alaska Panhandle. A descendant of early Long Island and Pennsylvania settlers, he spent three years as a reporter on large Eastern dailies and two on frontier newspapers in British Columbia. His work has appeared in Polish, Scandinavian, and French, and also in Braille. He has written a number of books with settings in British Columbia, such as *North to the Unknown* (Dodd), and has written for juvenile magazines as well.

KATHERINE EVANS is a Chicago artist who is best known for her delightful illustrations of Charles Tazewell's *The Littlest Angel* (Childrens Press).

HELEN and ALF EVERS live in New York City with their two daughters and their son during the winter but in the summer go to their house at the foot of a lovely mountain in Woodstock, New York. They have written and illustrated many delightful juvenile books, one of which is *All about Copy Kitten* (Rand).

| Helen Evers | Walter Farley | Georgene Faulkner | Eugene Field |

ELEANOR FARJEON never went to school, but grew up in the Bohemian literary and dramatic world of London presided over by her father, a novelist, and her mother, a daughter of Joseph Jefferson, the great American actor. At the age of sixteen she and her brother collaborated on an opera, *Floretta*, for which she wrote the verse. Except for a visit to America to see her grandfather, and a wartime sojourn in a Sussex cottage, she has lived in London. Her first success came during World War I with two series of *Nursery Rhymes of London Town*. *Martin Pippin in the Apple Orchard* (Stokes) was written in Sussex. Her literary contributions include fantastic fiction, lovely poems, music, children's tales and games, one novel, and, more recently, plays. One of her editors speak of her genuine childlike zest and says, "Joy, I think, is the keynote of all her stories, her poems, her people, and her music."

WALTER FARLEY claims that his one great love as a boy was horses. It still is. His first book, *The Black Stallion* (Random), was most popular and was followed by *The Black Stallion Returns* (Random), *Son of the Black Stallion* (Random), and several others. The most recent is *The Black Stallion's Filly*. More than fifty thousand boys and girls competed in Mr. Farley's contest to name this filly and the boy who won it received a pure-bred Arabian colt. After being in World War II, Mr. Farley bought a Pennsylvania farm where he lives with his wife and daughter. His favorite pastime is raising and breeding his own horses. "The Black Stallion's Race" (Volume 14:162) comes from his book *The Black Stallion*.

GEORGENE FAULKNER, known the country over as "the Story Lady," is the creator of *Melindy's Medal* (Messner) and *Melindy's Happy Summer* (Messner). Miss Faulkner was originally a kindergarten teacher. The Library Committee of the Chicago Women's Club sent her to the large fieldhouse "Back of the Yards," where she began to tell stories to the poor children. Experiences on the playgrounds of Brooklyn and on Chautauqua platforms led her to writing children's stories for magazines and newspapers. These were later republished in the Story Lady Series of books. Miss Faulkner still tells stories to the younger children who attend the famous Faulkner School in Chicago. "The Most Wonderful Thing in the World" (Volume 10:69) comes from *Melindy's Medal*.

EUGENE FIELD (1850–1895), the beloved children's poet, was a successful journalist who wrote a column for many years in the *Chicago Daily News*. In it appeared most of his stories and verses, later to be put in book form. His companionship with his eight children gave him constant inspiration in his work. Many favorite poems are found in his *Poems of Childhood* (Scribner).

RACHEL FIELD (1894–1942), has the distinction of being the first woman to win the Newbery Medal. Her book, *Hitty: Her First Hundred Years* (Macmillan), won this award. When she was a little girl she wrote poems and illustrated them for the *St. Nicholas* League. As she grew older she kept on writing poetry both for children and for adults. Then she began to write one-act plays, many of which are still produced all over the United States. Later on she went to Hollywood and spent five years as a motion-picture editor. She will always be remembered for her many outstanding juve-

Rachel Field   Charles J. Finger   Marjorie Flack

niles and for her famous adult books, *Time Out of Mind* (Macmillan) and *All This, and Heaven Too* (Macmillan), which were written not long before her death. Most of her life was spent in New York City, but in the summer she loved to go to the Maine coast. "Hitty's Shipwreck" (Volume 12:81) is taken from her famous book, *Hitty: Her First Hundred Years.*

CHARLES J. FINGER's books for children reflect his varied life of travel and adventure. These travels led him from the Klondike gold fields to the Antarctic, encompassing South America, Africa, Mexico, and Canada. His literary career began when he wrote stories for boys' magazines. He later was editor of *Reedy's Mirror* and *All's Well.* From 1906 to 1920 he served as general manager for a group of Ohio railroads. Then he settled with his family in the Ozarks and devoted himself to writing. His *Tales from Silver Lands* (Doubleday) won the Newbery Medal, and *Courageous Companions* (Longmans) brought him the $2,000 Longmans, Green Juvenile Fiction Prize.

BOB FINK is a New York artist who specializes in illustrating stories for boys.

MARJORIE FISCHER is a contemporary writer for juvenile magazines.

AILEEN FISHER is a typical country woman by choice. Working in Chicago when a young girl, she found that the city merely stifled her, so in 1932 she went to Colorado. There she and a friend own a two-hundred-acre ranch in the mountains with, as she says, "a view of a glacier and not a single house." In this quiet and beautiful place she writes her childlike poems. "And there is always time for wood carving, mountain climbing, and eating over a campfire," she adds. *Up the Windy Hill* (Abelard), *That's Why* (Nelson), and *Over the Hills to Nugget* (Aladdin) are her books of children's verse and prose.

BARBARA FITZGERALD grew up in Canada but is living in Chicago. She has designed some covers for children's records, has done some amusing illustrations for *The Children's Treasury* (Consolidated), and has illustrated some stories for *Children's Activities.* Her fairy drawings and her funny little animals are original and distinctive.

MARJORIE FLACK is both author and illustrator of many popular stories for young children. These tales, told first for the amusement of her daughter, are built around real incidents and happenings of everyday life. Among her own favorites are *Story about Ping* (Viking), *Tim Tadpole* (Doubleday), and, of course, *Angus and the Ducks* (Doubleday).

SEYMOUR FLEISHMAN, a Chicago artist with a good sense of humor, studied at the Chicago Art Institute. After four years in the army he has returned to Chicago where he is kept very busy illustrating books for children.

ESTHER FORBES has twice received outstanding recognition in the field of historical writing. *Paul Revere and the World He Lived In* (Houghton) won the Pulitzer Prize

214

in 1942 as the best book dealing with American history, and *Johnny Tremain* (Houghton) was a Newbery Prize winner. Most of her life has been spent in the house in Worcester, Massachusetts, where she lived as a child. At the age of thirteen she tried her hand at a novel. After attending Bradford Academy and the University of Wisconsin, she joined the editorial staff of Houghton Mifflin Company. During World War I she worked in the harvesting fields near Harper's Ferry, Virginia. After her marriage she spent some time abroad, and her first published novel, *Oh Genteel Lady* (Houghton), won recognition before she returned home. "Disperse, Ye Rebels" (Volume 11:238) comes from *Johnny Tremain*.

CAROLYN FORSYTH, a Chicago writer, began to make up poems when she was nine years old. Her juvenile stories and verse appear in magazines and anthologies. She has also written plays and lyrics for songs. Miss Forsyth's collection of verse won a prize of the Midwestern Writer's Conference.

GENEVIEVE FOSTER, when she was a little girl in southern Wisconsin, had an art studio on the top floor of her house that she shared with two of her friends. She always liked to draw. She liked school, too, except for history which she found confusing. After graduating from the University of Wisconsin, she came to Chicago where she studied and became a commercial artist. Then she married, and when her two children were old enough she began illustrating again. When she began to write books of her own she decided to find out what she had always wanted to know about history. It was then she wrote and illustrated *George Washington's World*, *Abraham Lincoln's World*, and *Augustus Caesar's World* (Scribner's). Among her other books are *Birthdays of Freedom* (Scribner's) and her series called "An Initial Biography" including *Abraham Lincoln, George Washington, Andrew Jackson*, and *Theodore Roosevelt* (Scribner's).

ELSIE MELCHERT FOWLER, whose verse appears in juvenile magazines, lives in Oak Park, Illinois. Her story, "The Odd One," won a prize given by the Chicago branch of the National League of American Pen Women.

J. G. FRANCIS, many years ago, used to write nonsense rhymes for *St. Nicholas* and illustrate them with absurd pictures. *A Book of Cheerful Cats and Other Animated Animals* (Appleton-Century) is still loved by children today.

GEORGE CORY FRANKLIN is one of the most noted storytellers of the Rocky Mountain region. He was born in Kansas and now lives in Victorville, California, spending his summers in Del Norte, Colorado. Mr. Franklin has been an assayer, a mining engineer, and an explorer. Since beginning to write professionally, he has contributed more than a thousand stories to various national magazines. His hobbies are trapshooting, camping, exploring, and prospecting. He knows the Colorado mountain region and all the animals that live there. These animals, along with actual experiences with them, are in his stories. Among his books are *Back of Beyond* (Aladdin), *Wild Animals* (Houghton), *Monte* (Houghton), *Tricky* (Houghton), and *Bravo the Bummer* (Houghton).

| Seymour Fleishman | Esther Forbes | Genevieve Foster | George Cory Franklin |

HAZEL FRAZEE is a Chicago artist and illustrator who is following in her mother's steps. She attended the Chicago Art Institute, then began to illustrate books and stories for magazines such as Rand McNally's *Child Life*. She made many of that magazine's fine covers. She is very original and has a good sense of humor. Recently she has become interested in textile designing and experimenting with new mediums. Her latest specialty is "lumi-prints," a process which combines drawing and painting with photography.

ESTHER FRIEND, a Chicago artist, used to decorate the borders and frontispieces of her schoolbooks with dancing children and prancing animals. When she was twelve, she sold a poster to a drygoods store for two dollars, and two years later she spent her free hours serving as an apprentice in a commercial art studio. Soon her mother sent her to the Chicago Art Institute and later took her to Paris where she continued her studies. She has illustrated a number of children's books, and now does delightful animals in ceramics as well. Her husband, Carl Lichtenstein, handles the manufacturing of these popular little figures. Recently they moved to Indianapolis.

MARGARET FRISKEY grew up in Moline, Illinois, and spent most of her summers with at least one foot in a boat. She later went to Northwestern University, married, and settled in Evanston. She wrote her first books to the specifications of her own three children. Now that her children are grown, she commutes to Chicago every day, for she is the editor of The Childrens Press. Her hobbies are gardening, sailing, and books. Among her own books are *Chicken Little Count to Ten* (Childrens Press), *Seven Diving Ducks* (McKay), and *Johnny and the Monarch* (Childrens Press).

HILDA FROMMHOLZ's scholarships took her through Parsons New York School of Fine and Applied Art. The young Brooklyn artist then began to illustrate a number of books and to draw very attractive young girls and boys for stories in *American Girl*. She has also drawn fashions and advertising illustrations. With her husband, Victor Ulric, she has traveled in Europe and in South America, but she still calls New York her favorite city. Here, in her home, she re-does old furniture and makes ceramics. She is also fond of mystery stories, fancy shoes, and amber with two-billion-year-old insects in it. "Being an artist is my vocation and avocation," she says. "And I feel it will always be for me a joyous one."

A. B. FROST (1851–1928) was an outstanding illustrator of his day. He is famous for his Uncle Remus pictures and his illustrations for Stockton's *Rudder Grange*.

FRANCES FROST began her career as a reporter. From 1929 to 1931 she was an instructor in creative poetry at the University of Vermont. Besides writing much outstanding poetry for children, she is the author of several novels, and has been a contributor of verse and fiction to the *New Yorker, American Mercury,* and *Saturday Evening Post*. Recent juvenile books are *Maple Sugar for Windy Foot* (Whittlesey), *The Cat That Went to College* (Whittlesey), *Little Fox* (Whittlesey), and *Rocket Away!* (Whittlesey).

Hazel Frazee   Esther Friend   Margaret Friskey

Hilda Frommholz   Frances Frost   Robert Frost

ROBERT FROST, a ninth generation New Englander, published his first book, *A Boy's Will*, in England in 1913. Since his return to America in 1915, he has been farmer, college professor at Amherst and the University of Michigan, and poet in residence. Mr. Frost was awarded the Pulitzer Prize three times; for *New Hampshire* (Holt), for *Collected Poems* (Holt), and for *A Further Range* (Holt). A good selection of his remarkably fine poetry is found in *Poems of Robert Frost* (Holt). Many people remember Robert Frost's definition of a poem. "A poem begins with a lump in the throat . . . a complete poem is one where an emotion has found its thought and the thought has found the words."

ROSE FYLEMAN, known to her British public as "R. F.," left a professional musical career for writing. Since 1916, when she began to contribute poems to *Punch*, R. F. has traveled extensively on the Continent and in America, and has written such fine books for children as *Fairies and Friends* (Doubleday), *Fairies and Chimneys* (Doubleday), *The Rose Fyleman Fairy Book* (Doubleday), *Gay Go Up* (Doubleday), and *The Doll's House* (Doubleday).

FLAVIA GÁG is a New York artist who has done a number of outstanding illustrations for children's magazines and also for children's books. Her pictures for Robin Palmer's *The Barkingtons* are delightful. She, like her famous sister Wanda Gág, was born in Minnesota and grew up there.

WANDA GÁG (1893–1946) was a distinguished etcher, artist, illustrator, and author of numerous children's books. These included such classics as *Millions of Cats* (Coward-McCann), *The Funny Thing* (Coward-McCann), and *Gone Is Gone* (Coward-McCann). She was born in Minnesota of Bohemian parents. After coming to New York to study and work, she had a one-man show, the first of many exhibitions all over the country. The last twenty years of her life were spent at "All Creation," her home in Milford, New Jersey.

PAUL GALDONE has been well known in the book world of adults for a long time. Recently his lively and humorous drawings for children's books have won special attention. Among these books are the *Miss Pickerell* Books (Whittlesey) by Ellen Mac-

Rose Fyleman   Wanda Gág   Paul Galdone

217

Phillis Garrard   John Gee   Etta F. Gilbert

Gregor, *Rocket Away* (Whittlesey) by Frances Frost, *Star of Wonder* (Whittlesey) by Robert R. Coles, and *Skeleton Cave* (Holt) by Cora Cheney. Mr. Galdone and his family live in New York City.

ALICE CREW GALL, who died in 1949, used to collaborate with her brother, Fleming Crew, on many interesting stories about animals. Their first stories were sent back and forth in letters, as they did not live in the same city. Later, however, they moved back to their childhood home in McConnelsville, Ohio. (See *Fleming Crew.*)

LOUISE AYRES GARNETT was an Evanston composer, a fine poet, and a writer of a number of books for children, including *Three to Make Ready* (Baker), *The Merrymakers* (Rand), and *Muffin Shop* (Rand).

PHILLIS GARRARD (Rowley) is an outstanding poet and writer of distinguished juveniles. She lives in Bermuda, where she has been secretary with the Bermuda Government Transportation Board. She was born in London and educated in England, New Zealand, and Canada. She wrote four "Hilda" books (Blackie), *Nancy, Canadian Schoolgirl, Those Cartwright Twins* (Appleton), *Banana Tree House* (Coward-McCann), *Bermuda Ballads* (with Jack Williamson), and *The Book of Ralf* (Bobbs-Merrill), which gives more adventures of the hero of "Dungeon Deep" (Volume 12:108). Two of her books, *Jenny's Secret Island* (Winston) and *Running Away with Nebby* (MacKay), were Junior Literary Guild selections. Her hobbies are swimming, horseback riding, gardening, and flower painting.

JIMMY GARTHWAITE is a contemporary writer whose stories appear in juvenile magazines. A collection of his verse is found in *Puddin' and Pie* (Harper).

JOHN GEE was born in Southbridge, Massachusetts, but soon came to Chicago where he went to its famous Art Institute. For many years he has illustrated children's stories for juvenile magazines and children's books as well. His drawings are full of humor and originality. He has taught composition and illustration in a number of art schools in Cleveland, Chicago, Denver, Los Angeles, Santa Barbara, and Sarasota, Florida, where he now lives. In Florida his paintings of tropical blooms, which are exhibited in the universities at Tallahassee and Gainesville, are well known. He feels "the great ones who write for children are the finest people on earth." Perhaps that is why his own whimsical work has such a great appeal to boys and girls.

TODROS GELLER was a nationally known painter, graphic artist, and craftsman. He served as director of art of the College of Jewish Studies. Later he was supervisor of art of the Board of Jewish Education. Many nationally known artists received their first training under him. He was the founder and guiding spirit of the American-Jewish Arts Club, and the Todros Geller art gallery in Chicago is named after him.

ETTA F. GILBERT has been writing for twenty years, mostly for children. In that time she has sold nearly two hundred poems, stories, plays, and articles. One of her

Kenneth Gilbert   Nan Gilbert   Paul T. Gilbert   Denise Giraud

daughters, an artist, has illustrated many of her amusing poems, and she has a son who is in the publishing field. Mrs. Gilbert has done some radio work, writing scripts and appearing on programs. Her home is Cleveland, Ohio.

KENNETH GILBERT grew up in Wisconsin, and learned about the wilderness and the ways of wild animals from his friends, the fur trappers. Since then he has written many stories about animals. He left Wisconsin, and after travels in the Orient, Central America, and Alaska, he made the Pacific Northwest his home. Four of his books have been chosen by the Junior Literary Guild. Among them are *Arctic Venture* (Holt) and *Triple Threat Patrol* (Holt).

NAN GILBERT lives in Oregon with her "husband, two children, some dogs, and a turtle." In addition to writing hundreds of children's stories, she works at a local radio station. Her favorite sports are tennis and bowling.

PAUL T. GILBERT, a well-known newspaperman, was an outstanding writer of nonsense stories for children. His amusing "Bertram" stories have delighted readers of all ages. His knowledge of animals was gained firsthand when he traveled with a circus as a reporter. In those days he enjoyed dressing up and performing with the clowns. A collection of sixteen of his stories is found in *Bertram and His Marvellous Adventures* (Dodd). Another of his funny books is *Egbert* (Harper). His last story, before his death in 1953, was "Bertram's Trip to the Moon," which appeared in *Child Life Magazine*.

DENISE GIRAUD was born in Lake Forest, Illinois, but spent four years in France when a child. She attended high school in Chicago and then went to the Art Institute, where she received a Bachelor of Fine Arts degree. She is in the art department of the Spencer Press. Her favorite hobby is photography.

LOUIS S. GLANZMAN is a contemporary artist who illustrates children's stories.

MARGUERITE GODE, who lives in Des Moines, Iowa, is a contemporary writer whose stories appear in juvenile magazines.

MARJORIE GORDON, on graduating from Columbia University, returned to her home in Chicago to take her M.A. at the University of Chicago. She teaches in the nursery school there. One of her hobbies is Old English folk music. She collects folk songs and belongs to a club that sings them. For some months she did editorial work for the Spencer Press.

VIVIAN G. GOULED is a contemporary writer, living in Montclair, New Jersey, whose work appears in juvenile magazines.

FRANCES BARBARA GRAFE lives in Bloomington, New York. She is a contemporary writer whose verse appears in juvenile magazines.

219

KENNETH GRAHAME (1859–1932) wrote *Wind in the Willows* (Scribner's), a children's classic, which was one of the bedtime stories he told to his son. "The Open Road" (Volume 2:20) was one of the stories in this book. Kenneth Grahame was a businessman and before his death he was secretary of the Bank of England. His writing was done in his free time. Among his books were his famous *Reluctant Dragon* (Holiday) and his fine *Dream Days* (Dodd) and *Golden Age* (Dodd). He is also remembered because of his outstanding anthology, *The Cambridge Book of Poetry for Children.*

HARDIE GRAMATKY is a transplanted Texan, raised in California, who now lives in Connecticut. Here he has written and illustrated such outstanding stories for children as *Little Toot* (Putnam), *Hercules* (Putnam) (See Volume 1:200), *Creeper's Jeep* (Putnam), and *Sparky* (Putnam). While on the West Coast he ghosted a well-known comic strip and was an animator for Walt Disney. Then he came East and did "pictorial reporting" for *Fortune, Colliers, Cosmopolitan,* and *Reader's Digest.* During World War II he supervised training films for the Army Air Force. A fine artist, he has exhibited in every large museum in America. His paintings hang in permanent collections in the Brooklyn Museum, Chicago Art Institute, and Toledo Museum.

ELIZABETH JANET GRAY, once a tutor of the Japanese Crown Prince, always wanted to be an author. As a child she contributed an article to the *Young Churchman.* Her first book, published when she was twenty-three, was followed by many more. Some of these are *Adam of the Road* (Viking), a Newbery Prize winner, *Young Walter Scott* (Viking), *Beppy Marlowe* (Viking), *The Fair Adventure* (Viking), and *Sandy* (Viking), winner of a Herald Tribune Spring Festival Prize. She also won the Constance Lindsay Skinner Award of the Women's National Book Association. "Adam to the Rescue" (Volume 12:240) comes from *Adam of the Road.* "Big Moment" (Volume 10:185) comes from *The Fair Adventure.*

HELEN GREGUTT, who lives on Long Island, is a contemporary writer whose stories appear in juvenile magazines.

ZANE GREY (1872–1939) was proud of being a descendant of that same Betty Zane who saved Fort Henry. He wrote his first book about her which, as he couldn't sell it, he had printed himself. He grew up in Zanesville, Ohio, and went to the University of Pennsylvania, where he played baseball. Although he was a successful dentist, he decided to devote all his time to writing. For many years he was unable to sell any of his books but, despite poverty and hardships, he continued to write them. Then he went out West with Colonel "Buffalo" Jones. Here he lived with rangers and wild-horse hunters and had many adventures, but he still could not sell his work. The first book he sold was *The Heritage of the Desert* (Harper) and not many people bought it. His next novel, however, was *Riders of the Purple Sage* (Harper) which sold a million copies. From this time on his work grew very popular and he wrote fifty-four novels that all sold well. During his later years he lived happily with his wife and three children in Altadena, California.

Hardie Gramatky   Elizabeth Janet Gray   Zane Grey   Jacob Grimm

Wilhelm Grimm   Arthur Guiterman   Berta Hader   Elmer Hader

WILLIAM ELLIOT GRIFFIS (1843–1928) was sent to Japan by Rutgers University after he graduated from that college. In Japan, he established schools based on American principles of education. He also taught at the Imperial University at Tokyo. When he returned to the United States, he wrote many books about Japan. *The Mikado's Empire* was his most important one. He later became a minister, but he continued to write and to lecture, too.

JACOB (1785–1863) and WILHELM (1786–1859) GRIMM were brothers who have been called the founders of folklore science. They lived together in Germany all their lives, working, studying, writing almost as one. They wrote tales of princes, princesses, giants, dwarfs, dragons, and enchanted castles which all children love. They did exhaustive research in old manuscripts and books, and they conversed directly with many people in Germany who gave them stories they had heard from their grandparents. Among the favorite stories of theirs are *The Twelve Brothers, Cinderella, Red Riding Hood,* and *Hansel and Gretel.*

ARTHUR GUITERMAN (1871–1943), often called "the most American of poets," was born in Vienna, Austria, of American parents, but was educated in New York City. After his marriage, he divided his time between New York and his wife's summer home in Vermont. He and his wife also did much traveling. Gay, lighthearted poems record the experiences of their frequent jaunts in his native country and abroad. Love lyrics to Vida, patriotic ballads about great Americans, deeply philosophical poems were interspersed with stories, plays, articles, and the libretto of an opera. Among his many volumes are *Chips of Jade* (Dutton), *Gaily the Troubadour* (Dutton), and *I Sing the Pioneer* (Dutton).

JAMES MURRAY HADDOW was born in Scotland but studied art in Chicago at the Art Institute and later studied privately under various artists. He is now a naturalized citizen who has been an instructor of drawing and painting at the American Academy of Art and at his own art school. His work has been exhibited in galleries elsewhere and he has won various prizes with it. He has been president of the Society of Chicago Painters and Sculptors and has a studio in Chicago.

BERTA and ELMER HADER together write and illustrate many outstanding books for children. They are husband and wife and work in their own lovely stone house overlooking the Hudson River not far from New York, a house they built themselves. Both of them like to travel and have given book talks and drawn pictures for child audiences everywhere. Most of their stories deal with familiar situations and are full of action. The same is true of their illustrations, which appeal to children. They work out their books together, both of them writing and drawing and then revising each other's ideas. Some of their best-liked books are *Midget and Bridget* (Macmillan), *Billy Butter* (Macmillan), *Spunky* (Macmillan), *Cricket* (Macmillan), and *Mighty Hunter* (Macmillan). *The Big Snow* (Macmillan) won the Caldecott Award. "Bridget on Fortune's Trail" (Volume 14:55) is an episode from Berta and Elmer Hader's *Midget and Bridget.*

Sylvia Haggander   Paul Hamlin   Nathaniel Hawthorne

SYLVIA HAGGANDER is a native New Yorker who won two scholarships at Parsons New York School of Fine and Applied Art. The second brought her a year's study in France and Italy before she returned to Parsons to teach for one year. Since then she has free-lanced and her delightful drawings of teen-aged girls and boys appear in *Woman's Home Companion, American Girl,* and in many books. Her hobby is cooking and she divides her time between Mt. Vernon, New York, a farm in Pennsylvania, and Fort Myers in Florida.

LUCRETIA HALE (1820–1900) was the sister of Edward Everett Hale, the famous American clergyman and writer. Her father was an editor and all the family liked to write. Lucretia Hale's great literary work was her famous *Peterkin Papers* (Houghton), a group of stories about the humorous, irresponsible Peterkin family, which several generations of children have enjoyed. These tales were originally told to the daughter of her best friend.

JENNIE HALL is a contemporary writer whose stories appear in numerous anthologies. A good selection of her stories is found in *Buried Cities* (Macmillan).

PAUL HAMLIN is a contemporary artist who lives in Chicago. He was born in Ohio and attended art schools in Cleveland and Toledo. He also went to the New England School of Design in Boston. He has been an advertising artist in various midwestern cities and has done story-illustrations for many national magazines. He has exhibited his paintings in galleries throughout the country and has won many awards. In World War II he did work for the Army Engineer publication and did intelligence work at Fort Belvedere, Virginia.

JOEL CHANDLER HARRIS (1845–1908), creator of the classic *Uncle Remus,* spent his life in Georgia. While an apprenticed typesetter on a Southern plantation newspaper, he spent his evenings in the slave quarters hearing the Negroes sing and tell stories. His Br'er Rabbit tales and all his other stories are actual folk tales told to him by these people. After the War between the States he worked on various papers for which he first wrote the Uncle Remus stories. These were later collected and published in book form. To him a child saying, "You have made some of us happy" was the greatest reward a storyteller could have.

HENRY SYDNOR HARRISON (1880–1930), American novelist, was born in Tennessee. He went into journalism after graduating from Columbia. Later he went to Charleston, West Virginia, and wrote. His first adult novel, *Queed* (Houghton), was an immediate success and he found his short stories in great demand. From that time on he was a regular contributor to the *Atlantic Monthly* and other magazines. "Miss Hinch" is his most famous short story.

NATHANIEL HAWTHORNE (1804–1864), a great American novelist, lived most of his life in Massachusetts. At Bowdoin College he was a classmate of Longfellow and Franklin Pierce. He could not make a living at literature and, therefore, held various

Robert A. Heinlein   Marguerite Henry   O. Henry

government positions in customhouses. Three of his classics written for children are *Grandfather's Chair* (Houghton), *A Wonder Book for Boys and Girls* (Houghton), and *Tanglewood Tales* (Houghton). His granddaughter, Hildegarde Hawthorne, is a present-day writer for children and is well known for her biographies. She tells the story of her grandfather in *The Romantic Rebel* (Appleton-Century).

MARJORIE HAYES is a former schoolteacher who likes to write for children. Her first book was *The Little House on Wheels* (Little). Since then she has written articles on children's books for the educational page of the *Christian Science Monitor*, and has illustrated a weekly nature article for a children's page of a newspaper. Some of her other books are *Robin on the River* (Little) and *Little House on Runners* (Little).

I. HEILBRON is a contemporary artist who has illustrated many textbooks and has done advertising art. He lives in Chicago.

ROBERT A. HEINLEIN graduated from Annapolis. Five years of the Navy was followed by more school "as well as politics, silver mining, real estate, traveling, and also loafing." He started writing in 1939 but stopped for World War II, when he was a mechanical engineer at the Naval Aircraft Factory in Philadelphia. He is married to a former Wave. Mr. Heinlein says of his writing and himself, "I write speculative stories about the future because such stories have been my favorite reading since childhood. I'd like to live long enough to see the opening years of space travel, and expect to; other than that I seem to have no special ambitions." Among his books in the field of science fiction are *Space Cadet* (Scribner), *Rocket Ship Galileo* (Scribner), *Between Planets* (Scribner), and *The Rolling Stones* (Scribner).

MARGUERITE HENRY knew she wanted to write from the time she was ten years old and played at reading proof in her father's printing company. Her first writing took the form of magazine articles, but after publishing her first juvenile book, she knew that was the kind of writing she liked best. Since then Mrs. Henry has written many delightful books for children, among them *Misty of Chincoteague* (Rand), *The Little Fellow* (Rand), *Justin Morgan Had a Horse* (Rand), which won the Junior Scholastic Gold Seal Award, and *King of the Wind* (Rand), which won the Newbery Award. She lives in the village of Wayne, just west of Chicago. Here she keeps her well-loved horses, Misty, a Chincoteague pony, and Friday, a Morgan horse. The neighborhood children often come to see them. "King of the Wind and the Queen's Plate" (Volume 14:123) comes from *King of the Wind*.

O. HENRY (William Sydney Porter) (1868–1910) is one of America's most famous short-story writers. O. Henry was born in Greensboro, North Carolina, and had little formal schooling. His first book, *Cabbages and Kings* (Doubleday), brought him to the attention of the reading public, but his fame rests on such short stories as "Gift of the Magi," "The Last Leaf," and "Roads of Destiny." Unexpected twists of plot and a rapid colloquial style help to make the stories of this great American writer very effective.

OLIVER HERFORD (1863–1935), poet, illustrator, and humorist, was born in England but came to the United States when he was six. He wrote and drew for the old *Life*, for *Harper's Weekly*, and for other magazines. He also wrote and illustrated fifty books of clever nonsense. His oral humor was remembered as often as his verse and he was called "the most quoted man in America." Some of his books are: *Rubaiyat of a Persian Kitten* (Scribner), *The Kitten's Garden of Verses* (Scribner), *The Jingle-Jungle Book* (Century), and *This Giddy Globe* (Doran).

GEORGE HERZOG was born in Hungary, studied at the University of Berlin, and came to the United States in 1925. Here he received his doctor's degree at Columbia and did research work at the University of Chicago and at Yale. He was a member of the University of Chicago expedition to Liberia in 1930, and has made numerous visits to American Indian reservations. Mr. Herzog is a specialist in primitive music and languages, and at present is a member of the Anthropology Department of Columbia University. He is co-author of *The Cow-Tail Switch* (Holt).

MAURICE HERZOG, author of *Annapurna* (Dutton), was the level-headed leader of the French expedition to the Himalayas. Here he scaled Annapurna, at that time the highest mountain ever climbed by man. During his childhood, Maurice Herzog spent much time climbing mountains with his father and with his seven brothers and sisters. Mountain climbing and skiing are still his favorite sports. During World War II he fought for four years with the French Army and finally was a captain, commanding an army of the renowned Alpine Troops. He wrote his famous book in an American hospital at Neuilly, where he was recovering from the effects of his greatest climbing achievement. "One writes best," he believes, "when one is suffering, when one is reduced to complete immobility." Though he froze and lost all his fingers and toes when he led the nine men up the great mountain, the author does not dwell upon this in his book. Instead, he brings out the spiritual experience that they underwent and the wonderful teamwork and cooperation found among men under trying circumstances.

THOR HEYERDAHL, famous for his theory of Polynesian-American migrations, and author of *Kon-Tiki* (Rand), was born and educated in Norway. From boyhood he was interested in the natural sciences, even starting a one-room zoological museum at the age of seven. His first trip to Polynesia was made with an expedition of the Oslo University Museum. During World War II he served with the Free Norwegian Air Force created in Canada. In 1947 he organized the Kon-Tiki Expedition to prove that South American aboriginal people could have reached the Polynesian islands from South America by balsa-raft. He built a balsa-raft, which he manned with a crew of six. In 101 days, filled with tremendous excitement and adventure, they covered 4300 miles and reached their goal. During the perilous trip they made many scientific observations. Thor Heyerdahl continued his research in the United States and Europe. *Kon-Tiki* was published in Norway and has been translated into Swedish, Dutch, Finnish, German, English, and Italian.

WILLIAM HEYLIGER, a consultant editor of *The Children's Hour*, was born in New Jersey and was educated in the public schools there. When he was just a boy he was captivated by the stories of Richard Harding Davis and wanted to be a writer, too. His first story was promptly rejected. He had sent it, written in longhand and tied with blue ribbons, to the *Saturday Evening Post*. As he grew older he went into the mercantile business and then did newspaper work. After this he began to write popular sports stories for boys. Mr. Heyliger is the father of three boys (he has eight children). He has camped with boys, talked to schoolboys in ten states, and has written books for them continuously. He and his wife, Fleur Conkling, the writer, live at Drexel Hill, Pennsylvania. Among the forty-five books that he has published are *S O S Radio Patrol* (Dodd), *High Benton* (Appleton-Century), *Backfield Comet* (Appleton-Century), *The County Pennant* (Appleton-Century), and *The Macklin Brothers* (Appleton-Century).

Maurice Herzog   Thor Heyerdahl   William Heyliger   Helen Train Hilles

HELEN TRAIN HILLES was born in New York. Her father, Arthur Train, was the well-known author of the famous "Mr. Tutt" stories. She is married and has two daughters. In addition to her many short stories appearing in magazines and anthologies, she has done several books for children: *A Mile of Freedom* (Macmillan), *Cowboy Holiday* (Macmillan), and *Play Street* (Random). She and her family spend part of their time on a farm in Millbrook, New York, where they raise livestock. She tells about her farming adventures there in a book for older readers called *Farm Wanted* (Messner).

GORDON HILLMAN is a contemporary poet. His work has appeared frequently in the *Christian Science Monitor*.

EMILY HILSABECK has taught poetry to children and has written occasional verse. She has organized a poetry club at Woodlawn Library in Chicago and also poetry groups at Chicago Boys Clubs. Mrs. Hilsabeck reviews children's books for the *Chicago Schools Journal*. Her poems have appeared in *Jack and Jill* and in various other magazines and newspapers.

INEZ HOGAN was born in Washington, D. C., and studied illustration and painting both there and in Paris. On her return from Europe she became art supervisor in the public schools of Washington and New York. After trying her hand at illustrating other people's books, she decided she would like to write stories for children, herself. She then both wrote and illustrated the famous "Nicodemus" books (Dutton), and the popular "Twin" series (Dutton). After her marriage to Randolph Bowers she went to live in Provincetown, Massachusetts.

JANICE HOLLAND is a native Washingtonian who likes to illustrate children's books. She has over thirty to her credit and has written some of them herself. She attended Pratt Institute in Brooklyn and worked fifteen hours a day on her first book *Distant Lands* (Silver Burdett). She has been busy free-lancing ever since. Miss Holland, when she was in her teens, spent a season in summer stock—on the marionette circuit. "We gave the show and passed the hat," she explained. *They Built a City* (Scribner), the story of Washington, D. C., she both wrote and illustrated. "I don't think that anyone could have half as much fun reading my books as I have had doing them," she says.

MARION HOLLAND, author of *Billy Had a System* (Knopf), has a busy life in Chevy Chase, Maryland, for she is the mother of five children, as well as a housewife, an author, and an illustrator. After graduation from Swarthmore College, she went to Columbia, and then to work as a display artist in various department stores. Eventually, she began writing and illustrating her own stories about Billy and Fats and wrote features published in juvenile magazines.

RUPERT SARGENT HOLLAND was educated at Harvard where his English professor told him, "The only way to write is to go ahead and write." He did, and was editor of the college magazines. Following a degree from the University of Pennsylvania, he practiced law for some years, writing whenever he could. The boyhood adventures of famous men had always interested him and he wrote a series of stories about them for *St. Nicholas*. These later appeared in book form and were followed by six others. He has also written a number of Boy Scout stories, mystery and adventure stories, and some verse for children's magazines. Among his books are *Freedom's Flag* (Macrae Smith), a biography of Francis Scott Key, and *Plays of American Colonies* (Harper). Some of his stories were written at Prout's Neck, Maine, where he, his wife, and his three children spend their summers. In the winter he lives west of Philadelphia, not far from Valley Forge.

OLIVER WENDELL HOLMES (1809–1894) was one of America's most versatile men of letters. Not only was he an author, poet, and humorist, but he was also a distinguished professor of medicine. His ridiculous verse is especially appealing to children and may be found in his *Complete Poetical Works* (Houghton). His love of fun was inherited by his famous son, Chief Justice Oliver Wendell Holmes.

ELIZABETH HONNESS was born in New Jersey, spent most of her childhood in the Catskill Mountains, and now lives with her husband, J. A. McKaughan, and her daughter in Philadelphia. She is a graduate of Skidmore College and likes to paint, to write poetry, to make doll clothes, and to concoct strange dishes for which her family are willing guinea pigs. She was, for some years, assistant editor of *American Girl*. She is the author of eight books for children, among them *The Great Gold-Piece Mystery* (Lippincott), *Mystery of the French Diamonds* (Lippincott), and *The Tail of the Sorry Sorrel Horse* (Nelson).

FLORENCE and MARGARET HOOPES are two contemporary artists who live in Philadelphia, and have illustrated many magazine stories and many textbooks. They are particularly well known for their drawings of delightful children.

DOROTHY HOSFORD was born in Pittsburgh and graduated from Margaret Morrison College, Carnegie Institute of Technology. Her years at the Carnegie Library School gave her a real and lasting interest in children's books. And now, with her twin boys, she has spent many pleasant hours of storytelling. The stories of the Norse gods have been in special demand, and she has told and retold the legends many times. Among her books are *By His Own Might* (Holt), *Sons of the Volsungs* (Holt), and *Thunder of the Gods* (Holt).

A. E. HOUSMAN (1859–1936), educated at Oxford, became a professor of Latin at the University of London and at Cambridge University. He came from a talented family; his brother, Laurence Housman, was an illustrator and man of letters, and his sister Clemence an artist. Mr. Housman was a poet and classical scholar. His great book, *The Shropshire Lad* (Holt), first published in 1896, made him internationally famous. A second volume of his adult verse appeared twenty-six years later. This was *Last Poems* (Holt).

LAURENCE HOUSMAN, brother of A. E. Housman, is an author, a dramatist, and a well-known illustrator in England. A favorite juvenile book is *Moonshine and Clover* (Harcourt), a charming selection of fairy tales. The illustrations were designed by the author and engraved by his sister. He is best known, however, for his work in the adult field.

RICHARD HUGHES, the English author, began writing plays while an undergraduate at Oxford. His first collection of verse was published then, too. It was *Gypsy Night* (Golden Cockerel Press). Later he turned to short-story writing and a book of collected stories appeared. Two of his children's books are *The Spider's Palace* (Harper) and *Don't Blame Me!* (Harper). He loves children and often has them visit him in his stone cottage in Wales.

| Emily Hilsabeck | Oliver Wendell Holmes | Elizabeth Honness | Dorothy Hosford |

ELEANOR HULL is a contemporary writer. She is the author of *The Boy's Cuchulain* (Crowell).

LEIGH HUNT (1784–1849) was an English poet and also a critic and essayist. Throughout his life he was connected with various newspapers and magazines. He was educated at Christ's Hospital, London, where he was a classmate of Coleridge and Charles Lamb. He was a close friend, also, of Keats, Shelley, and Byron. Some of his poems, written over a hundred years ago, are still very popular.

MABEL LEIGH HUNT is a native Hoosier. After training in children's library service at Western Reserve University she returned to her home in Indianapolis. Here she began her work with children, serving for ten years as a librarian. In 1938 she decided to devote her entire time to creative writing. Her first book, *Lucinda* (Lippincott), was based on her mother's reminiscences of a Quaker childhood. Among Miss Hunt's many books are *Billy Button's Butter'd Biscuit* (Lippincott), *Have You Seen Tom Thumb?* (Lippincott), *Better Known as Johnny Appleseed* (Lippincott), *Ladycake Farm* (Lippincott), and *Singing Among Strangers* (Lippincott).

FRANCES TIPTON HUNTER is a contemporary artist who lives in Philadelphia. One of her books is the *Frances Tipton Hunter Picture Book* (Whitman). Her very outstanding work has frequently been found on the covers of such magazines as the *Saturday Evening Post* and *Collier's*. Many of her charming children have appeared in national advertising.

MIRIAM HURFORD is a contemporary artist who lived for many years in Chicago and did illustrations for *Child Life Magazine* and for *Now We Are Three* (Consolidated). Most of her work, however, has been found in Scott Foresman textbooks. She and her artist husband are now living in New Mexico.

SCHARMEL IRIS is a fine poet who now lives near Chicago. The manuscript of his book of outstanding poems, *Bread Out of Stone* (Regnery), was lost for many years, along with a preface by William Butler Yeats saying, "Of poets writing today there is no greater." This manuscript was found and published in 1953.

WASHINGTON IRVING (1783–1859) was the first great American author to gain fame abroad and at home. As a boy, his interest in reading and writing was encouraged by his ten brothers and sisters. His characters, Rip Van Winkle and Ichabod Crane, are still favorites of both young and old, and his Knickerbocker legends are an enjoyable part of the local history of New York. In his later years he lived on his estate, Sunnyside, on the Hudson River near Sleepy Hollow.

WALLACE IRWIN as a boy was taken to a wild western mountain camp where his father looked for gold and found none. He was educated at Stanford University, and later became a reporter on the *San Francisco Examiner*, then editor of the magazine founded by Bret Harte. After moving to New York he was on the staff of *Collier's Weekly*. It

| Mabel Leigh Hunt | Wallace Irwin | Bertha Ten Eyck James | Will James |

was there he created his famous "Letters of a Japanese Schoolboy," which Mark Twain and many others loved, and which appeared in many newspapers and magazines for over a period of thirty years. He has written a dozen popular novels and over one hundred short stories, many of which were published in the *Saturday Evening Post*. His wife is also a novelist, Laetitia Irwin, and his brother is Will Irwin, another well-known writer. A selection of his verse is found in *Random Rhymes and Odd Numbers* (Macmillan).

ELIZABETH RHODES JACKSON is the wife of a Boston architect. Her own children are put into her delightful book *Beacon Hill Children* (Page).

LEROY F. JACKSON was born in Canada but came to the United States when just a small boy. He has taught and directed schools in North Dakota, Minnesota, Washington, and North Carolina. He has written several books of nonsense rhymes for younger children. Many of his much praised verses are found in *Jolly Jingle Picture Book* (Rand) and *The Peter Patter Book* (Rand).

JOSEPH JACOBS (1854–1916) was born in Australia and spent most of his life in England. The beautiful fairy tales he has retold he read first to his three children when they were small. Later they were put into book form. Mr. Jacobs is considered one of the great modern scholars of folklore. Among his books are *Celtic Fairy Tales* (Putnam), *English Fairy Tales* (Putnam), *Indian Fairy Tales* (Putnam), and *Johnny-Cake* (Putnam). He was also an authority on Jewish culture and history.

HAYM JAFFE is co-author, with Joseph Cottler, of *Heroes of Civilization* (Little), a collection of fine biographies.

BERTHA TEN EYCK JAMES says, "I was born in Los Angeles at the top of a hill called the Angels' Flight and in a house which had a hedge of calla lilies. I had one older sister, one next sister, one brother, and a baby sister. I started to write poetry before I could print. I had to save my poems in my head until someone would write them down for me. My father did not believe in schools, so I spent my childhood playing outdoors, writing poems, and telling stories to my sisters and brothers. After a lot of lovely long years like that my father went to Europe, so he could not teach us any more. I went to high school for one year and to the University of Chicago for six years, where I got my degree. Then I was married and spent many years writing poetry and telling stories to my three boys and one daughter." The poet did not mention that she won the Fiske prize for poetry at the University of Chicago and that her husband is Daniel Catton Rich, director of the Art Institute of Chicago.

S. T. JAMES is a frequent contributor to *Collins Young Elizabethan*, a magazine for young people published in London, England.

WILL JAMES (1892–1942) was born in Montana. His parents died when he was a little boy, and he was adopted by a French-Canadian trapper and prospector. His educa-

228

Florence Page Jaques   Francis Lee Jaques   De Witt Whistler Jayne   Eleanor Jewett

tion came from old magazines and catalogues, and he first drew with charcoal from a branding fire. An expert cowboy at fourteen, he rode with many of the biggest outfits from Canada to Mexico. An accident when he was thirty-two, in which a bucking horse fell on him, stopped his cowpunching. Urged by a friend, he submitted an article about bucking horses to *Scribner's Magazine.* From that time until his death, Will James wrote books and illustrated them. Some of his books are *Smoky* (Scribner), which won the Newbery Medal, *Young Cowboy* (Scribner), *The American Cowboy* (Scribner), and *Cowboys North and South* (Scribner). "The Squeak of Leather" (Volume 14:211) comes from *Smoky.*

FLORENCE PAGE JAQUES began her career by writing poetry and nursery tales for juvenile magazines. After graduating from college she attended Columbia University in New York, and there met her artist husband, Francis Lee Jaques. His work at the American Museum of Natural History took them on many expeditions, some of which resulted in their joint books, *Canoe Country* (University of Minnesota Press), *Snowshoe Country* (University of Minnesota Press), and *Canadian Spring* (Harper). They now live in a country home in Minnesota.

FRANCIS LEE JAQUES, born in Geneseo, Illinois, was with the American Museum of Natural History for eighteen years, painting many exhibit backgrounds for that and various other museums. A noted etcher and painter of wildlife, he has been a member of expeditions to many parts of the world; expeditions to Panama, Peru, the Bahamas, the Bering Sea and the Arctic Ocean, the South Seas and the Marquesas Islands, visiting Tahiti, Pitcairn and Easter Island, and the Galapagos. Mr. Jaques has illustrated many books, among them *Canoe Country* (University of Minnesota Press) and *Canadian Spring* (Harper), written by his wife Florence Page Jaques.

DE WITT WHISTLER JAYNE spent his childhood in Boston and on the East Coast, always near the ocean and the ships he loves to paint. He graduated from Wheaton College in Illinois, and had his art training at the Pennsylvania Museum School of Art. He also did graduate work in art and archeology at the University of Chicago. After being the head of the art department of Wheaton College for nine years and working for a while as an art director, he became a free-lance illustrator. His outstanding illustrations are found in various books and magazines. His mother was a Whistler and comes from the same family as the famous artist, James McNeill Whistler.

ELEANOR JEWETT, well-known art editor and special article writer for the *Chicago Tribune,* spends her summers in Traverse City, Michigan, and her winters with her family in Winnetka, Illinois. Her delightful juvenile verse is well known as well as her verse for adults, published in her book called *The Wind's Whistle* (Ralph Fletcher Seymour).

EMILIE FENDALL JOHNSON was born in Baltimore, Maryland, and educated there at Madam Le Fevre's School. After her marriage to Oscar Johnson, she lived for a number of years in Chicago. She has always been interested in children and was a volunteer social service worker at Children's Memorial Hospital. More recently she has lived in Palm Beach, Florida. She has contributed many poems to children's magazines and is the author of *The Umbrella Bird* (Falmouth) and *A Little Book of Prayers* (Viking).

OWEN JOHNSON (1887–1952) was born in New York City. At the age of six he wrote a story for *St. Nicholas* and received a dollar for it. When twelve he put out a paper with the assistance of a friend, the son of the poet Richard Watson Gilder. While attending Lawrenceville School he founded a school paper and wrote his first novel, *The Eternal Boy* (Grosset). His next book, *Stover at Yale* (Little), was written while attending Yale. He was employed as a police court reporter, and was in France during World War I, receiving the Chevalier Legion D'Honneur. Among his books are *Blue Blood* (Little), *Skippy Bedelle* (Little), *Humming Bird* (Little), and *The Spirit of France* (Little). No one who ever chuckles over his stories about Hickey, the Varmint, Turkey, the Tennessee Shad, and Doc MacNooder at Lawrenceville will ever forget them. "The Third Round" (Volume 10:199) comes from *Stover at Yale*. "Beauty's Sister" (Volume 10:125) comes from *The Prodigious Hickey*.

SIDDIE JOE JOHNSON spent her childhood roaming the countryside of southern Texas. She started writing poems when she went to school but considered them to be "very bad." At Texas Christian University she was the campus poet. Since graduating from college she has done library work with children. She is children's librarian at the Dallas Public Library, has a radio program for boys and girls, and teaches children's literature at Southern Methodist University. She is a consultant editor of *The Children's Hour*. Her first book for boys and girls, *Debby* (Longmans), was about herself as a child. *Texas: The Land of the Tejas* (Random), *Cathy* (Longmans), and *Susan's Year* (Longmans) followed. "The Story Hour" (Volume 6:95) comes from *Susan's Year*.

ELIZABETH JONES lives in Poland, New York, where she writes delightful verse for children.

ELIZABETH ORTON JONES feels that she inherited her pleasure in making books for children from her grandfather Orton. He had a bookstore in Geneva, New York, and wrote stories and plays for children. Like him, Miss Jones was always drawing and making up stories. Her parents exposed her to good literature, music, art, and to the democratic way of life through contacts with people of different nationalities and walks of life. This is reflected in *Maminka's Children* (Macmillan), *Ragman of Paris* (Oxford), and *Twig* (Macmillan). She received the Caldecott Medal for her illustrations of Rachel Field's *Prayer for a Child* (Macmillan). She now lives in her own house in Mason, New Hampshire, where she has a woods with squirrels and rabbits for neighbors, and where she writes many of her books and draws her delightful pictures.

THOMAS ORTON JONES, when living in Highland Park, Illinois, wrote *Minnie the Mermaid* (Oxford) with his sister, Elizabeth Orton Jones.

Emilie Fendall Johnson   Siddie Joe Johnson   Elizabeth Orton Jones

CLAIRE JOSLYN is a Chicago lecturer who long ago composed the lovely lullaby in *The Children's Hour* for her own children.

BETTY JUMP, an author from South Bend, Indiana, has contributed many poems to children's magazines.

CARL S. JUNGE, a Chicago artist known the world over for his fine bookplates, amuses himself by writing very outstanding nonsense verse which delights others when it appears in magazines and newspapers. He has art work in permanent exhibits in the Metropolitan Museum, New York, the Museum of Fine Arts, Boston, and the British Museum.

CHESLEY KAHMANN, a New Jersey author, has contributed many short stories to children's magazines. Among her books are *XDY and the Soap Box Derby* (Random), *Gypsy Melody* (Random), and *Sinfi and the Little Gypsy Goat* (Random).

JOHN KEATS (1795-1821) was one of the greatest English romantic poets. After the death of his parents he was apprenticed to a surgeon but was very unhappy in his hospital work. When a friend gave him a copy of Edmund Spenser's *Faerie Queene* he was so inspired that he devoted his life entirely to writing. He died three years later at the age of twenty-six. Boys and girls today still read and enjoy such beautiful poems of his as "Ode on a Grecian Urn," "Ode to a Nightingale," and "The Eve of Saint Agnes."

ERIC P. KELLY was born in Amesbury, Massachusetts, and was educated at Dartmouth. His early years were spent as a journalist. During World War I he did relief work among the Polish legions in France, whom he accompanied back to Poland. He traveled and studied there for three years, returning to the United States as an instructor at Dartmouth. In 1925-1926 he was a lecturer and student at the University of Krakow in Poland. Among his prized possessions is one of the ancient trumpets used for centuries by the trumpeters of Krakow, and out of this grew his book, *The Trumpeter of Krakow* (Macmillan), a Newbery Prize winner. Mr. Kelly is also the author of *The Blacksmith of Vilno* (Macmillan), *The Golden Star of Halich* (Macmillan), and *Christmas Nightingale* (Macmillan). "The Broken Note" (Volume 8:294) is from *The Trumpeter of Krakow*.

ALICE GEER KELSEY was born in Danvers, Massachusetts. After college, she married and left America on the second boat taking relief workers to the Near East. This was after World War I. While her husband did agricultural and general relief work she worked with war orphans at Merziform. Her fine collection of Turkish stories, *Once the Hodja* (Longmans), was gathered during this time. Later she came back to Ithaca when her husband joined the faculty of Cornell. Here, with her four children, she stayed until World War II, when she served with UNRRA in Athens. Her book, *Racing the Red Sail* (Longmans), gives a vivid picture of Greece. The Kelseys' major hobby is camping in the Adirondacks. This is how they spend their vacations.

Carl S. Junge   John Keats   Eric P. Kelly   Alice Geer Kelsey

231

LOUISE ANDREWS KENT remembers doing, when she was a child, much the same things as children do now: coasting, camping, skating, climbing trees, riding horseback, fishing, and playing baseball. After graduating from Simmons College she married Ira Rich Kent, later the editor of Houghton Mifflin Company. She has two daughters and lived for many years in Brookline, Massachusetts. Mrs. Kent is the author of eleven fine books, and joint author of two more. She has also contributed short stories to magazines and has written a newspaper column for a Boston paper. Her most popular book for adults is *Mrs. Appleyard's Year* (Houghton). *Douglas of Porcupine* (Houghton) is her own favorite book and is a favorite book of many boys and girls, too. "An Island Christmas" (Volume 6:277) is a celebration found in *Douglas of Porcupine*. "On Kublai Khan's Service" (Volume 12:313) is part of *He Went with Marco Polo*.

ALEXANDER KEY wanted to be an artist, "another Velasquez," as he puts it, so he studied at the Chicago Art Institute. Soon after that he found himself drawing for juvenile magazines and illustrating books. This led him to writing books. Although born in Maryland, he considers himself a native of Florida, where he spent his early years along the banks of the Swanee River. He now lives with his wife and young son on the Gulf Coast, "in a palm grove full of raccoons and mosquitoes beside a lagoon full of sharks. The seams of my house are splitting with books, but I'm still collecting them, writing them, and illustrating them," he says. He has written seven books and illustrated about seventy. One of his best known is *With Dan'l Boone on the Caroliny Trail* (Winston). "Strangers in the Wilderness" (Volume 11:150) comes from this book.

JOYCE KILMER (1886–1918), after graduating from Rutgers University, was a teacher, a book salesman, and an editor. He was killed in action during World War I. Some of his beautiful, well-known poems can be found in *Trees and Other Poems* (Doubleday).

EDITH KING, who sometimes signs her poems E. L. M. King, was born in South Africa and has spent much of her life there. For eleven years she was principal of a school for girls. She loves the country and enjoys writing about it in her many delightful poems for boys and girls. Two fine collections of hers are *Fifty Country Rhymes for Children* (Appleton) and *Fifty New Poems for Children* (Appleton).

KENNETH KING, an English author, is a frequent contributor to *Collins Young Elizabethan*, a magazine for young readers published in London.

RUDYARD KIPLING (1865–1936) spent most of his early life in India. It was here that he heard the native tales of jungle animals used in his later books. At seventeen he became assistant editor of the *Civil and Military Gazette* of Lahore, for which he began writing verse as fillers. In 1890 Kipling left India and returned to England by way of the United States, where he married and lived for several years. He then settled in a quiet English village, where he devoted himself to writing. His *The Light that Failed* (Doubleday), *Soldiers Three* (Doubleday), *Actions and Reactions* (Doubleday), *Kim* (Doubleday), *Stalky and Co.* (Doubleday), and many other books

232

are liked by adults. Best known of his children's stories are the *Jungle Books* (Double-day), the *Just So Stories* (Doubleday), and *Captains Courageous* (Doubleday). He received the Nobel Prize for Literature and the Gold Medal of the Royal Society of Literature.

OLIVE BURNS KIRBY is a contemporary writer who has written many short stories for juvenile magazines. Her winters are spent in Florida and the summer months in Toronto, Canada.

JIM KJELGAARD came from a large family. He had four brothers and one sister, and remembers a wonderful childhood spent on a farm in Pennsylvania. Outside of school all his free time was spent fishing, hunting, and trapping. Before turning to writing, Mr. Kjelgaard at one time or another was a laborer, teamster, factory worker, plumber, and surveyor's assistant. He is married and has a daughter. Five of his popular books for boys are *Big Red* (Holiday), *Forest Patrol* (Holiday), *Rebel Siege* (Holiday), *Cracker Barrel Double Shooter* (Dodd), and *Haunt Fox* (Holiday).

ROLF KLEP is a contemporary author-artist who wrote and illustrated *Album of the Great* (Knopf).

EMILIE BENSON KNIPE and ALDEN ARTHUR KNIPE (1870–1950) are a wife and husband team who have collaborated on writing several juvenile books. *The Lucky Sixpence* (Appleton) is one of their best known volumes. "Six Bells" (Volume 12:152) comes from this book.

ARTHUR KRAMER is a Chicago poet and advertising man. His poems have appeared in *Poetry* and many other magazines. His humorous verse has come out in *Child Life* and in various humorous newspaper columns.

FRITZ KREDEL was born in Germany, and after two years of college went to Offenbach, Vienna, and Florence, to study art. In 1938 he came to the United States and became a citizen; here, known for his distinguished illustrations for adult books and children's books. Among the books he has illustrated is *The King of the Golden River* (World).

SIDNEY LANIER (1842–1881) was born in Macon, Georgia. His earliest love was for music and he was a gifted flute player. He served in the Confederate army and contracted tuberculosis from which he never recovered. For a short time he lectured on literature at Johns Hopkins University. He retold, in lovely prose, stories of Froissart and King Arthur. Some of his most famous poems are "The Song of the Chattahoochee," "The Marshes of Glynn," and "A Ballad of Trees and the Master."

DOROTHY P. LATHROP, one of the most gifted of present-day illustrators of children's books, was born in Albany, New York. Her mother was a painter and her first interest in art came from playing in her mother's studio and being encouraged to use her mother's brushes and paints. Her sister, Gertrude, is a noted sculptor and the two share a studio in Falls Village, Conn. Dorothy Lathrop studied at Teachers College, Columbia University, and taught for two years. She studied art at the Pennsylvania Academy of Fine Arts and the Art Student's League in New York. She has illustrated some thirty books for children and has also written the text for eight of them. She works in oil, water color, pen and ink, and with lithographic pencil. Her pictures of fairies are among the finest portrayals of fairies in the history of book illustration. She is equally successful in drawing animals, most of which she draws from live models. Indeed, she and her sister have a studio set back among the apple trees where, she says, "Many wild animals, birds, and flower models walk conveniently up to our windows." *Who Goes There?* (Macmillan) and *Hide and Go Seek* (Macmillan), which she also wrote and illustrated, are extraordinarily beautiful and show an accu-

Dorothy P. Lathrop   Mildred Lawrence   Marie Lawson

rate and sympathetic understanding of animal life. In 1938 she received the Caldecott Medal. This was the first award ever given to a picture book for children. She received it for her *Animals of the Bible* (Lippincott). Miss Lathrop's contribution to children's books is a large one, and each year she adds new volumes of beauty.

ELEANOR F. LATTIMORE was born in China. She was the fourth in a family of five children. Her childhood experiences are reflected in many of her books: *Little Pear* (Harcourt), *Peachblossom* (Harcourt), *Questions of Lifu* (Harcourt), *Story of Lee Ling* (Harcourt), and *Holly in the Snow* (Morrow). When her family came to America she attended art school in California and New York. She always liked to draw best, but in order to get some stories to illustrate she started writing them, and she has illustrated her own books ever since. At present, Eleanor Lattimore lives in South Carolina with her husband and two sons.

MILDRED LAWRENCE was born in Charleston, Illinois. After graduating from college she held various positions on a Flint, Michigan, newspaper. Now she is married and has one daughter. Most of her children's books have sprung from projects of the Lawrence family: *Peachtree Island* (Harcourt), *Sand in Her Shoes* (Harcourt), and *The Homemade Year* (Harcourt). She has contributed short stories for children to many juvenile magazines, and is also the author of adult short stories. At present the Lawrences live in Orlando, Florida, traveling north each summer. Recently they went to Europe.

MARIE LAWSON was born down in Georgia, studied at the New York School of Fine and Applied Art, and has beautifully illustrated many books, including *Pocahontas and Captain John Smith*, a "Landmark" book (Random). She has also written some books herself. She is married to Robert Lawson, the author-artist, and they live at Rabbit Hill, Westport, Connecticut. Here, when she isn't at her drawing board, she gardens and collects china.

ROBERT LAWSON, who through his writing and drawing has won both the Newbery and Caldecott Medals, was born in New York City, was brought up in New Jersey, and served in World War I. He was in the camouflage section with the Fortieth Engineers in France. After the war he did stage design, etching, and commercial art, but in 1930 began to illustrate books. A few years later he decided that he liked to do that best, and he has been doing it ever since, illustrating fifty-odd volumes such as *Ferdinand, Adam of the Road,* and *Mr. Popper's Penguins.* He wrote sixteen of these books. Among these are *They Were Strong and Good* (Viking) the Caldecott winner, and *Rabbit Hill* (Viking) the Newbery prize winner. He and his wife, Marie A. Lawson, the author-illustrator, live and work at their home in Connecticut.

EDWARD LEAR (1812–1888) was the youngest of twenty-one children. At fifteen he was supporting himself by drawing birds and illustrating the works of naturalists. He spent some years on the estate of the Earl of Derby. Here he drew birds and here he first began to make up nonsense verse and absurd pictures for the children of the

Robert Lawson   Mahrea Cramer Lehman   Margaret Leighton   Joan Leitz

family. Many years later these were published as *The Book of Nonsense*. Some of his other amusing books are *The Pelican Chorus, The Jumblies, The Book of More Nonsense*, and *Nonsense Songs*. Lear still considered painting his first love and at one time taught painting to Queen Victoria. A number of these books have been reissued by Warne of London.

AGNES LEE was a Chicago poet whose beautiful poems used to appear in *Poetry, a Magazine of Verse*, and whose collection of verse, *New Lyrics*, was published by Ralph Fletcher Seymour.

MELICENT HUMASON LEE (1889–1943) contributed many short stories to juvenile magazines. One of her well-known books is *Marcos, A Mountain Boy of Mexico* (Whitman).

MAHREA CRAMER LEHMAN went to John Herron Art Institute in Indianapolis and came to Chicago to study at the Academy of Fine Arts. She married Paul Lehman, another student there, when he came home from World War I. Starting with five dollars, they gradually worked up a successful commercial art business. They both taught at the Academy, and after his death she continued teaching there. She has exhibited her outstanding portraits and many of her humorous sketches, as well as her very fine pictures of cats, in various galleries in Chicago. She has recently been traveling and sketching in England, Ireland, and France.

LOUISE LEIGHTON is a contemporary writer. She has contributed verse to juvenile magazines.

MARGARET LEIGHTON was born in Oberlin, Ohio. Her father was a college professor. During his vacations and sabbaticals he liked to take his family traveling, sometimes in Europe, sometimes in the United States. Margaret Leighton remembers especially a summer in a German forest, a trip by tally-ho coach through the Scottish Highlands, a winter at a French school in Paris, and a voyage through the Mediterranean Sea. She lives now in an old house covered with vines, near the shore of the Pacific, so near that she can hear the surf on the beach all night long. She has four children who appear, thinly disguised, in *The Secret of the Old House* (Winston) and *The Secret of the Closed Gate* (Winston). Both her older children are talented artists. Jim has illustrated one of his mother's books, *The Sword and the Compass* (Houghton), and Mary illustrated another, *The Secret of Bucky Moran* (Farrar).

JOAN LEITZ was born in South Haven, Michigan, the only one in her family to become interested in art as a career. After leaving the Chicago Art Institute, she was employed in a small advertising studio, and then started working for the Spencer Press.

MAURICE LESEMANN, an outstanding poet, began writing in his early teens. While still a student at the University of Chicago, and president of its Poetry Club, he won a prize from *Poetry Magazine*. Now he is a busy advertising man in California, but when he finds time he still writes distinguished verse.

235

MERIDEL LE SUEUR is a contemporary writer. She is the author of *Little Brother of the Wilderness* (Knopf) and *River Road* (Knopf).

ELIZABETH FOREMAN LEWIS was born in Baltimore, Maryland. After receiving her education in the United States, she taught school in Chungking and Nanking, China. She is married to John A. Lewis of Sioux City, Iowa, and has one son. Her fine short stories, both juvenile and adult, have been translated into many languages. *Young Fu of the Upper Yangtze* (Winston) won the Newbery Medal. Other books of hers are *When the Typhoon Blows* (Winston), *Ho-Ming* (Winston), and *China Quest*.

GLADYS FRANCIS LEWIS makes her home in Canada and is the author of *The Black Stallion and the Red Mare* (Copp).

JANET LEWIS is a distinguished poet and a prize-winning novelist. She and her husband, Yvor Winters, the poet, live with their family in California.

BURR W. LEYSON is a member of the Institute of the Aeronautical Sciences. He has written many non-fiction books dealing with a variety of subjects. Among these are *Modern Wonders and How They Work* (Dutton), *Plastics in the World of Tomorrow* (Dutton), *Career in the Steel Industry* (Dutton), and *Wings of Defense* (Dutton).

STAN LILSTROM is a contemporary artist who lives in a Chicago suburb. Many of his religious illustrations are found in *Sears Concise Bible* (Spencer Press). He did many illustrations for *War and Spy Stories* (Consolidated) and *Humor Stories* (Consolidated). He has also done several covers for national magazines.

CHARLES A. LINDBERGH made the first solo flight across the Atlantic Ocean in 1927. In *We* (Putnam) he describes his own life and his transatlantic flight, together with his views on the future of aviation. He is married to Ann Morrow Lindbergh who has shared in many of his aviation ventures. His latest book is *Spirit of St. Louis* (Scribner). "New York to Paris" (Volume 15:246), his own description of his flight, was published in *We*. In 1954 Lindbergh was awarded the Daniel Guggenheim Medal for his contributions to aeronautics, and was made Brigadier General in the U.S.A.F. Reserve.

FRANK B. LINDERMAN (1869–1938) at the age of sixteen left home to go West into the territory of Montana. He lived there for years, hunting and trapping, sometimes living with the Indians who were his friends. When the railroad came, Mr. Linderman turned to mining, becoming an assayer and chemist. Before his death he had been secretary of the Montana State Mining Association, a member of the Legislature, and also of the American Indian Defense Association. *Indian Why Stories* (Scribners) is one of his best books.

ASTRID LINDGREN has long been a storytelling mother for her children and their friends. She is the author of *Pippi Longstocking* (Viking) which Swedish children have en-

Elizabeth Foreman Lewis

Charles A. Lindbergh

Willis Lindquist

Vachel Lindsay   Hugh Lofting   Jack London

joyed for several years. With the American edition we, too, are now able to read about Pippi's rollicking escapades. "Pippi Acts as a Lifesaver" (Volume 13:94) comes from this delightful book.

WILLIS LINDQUIST was first a lawyer. When World War II came, he served with the Merchant Marines. Since his return to civilian life he has been living in New York and devoting all his time to free-lance writing. Much of his writing has to do with nature and with far countries. He has traveled around the world, taking pictures and writing for *The National Geographic, Nature,* and *Travel. Burma Boy* (Whittlesey) was a Junior Literary Guild selection.

MAUD LINDSAY has written many stories for younger children that have been reprinted in anthologies.

VACHEL LINDSAY (1879–1931), poet of the Midwest, was born in Springfield, Illinois, in a house where Lincoln had often been entertained. His desire to be an artist was so keen that after three years of college he got a job at Marshall Field's, and attended the Art Institute of Chicago at night. After three years of study he tried to get a job in New York, but without success. Discouraged, he took to the highways of America, peddling his only printed poem for his supper, and reciting verses. Recognition as a poet came with the publication of *General Booth Enters Heaven* (Macmillan) and *The Congo and Other Poems* (Macmillan). "Abraham Lincoln Walks at Midnight" was written at the outbreak of World War I and is one of his most memorable poems. For the last ten years of his life he was constantly in demand as a lecturer and reader. *The Chinese Nightingale and Other Poems* (Macmillan) and *Johnny Appleseed and Other Poems* (Macmillan) are two more of his fine volumes of poetry.

HUGH LOFTING (1886–1947) was born in Maidenhead, England. After completing his education, he became a civil engineer and built railroads in West Africa and Canada. It was during World War I, while serving as a soldier in the British army that he first originated Dr. Dolittle. He made up stories about him and made up funny pictures, too, and sent them home to his two children. His wife persuaded him to have them published and they appeared as *The Story of Dr. Dolittle* (Lippincott). His second book, *The Voyage of Dr. Dolittle* (Lippincott) won the Newbery Medal. From that time on, Mr. Lofting devoted himself to writing clever nonsense for children. There are ten books in the Dr. Dolittle series, and two about Mrs. Tubbs. "Dr. Dolittle and the Pushmi-Pullyu" (Volume 4:158) was taken from *The Story of Dr. Dolittle.*

JACK LONDON (1878–1916) educated himself by reading in the Public Library. At fifteen he joined the oyster pirates around San Francisco. Later he shipped as a sailor on a schooner and took a turn at salmon fishing. At seventeen he sailed for the Japanese coast on a seal-hunting expedition. His first literary success was achieved when he won a prize offered by *The San Francisco Call* for a descriptive article. However, before settling down to writing, he sought gold in the Klondike, was a sailor again, as well as a newspaperman, and a war correspondent. He became famous when *The Call of*

Elizabeth-Ellen Long   Henry Wadsworth Longfellow   Adelaide Love   Kay Lovelace

the Wild (Macmillan) was published. He continued to be a vagabond and rover, finally settling in California. He wrote over fifty books which achieved tremendous popularity. Among them were *White Fang* (Macmillan), *Martin Eden* (Macmillan), and *South Sea Tales* (Macmillan). "For the Love of Man" (Volume 14:275) came from his famous book *The Call of the Wild*.

ELIZABETH-ELLEN LONG has contributed between five and six hundred poems to most of the popular magazines for children and adults. She was born in Troy, New York, but has lived in Southern California most of her life. After graduation from Scripps College she married George F. Tibbals and now has a son and a daughter. Many of her poems have appeared in anthologies. They have also been reprinted in Braille, set to music, and included in school textbooks. Her favorite poems may be found in *These I've Loved* (Saunders). Elizabeth-Ellen Long "likes museums and art galleries, needlework, gardening, and old coins and stamps"; her chief dislikes "are big cities, women's clubs, gossip, and people who take themselves too seriously." "Only ambition: to live as long as I can in a world which becomes more interesting every day," she says.

HENRY WADSWORTH LONGFELLOW (1807–1882) was for many years a professor of foreign languages and literature at Bowdoin College and Harvard University. He began his poetical career while still at college and continued writing poetry until his death. Loved by children are many of his American tales in verse form such as "The Song of Hiawatha," "Tales of a Wayside Inn," and "The Courtship of Miles Standish." His complete poems can be found in *Complete Poetical Works* (Houghton). Here you will find his famous poem, "The Children's Hour." Longfellow is one of the poets whose work will always live in the hearts of all people the world over and in the hearts of children.

CLAIRE and GEORGE LOUDEN, a young couple, have traveled all over the world together. They both like to sketch and paint. They both like photography. In this way they make notes of the ways of people and get backgrounds for their many illustrations. One of their books is *Rain in the Winds* (Scribner's).

ADELAIDE LOVE writes both for children and for adults. A native of Massachusetts, she is a graduate of Smith College. She married Chase W. Love of Chicago, has one daughter, and lives in Evanston, Illinois. The very poetic titles of her five books are: *The Slender Singing Tree* (Dodd), *The Crystal Flute* (Dodd), *The Star and the Leaf* (Dodd), *Enchanted Drum* (Dodd), and *The Delicate Harp* (Dodd). She is a member of Midland Authors and other literary societies, and she is a real help to young writers. Her hobbies are golf and the study of precious stones.

KAY LOVELACE, a Chicago illustrator, was born on a farm near Vandalia, Illinois, the fourth child in a family of six. Her interest in art led her to study at the Art Institute of Chicago, where she won the Elizabeth Skinner scholarship in her sophomore year. She has worked at several of Chicago's leading studios, has exhibited in the Chicago and Vicinity Artists' Show, and had her own showing at Esquire Galleries. She recently

James Russell Lowell   Eloise Lownsbery   Betty MacDonald

spent two months in Europe, doing water colors and quick pen-and-ink sketches. She is a free-lance illustrator and a commercial artist as well.

ROBERT LOVEMAN was a poet whose poem, "April Rain" is still loved by many people. It has been set to music.

JAMES RUSSELL LOWELL (1819–1891) was one of New England's great poets. He graduated from Harvard Law School and while waiting for his law business to start he wrote poetry. He gained fame with his amusing satiric "Bigelow Papers," written during the Mexican War. Some of his most famous poems are "The Vision of Sir Launfal," "The First Snowfall," "The Courtin'," "To a Dandelion," and "The Commemoration Ode." In addition to his writing, he was a literary critic, teacher, editor, and diplomat. His poems can be found in his *Complete Poetical Works* (Houghton).

ELOISE LOWNSBERY graduated from Wellesley and shortly after that moved to California. Here one of her great joys was leading Camp Fire girls up to the top of Mt. Wilson to see the sunrise. In World War I she worked for the Quakers in France, where she came to know and love the French people. She married and then motored through Europe, Egypt, and Palestine with her husband. In recent years they have lived outside of Washington, D. C. She is the author of several fine medieval tales in which history is made interesting. Among them are *Boy Knight of Reims* (Houghton), *Camel for a Throne* (Houghton), *Lighting the Torch* (Longmans), *Out of the Flame* (Longmans), and *Saints and Rebels* (Longmans).

MARTIN LUTHER (1483–1546) was the leader of the Protestant Reformation in Germany. His childhood was a happy one. He was educated in law, but changed his vocation and turned to religion. He worked for church reform all his life, teaching, preaching, and writing. He was married and had six children.

HAMILTON WRIGHT MABIE (1846–1916), American editor, was also a distinguished lecturer, critic, and essayist. His one great desire was to encourage a love of good reading. He practiced law for eight years and then left it to edit the *Outlook*. His first book, *Norse Stories Retold from Eddas*, is still a favorite of children today. Some of his other books are *The Life of the Spirit* (Dodd) and *William Shakespeare* (Macmillan). He edited the famous "After School Library" and *Fairy Tales Every Child Should Know*.

BETTY MACDONALD lives on Vashon Island, which is a large wooded island that is found in Puget Sound across from Seattle. Here her life is filled with the tasks of "keeping her household, including her dogs and cats, husband, mother, children, and grandchildren in order." She also gardens and entertains a constant stream of visitors. She cares for "countless ducks, chickens, pigs, lambs, and an orchard." Her writing is, therefore, a "catch as catch can" procedure. Nevertheless, she has written such adult best sellers as *The Egg and I* (Lippincott) and *Anybody Can Do Anything* (Lippincott) and some children's books: *Nancy and Plum* (Lippincott), *Mrs. Piggle-Wiggle*

239

(Lippincott), and *Mrs. Piggle-Wiggle's Magic* (Lippincott). "The Won't-Pick-Up-Toys Cure" (Volume 4:136) came from her book *Mrs. Piggle-Wiggle*.

ELLEN MACGREGOR was born in Baltimore, Maryland, but her family moved to the West Coast shortly afterwards. She received a degree in library science from the University of Washington and since then her work in that field has taken her to many places, including Wyoming, California, Idaho, Florida, Oregon, Hawaii, and Illinois. She now lives in Chicago, and has many friends everywhere in the library field. She is the author of the amusing and popular "Miss Pickerell" books: *Miss Pickerell Goes to Mars* (Whittlesey), *Miss Pickerell and the Geiger Counter* (Whittlesey), and *Miss Pickerell Goes Undersea* (Whittlesey). "Mars and Miss Pickerell" (Volume 16:36) is just a sample of what goes on in *Miss Pickerell Goes to Mars*.

JOHN GILLESPIE MAGEE, JR., was a nineteen-year-old American pilot and wrote his poem "High Flight" shortly before he was killed in December, 1941, while in service with the Royal Canadian Air Force. "High Flight" has been called "the most beautiful poem of World War II."

BERTHA E. MAHONY was the distinguished editor of *The Horn Book* for many years. This is an outstanding magazine devoted to books and reading for young people. She is now president of Horn Book, Incorporated. Mrs. Mahony has written a great deal on the subject of children's books for various magazines. She is the co-author with Elinor Whitney of *Five Years of Children's Books* (Doubleday), *Realms of Gold* (Doubleday), and *Contemporary Illustrators* (Women's Educational and Industrial Union).

CHARLES MAJOR (1856–1913), American historical novelist, was born in Indianapolis, Indiana. He was always interested in reading English and French history of the Renaissance period, and turned to this age for the background of his own popular books. *When Knighthood Was in Flower*, his first attempt at writing, was an immediate success. It was followed by *Dorothy Vernon of Haddon Hall* (Macmillan) and the book boys like, *The Bears of Blue River* (Macmillan).

ANN MALCOLMSON is the author of *Yankee Doodle's Cousins* (Houghton), a collection of stories of some of the real and some of the legendary characters who have become the national heroes of American folklore. Her present home is in Alexandria, Virginia. For recreation she enjoys playing bridge and tennis.

ALIDA SIMS MALKUS was the eleventh of thirteen children and grew up in a haphazard manner, traveling about the country with her family. She remembers seeing the lumber rafts come down from Lake Superior, riding a donkey in Colorado, and doing all sorts of things children love. Very early she started composing verse and began drawing. After attending art school she made her home in the West, under the shadows of the Rocky Mountains. Here she grew to know and love the Indians and had many exciting adventures. Here she started writing newspaper and magazine articles, and short stories for young people. Her first book, *Raquel of the Ranch*

Ellen MacGregor

Corinne Malvern

Betty Martin

240

Country (Harcourt), was a story of her own life in the Southwest. This was followed by *Dragon Fly of Zuni* (Harcourt) and *Stone Knife Boy* (Harcourt).

CORINNE MALVERN says that all of her family roots are in Virginia. From the age of three and a half, her childhood was spent on the stage and in motion pictures. Although crippled for two years by a railroad accident, which halted her dramatic career, Corinne Malvern studied art and found a new career as a fine illustrator of thirty-eight children's books. Her art education was obtained at the Art Students' League in New York, and in California. She now divides her time between New York and Connecticut, where she indulges in her favorite hobby of gardening. She lives with her sister, Gladys Malvern, a well-known author of books for teen-agers.

JOHN MANNING is a Chicago humorist who has written many nonsense poems.

NORMA BICKNELL MANSFIELD is a juvenile author who has contributed stories to magazines and anthologies.

BETTY MARTIN is a lecturer and writer who lives in New York. She is the head of the Educational Record Department of R.C.A., Victor Division.

MABELLE E. MARTIN, after a childhood in Iowa, went to California. She went to the University of California, taught high school history in San Francisco, and taught also in Boston, Texas, and Washington, D. C. She is married, has two daughters, and writes articles on history for children's magazines. She now lives in Virginia.

JOHN MASEFIELD, when but fourteen years old, sought for adventure in all parts of the globe. From his native England, he was indentured to a merchant ship and sailed with her for nearly three years, through calm waters and stormy seas. With exactly five dollars in his pocket, and a small chest of clothes, he finally landed in New York City and lived in a Greenwich Village garret. Here he did all sorts of odd jobs to make his living, jobs in a livery stable, in a bakery, in a carpet factory, along the water front. Soon he found a bookstore and began to read Keats, Shelley, Milton, Dickens, Kipling, and Stevenson. Back in England again, he met Synge, Yeats, and other helpful poets, and began to write. All his experiences and early struggles come out in his early writing, as do his World War I experiences when he was a sensitive orderly in a Red Cross unit. His first book was *Salt Water Ballads* (Macmillan) and contains two of his great poems, "Sea Fever" and "Cargoes." Other books followed which finally brought him two outstanding honors. He received the Order of Merit and he became Poet Laureate of England. Masefield is married and has one son and one daughter. His home is at Burcole Brook on the banks of the Thames, where he does much writing. Masefield will always be best remembered for his great poetry, although he is also known for his plays, novels, biographies, and histories. Younger readers know his *Jim Davis* (Macmillan), *The Midnight Folk* (Macmillan), and *The Box of Delights* (Macmillan). *So Long To Learn* (Macmillan) is a book of his personal recollections.

Mabelle E. Martin

John Masefield

241

Fiore Mastri   Barbara Maynard   Robert McCloskey

MIRIAM E. MASON is the author of books for little children just beginning to read, and for older boys and girls, too. Among her books are *O Happy Day* (Lippincott), *Happy Jack* (Macmillan), *Little Jonathan* (Macmillan), *Matilda and Her Family* (Macmillan), *Susannah, the Pioneer Cow* (Macmillan), and *Timothy Has Ideas* (Macmillan). "Cake for Company Dinner" (Volume 4:185) is one of the funny experiences in *O Happy Day*.

FIORE MASTRI was born in Italy, where many great artists have been born. After coming to America, Mr. Mastri studied with John Norton, the painter of murals. He resides in Chicago with his artist wife Jackie Mastri. He has his own studio there. He specializes in fine illustrations for children's books, especially pictures of cowboys and airplanes.

ANDRE MAUROIS, the great French biographer and novelist, followed a career as an industrialist until World War I. Then as a liaison officer to the British Army he began to write down his observations and experiences. These were published in book form and thus he began his life as an author. He lives in Paris with his wife and children, and he is in constant demand as a lecturer. Three of his popular books for younger readers are *Eisenhower, the Liberator* (Didier), *Franklin, the Life of an Optimist* (Didier), and *Frederic Chopin* (Harper). "Ben Franklin's First Adventures" (Volume 15:164) was one of the episodes that appears in Andre Maurois' fine book about Franklin.

BARBARA MAYNARD grew up in Grand Rapids, Michigan, and graduated from the Chicago Art Institute. She won a travel scholarship there which took her to Europe for a year. She is primarily a water colorist, and she has exhibited her work in several galleries. She has illustrated *Fraidy Cat* (Rand) and *Let's Fly to Bermuda* (Whitman) and has done illustrations for *Compton's Pictured Encyclopedia*. She works in the art department of Compton's.

ROBERT MCCLOSKEY's first ambition was to be a musician, then an inventor, and in high school, while drawing for the school paper and annual, an artist. "It is just sort of an accident that I write books. I really think up stories in pictures and just fill in between the pictures with a sentence or a paragraph or a few pages of words," he says. During World War II, Mr. McCloskey was a sergeant, drawing training pictures for the army. Today he lives on an island off the coast of Maine with his wife and daughter. He won the Caldecott Medal for his book *Make Way for Ducklings* (Viking). Among his other books filled with his amusing stories and illustrations are *Homer Price* (Viking), *Lentil* (Viking), and *Blueberries for Sal* (Viking). Three of the Homer Price stories you will enjoy are: "The Case of the Cosmic Comic" (Volume 4:238), "The Case of the Sensational Scent" (Volume 7:30), and "Homer Price and the Doughnuts" (Volume 4:360).

ELLIS ATKINSON MCDONALD, a Georgia writer, has contributed poems to various juvenile magazines and anthologies.

242

PHYLLIS MCGINLEY grew up on a ranch in eastern Colorado and began writing poetry at the age of six. As a child she recalls watching bronco-busting instead of baseball, and having to ride her pony to school where she and her brother were the only pupils. After college she went to New York where she taught school. Later, she became a free-lance writer, copy editor for an advertising agency, and assistant editor of *Town and Country*. She is married to Charles Hayden and has two children. She contributes clever, light verse to various magazines, and is the author of such juveniles as *The Horse Who Lived Upstairs* (Lippincott) and *The Plain Princess* (Lippincott).

JANE MCHENRY, at the age of eight, composed her first story and typed it on her own typewriter. She says it had no plot but lots of punctuation. Since then she has edited school publications, won a senior essay contest, been on the editorial staff of Consolidated Books, and done some writing for the *Children's Treasury* (Consolidated) and for *The Children's Hour*. Mrs. McHenry lived abroad for five years in the Hague and in London, but now lives near Hinsdale, Illinois, with her husband, her son, and two Siamese cats. The cats have destructive tendencies and cause her to redecorate now and then. But her chief hobby is interior decorating, anyway.

JOHN DUKES MCKEE calls himself "a purveyor of nostalgia," more specifically of nostalgic Americana. Born in Kokomo, Indiana, he was educated at DePauw University and the Art Institute of Chicago, and then spent a year in Paris. He began his career by doing illustrations for *Child Life Magazine*. He now specializes in illustrating anything requiring an authentic nineteenth-century atmosphere. His pre-Civil War woodcut style is created by using a stylus-like tool to cut India ink off the scratchboard on which his drawings are made. His one-man exhibit of fifty landmarks of northern Illinois, in water color, has traveled throughout the Midwest, and recently he completed a series of woodcuts of these landmarks for illustrative purposes. His work has been exhibited in the Chicago Art Institute, in the Hoosier Salon, and in Philadelphia. He is a member of the "27 Designers." His special picture map, *American Folklore and Legends*, is very popular with schools and libraries.

LAURENCE MCKINNEY lives in Albany, New York, with his wife and three children. He has contributed humorous verse to various juvenile magazines and has had three adult books published: *People of Note* (Dutton), *Garden Clubs and Spades* (Dutton), and *Lines of Least Resistance* (Dutton).

MICHAEL MCLAVERTY is a well-known Irish novelist and short-story writer, who is the author of *The Game Cock and Other Stories* (Devin-Adair). He is a graduate of Belfast University and lives in Ulster.

MARIE MCSWIGAN is the author of the exciting *Snow Treasure* (Dutton). This book won the Junior Scholastic Gold Seal Award and is founded on an actual happening during World War II, when some children of Norway were willing to take great risks for their well-loved native land. "Secret in the Snow" (Volume 13:101) is a thrilling episode from this book. Another of her books is *Binnie Latches On* (Dutton).

Phyllis McGinley

Jane McHenry

John Dukes McKee

STEPHEN MEADER is famous for his stories about horses. He has lived for many years in Moorestown, New Jersey, but was born and raised in New England. The New England backgrounds of many of his stories reflect his own boyhood. In addition to contributing short stories to various magazines, he has written many fine books for young people: *Red Horse Hill* (Harcourt), *The Black Buccaneer* (Harcourt), *Longshanks* (Harcourt), *Away to Sea* (Harcourt), *Whaler 'Round the Horn* (Harcourt), and *The Fish Hawk's Nest* (Harcourt). "The Cutter Race" (Volume 10:302) came from *Red Horse Hill*. Mr. Meader is married and has four children.

ENID LaMONTE MEADOWCROFT started her literary career when she was a little girl by helping publish a newspaper called *Junior Pickwick Papers*. It sold for a nickel, and although she did not make much money, she did learn to enjoy putting ideas into words. For many years she taught school in Portland, Oregon, in New Jersey, and in New York. While doing this she often found herself making up stories to amuse her pupils, and when she felt the lack of interesting historical books for the children, she started to write them. Her stories make American history come alive. Her human tales of our own American people are presented in authentic historical settings. Some of her books are *Silver for General Washington* (Crowell), *On Indian Trails with Daniel Boone* (Crowell), *Abraham Lincoln* (Crowell), *Gift of the River* (Crowell), *Along the Erie Towpath* (Crowell), and *Benjamin Franklin* (Crowell).

CORNELIA MEIGS, consultant editor for *The Children's Hour*, was born in Rock Island, Illinois, a descendant of a family which has supplied illustrious names to United States history. She began writing in the days when she was teaching school. She tried out her stories on all her pupils and on her twelve nieces and nephews, some of whom lived with her. The criticisms of her child audience were carefully heeded. Later, Miss Meigs was an outstanding professor of English at Bryn Mawr College and spent her summers at her lovely Vermont farm, "Green Pastures," where she now does much of her writing. Her books have brought her outstanding recognition among those seeking the highest standards in children's literature. *Trade Wind* (Little) received the Beacon Hill Book Shelf prize and *Invincible Louisa* (Little) was awarded the Newbery Medal. Her short story, "Fox and Geese," won the *Child Life* prize story contest. Other well-liked books of hers are *Wind in the Chimney* (Macmillan), *Rain on the Roof* (Macmillan), *The Pool of Stars* (Macmillan), *The Wonderful Locomotive* (Macmillan), and *As the Crow Flies* (Macmillan). From *Invincible Louisa* was taken "Early Days with Invincible Louisa" (Volume 15:130).

MILDRED PLEW MEIGS was an outstanding writer for children's magazines. She wrote many amusing stories and lovely poems for younger boys and girls. Though Chicago was her home for many years, she was living in Florida when she died. Among her books was *Bonbon and Bonbonnet* (Rand).

JOHN MERRYWEATHER has won distinction in the fields of book and magazine illustrating, in commercial art, and in designing. He was born in Chicago and was graduated from Williams College. He received his art training at the Chicago Academy of

| Stephen Meader | Enid LaMonte Meadowcroft | Cornelia Meigs | John Merryweather |

244

| Decie Merwin | Edna St. Vincent Millay | Joaquin Miller | Mary Miller |

Fine Arts. He now resides in Highland Park, Illinois, and has his own Chicago studio. He has won awards for his outstanding pictures in exhibits in Chicago and New York. He is a member of the Society of Typographic Arts, the Cliff Dwellers, the Caxton Club, and the Baker Street Irregulars.

DECIE MERWIN claims that her early success as an illustrator was due to the development of the juvenile book field in the 1920's. As a child in Tennessee she loved to draw horses, dogs, and children. Her first earnings after she came North were spent on a trip abroad. Her success with stories calling for an Irish or English background stems from her love for the British Isles. After her marriage to Jack Bechdolt, she collaborated with him on the "Dulcie" stories (Dutton). Since then she has written and illustrated *Time for Tammie* (Oxford), *Pinktails* (Oxford), and *Robin and Mr. Jones* (Oxford).

EDNA ST. VINCENT MILLAY (1892–1950), winner of the Pulitzer Prize for *The Harp-Weaver and Other Poems* (Harper) and *A Few Figs from Thistles* (Harper), wrote verse from her childhood days in Maine, when she was a contributor to *St. Nicholas Magazine*, and she continued writing it throughout her life. Before entering college, she studied music and literature. "Renascence," called "one of the most brilliant poems of this generation," was written at the age of nineteen and won her nation-wide fame. She attended Barnard College and Vassar. Her first volume of poetry was published the year of her graduation, and while still at Vassar she won the cup awarded in the intercollegiate poetry contest. For a time she lived in New York, where she wrote short stories under a pen name. She was associated with the Provincetown Players both as an actress and as a playwright. She traveled abroad for two years. Two of her volumes of lovely poetry have been translated into Spanish, and her play *Aria Da Capo* was translated into French and performed in Paris. She also wrote *The King's Henchman* (music by Deems Taylor), which was produced at the Metropolitan Opera House. A fine collection of her work is found in *Edna St. Vincent Millay's Poems Selected for Young People* (Harper). Among her fine lyrics and sonnets for older readers are "Second April" and "Fatal Interview."

JOAQUIN MILLER (1841–1913) at the age of eleven went with his parents to Oregon in a covered wagon. Later, while gold mining he was attacked by Indians, but was found and nursed back to health by a friendly tribe. After that he did a number of things: studied law, drove mules through Arizona and Mexico, took express messages from Walla Walla to Idaho, edited a newspaper, and became a judge. He received recognition as a poet when his first book, *Songs of the Sierras,* was published at his own expense in London, England. He traveled for a few years before returning to the United States. Then he lived on a rugged hillside near Oakland, California, and wrote many beautiful and inspiring poems that live on and on. His California estate has since been converted into a memorial park in tribute to the poet.

MARY MILLER (Salem) traveled a great deal when she was a little girl. She began school in Spokane and went to fourteen different schools before she reached Chicago,

245

where she went to the American Academy of Art. After art school she started at the bottom in art studios, delivering packages, and then worked up gradually. Since marrying, she has been working at home, in Chicago, and now she has "four children's books that she has illustrated, several schoolbooks, three children, a ranch house, and a nice husband."

MARY BRITTON MILLER, although her parents died when she was four, had a happy childhood growing up with her four brothers and sisters in her grandmother's fine old New England home. She now lives in New York, and her delightful poems for children are found in *Menagerie* (Macmillan). She has also written three volumes for adults, *Without Sanctuary* (Macmillan), *Intrepid Bird* (Macmillan), and *Songs of Infancy* (Macmillan), which picture the thoughts and feelings of childhood.

A. A. MILNE is a London-born Englishman who left Cambridge to be a free-lance writer, and later became an assistant editor of *Punch*. After World War I when he served in France he devoted all his time to writing. His own son, Christopher Robin, was the inspiration for the delightful tales about Winnie the Pooh, Piglet, and Eeyore. These tales and verses have become classics and every house with children in it wants to own *When We Were Very Young* (Dutton), *Winnie the Pooh* (Dutton), *Now We Are Six* (Dutton), and *The House at Pooh Corner* (Dutton). Among other books for Christopher Robin are *The Christopher Robin Story Book* (Dutton), *The Christopher Robin Reader* (Dutton), and *The Christopher Robin Fairy Book* (Dutton). Mr. Milne, who is also an essayist and a successful dramatist, lives in a red house in a green square in Chelsea and is very fond of playing golf. "Eeyore's Birthday" (Volume 1:186) you will find in *Winnie the Pooh*.

LUCY SPRAGUE MITCHELL is an educator and the author of many delightful selections found in *The Here and Now Story Book* (Dutton) and *Another Here and Now Story Book* (Dutton). She is also a pioneer in the field of realistic stories for very young boys and girls.

ANNE MOLLOY, a contemporary writer, has contributed many short stories to juvenile magazines. Her book *The Monkey's Fist* (Houghton) is popular with teen-agers.

HARRIET MONROE wrote verse for adults which can be found in *Selected Poems* (Macmillan). She was the famous founder and first editor of *Poetry*, a magazine of verse. This magazine first discovered and published the works of almost all the famous living poets of America and England.

MARGARET PRESCOTT MONTAGUE has retold many fine myths and legends. A collection of these may be found in *Up Eel River* (Macmillan).

CARL MOON (1878-1948) decided he wanted to go out West when his mother read him Indian stories as a little boy. At twenty-three he fulfilled his dream. He had a studio in Albuquerque where many Indians visited him. He visited their villages, too. He was constantly busy with his camera, paint brushes, and writing pad, and contributed articles and pictures to magazines and newspapers. When he began a collection of Indian pictures in Arizona, he met and married Grace Purdie. They collaborated on their first two books, *Book of Nah-wee* (Lippincott) and *Lost Indian Magic* (Lippincott). Then each decided to write alone. Mr. Moon, however, illustrated his wife's books. In later years the Moons made their home in Pasadena, California. Among his books are *The Flaming Arrow* (Lippincott) and *The Painted Moccasin* (Lippincott).

GRACE MOON, wife of Carl Moon, always remembered her younger brother saying to her, when they were both quite small, "We must be Indians because we were born in Indianapolis, Indiana." This feeling persisted through the years, and Mrs. Moon

A. A. Milne   Grace Moon   Rosalie Moore   Dorothy Bayley Morse

always felt a deep attachment for the Indians. With her husband, she made long trips into the fascinating Southwest, living for months among the Indians. She says, "I fell head over heels in love with the little big-eyed, black-headed children—the little Chi-wees and Loks of Navajo and Hopiland, and began to write about them, too." Among her books are *Chi-wee* (Doubleday), *The Runaway Papoose* (Doubleday), *Far Away Desert* (Doubleday), and *Nadita* (Doubleday). "The Desirable Shawl" (Volume 9:14) comes from *Chi-Wee*.

ROSALIE MOORE was born in California and graduated from the University of California. Her volume, *The Grasshopper's Man and Other Poems* (Yale) was published in the Yale "Younger Poet's Series." Since then she received two Guggenheim Fellowships for creative writing. She also writes juvenile stories with her husband, Bill Brown.

SIR THOMAS MOORE (1779–1852) was a famous Irish poet and song writer who wrote "The Last Rose of Summer," "Oft in the Stilly Night," and many other well-loved verses, as well as his famous "Lalla Rookh," an oriental romance.

DOROTHY BAYLEY MORSE was born in New York City and still lives there. She graduated from Connecticut College for Women and then studied at the New York-Phoenix School of Design under the guidance of Norman Rockwell and Thomas Fogarty. After two years in the theater, she began her book illustrating. She has illustrated sixty-five books, many in the juvenile field. She is a sailing enthusiast, but her latest hobby is working with her husband fixing up an ancient farmhouse in Bedford Village, New York.

ELISE MORTON is a busy contemporary artist.

DHAN GOPAL MUKERJI (1890–1936) used his native India as the background for his many outstanding stories for children. He moved to the United States when he was twenty and received his Ph.D. from Stanford University. Mukerji's *Gay-Neck* (Dutton) won the Newbery Medal. Among his other popular books are: *Hindu Fables* (Dutton), *Jungle Beasts and Men* (Dutton), *Hari: the Jungle Lad* (Dutton), *Rama: the Hero of India* (Dutton), *Fierce Face* (Dutton), and *The Cow Golden Horn* (Dutton). Mr. Mukerji often talked to boys and girls at the school his son attended and read his stories to them. He felt that boys and girls of America would benefit from the ancient lores of India. "Until a nation appreciates the common culture of another nation it will not be able to understand the value of international peace," he said. "We need peace between nations because peace alone can augment the forces of true culture."

DINAH MARIA MULOCK (1826–1887) was born in England. At ten she was writing verse, and four years later her first published poem appeared in an English newspaper. In order to take care of a younger brother, she turned to writing as a career. Her first novel was published when she was twenty-three, and many books followed.

247

Dhan Gopal Mukerji   Ogden Nash   Harry Edward Neal   Mabel Neikirk

John Halifax, Gentleman is perhaps her most famous work, and although it was written for adults, it had an appeal to younger people, too. Two of her books which have been favorites with successive generations of children are *The Adventures of a Brownie* (Macmillan) and *The Little Lame Prince* (Macmillan).

OGDEN NASH'S verses for children are particularly delightful. Mr. Nash was born in New York, but claims "ten thousand cousins" in North Carolina. In this state his great-great-grandfather was a Revolutionary governor. After attending Harvard for one year, he taught for a year, was a bond salesman for two years, wrote greeting cards, was in the advertising department of Doubleday, and then joined the staff of the *New Yorker*. He was associated for a short time with Farrar and Rinehart before devoting his entire time to writing. *Many Long Years Ago* (Little) and *The Private Dining Room and Other New Verses* (Little) are two of his collections of very humorous poetry.

HARRY EDWARD NEAL has had short stories and articles published in the *Saturday Evening Post* and many other magazines. He has taught classes in writing and is the author of a how-to-write book called *Writing and Selling Fact and Fiction* (Funk). A juvenile of his is *Story of a Kite* (Vanguard). Born in Pittsfield, Massachusetts, Mr. Neal now lives in Washington, D. C., with his wife and two children. He writes at night and on week ends because he has a full-time regular job as Executive Aide to the Chief of the United States Secret Service, the famous "T-Men" law enforcement agency.

MABEL NEIKIRK'S father was a clergyman and she lived in many interesting places. In Wooster, Ohio, she fished for minnows with her three sisters. And then for several seasons she had a morning-glory house which her father made for her. At Cedar Crest College she edited *The College Folio*. Then, after graduation, during World War I she became a trained nurse. When illness, sometime later, made nursing difficult, she began writing stories. After "Oscar, the Trained Seal" was published in *Story Parade* magazine, many boys and girls wrote letters asking for more Oscar stories. So she wrote *All about Oscar, the Trained Seal* (Winston).

EDITH NESBIT (1858–1924), known as E. Nesbit, was an English poet, novelist, and writer of stories for children. She was born in London. She was described as "a daring and mischievous child and an incorrigible tomboy, with a large family of brothers and sisters." She drew upon the escapades of her childhood for several of her books. The best ones for which she is chiefly remembered are: *The Bastable Children* (Coward-McCann), which includes her three most famous stories, "Treasure Seekers," "New Treasure Seekers," and "The Wouldbegoods," and *The Five Children* (Coward-McCann) which includes "Five Children and It," "The Phoenix and the Carpet," and "The Story of the Amulet." These stories first appeared in the old *Strand Magazine* of London and have been tremendously popular not only with children of yesterday and today, but with May Lamberton Becker, Christopher Morley, Noel Coward, and other present-day writers.

| Charles Nordhoff | Margaret Norris | Sterling North |

DAVID M. NEWELL is both a writer and an illustrator. He has lived an out-of-door life in Florida and writes about animals he has actually encountered. He has made motion pictures with Grantland Rice and is on a television program called "The Sportsman's Club."

HELEN NICOLAY was born in Paris where her father was acting as American Consul General. Previous to this he had been President Lincoln's private secretary. Miss Nicolay tells how her father spent much time writing his ten-volume life of this great man. She helped him by taking his dictation and reading his proof. When her father died, she completed the book he was working on, and as a result was asked by the publishers to do *The Boys' Life of Lincoln* (Century). This was the first of her many biographies for young people that were to follow: *Andrew Jackson* (Appleton), *Alexander Hamilton* (Appleton), *Thomas Jefferson* (Appleton), *Ulysses S. Grant* (Appleton), *George Washington* (Appleton), and *MacArthur of Bataan* (Appleton). She lives in Washington and spends her summers in New Hampshire.

MADELEINE NIGHTINGALE, a contemporary English poet, is the author of *Ring-A-Ring O'Fairies* (Blackwell) and *Nursery Lays of Nursery Days* (Blackwell).

NICHOLAS NIRGIOTIS is a young Chicago writer who was born on the Island of Crete. He received his M.A. at the University of Chicago and is at present a teacher in Athens, Greece. During World War II he was a combat engineer in the army. For some months he did editorial work for the Spencer Press.

CHARLES NORDHOFF was half of the celebrated writing team of Charles Nordhoff and James Norman Hall. They wrote the famous books of historical fiction, *Mutiny on the Bounty* (Little), *Man Against the Sea* (Little), and *Pitcairn's Island* (Little). For fourteen years the two writers lived in Tahiti and wrote a number of sea novels there. As for Mr. Nordhoff's early life, he was born of American parents in London. He was brought up on his father's ranch in Mexico and after graduation from Harvard, he went to war. In 1918 he was awarded the Croix de Guerre.

MARGARET NORRIS was born on a farm near La Moille, Illinois. She was educated at Smith College and later became a reporter on a Chicago newspaper. It was in her work there that she first became interested in men engaged in hazardous occupations. Her book, *Heroes and Hazards* (Macmillan), dealing with just such people, was a Junior Literary Guild book. Much liked, too, are her stories about the White House presidents. Before her death in 1943 she contributed articles and stories to various magazines and newspapers. "Down in Davy Jones's Locker" (Volume 13:334) came from her book *Heroes and Hazards*.

STERLING NORTH was born in Wisconsin, and when he was eight years old wrote a poem for *St. Nicholas*. He wrote fifty more poems during his teens for such magazines as *Harpers, The Dial,* and *Poetry Magazine*. Though stricken with infantile paralysis at fifteen, he worked his way through the University of Chicago, where he

Jack O'Brien   Thomas C. O'Donnell   Tony Palazzo   Grace Paull

ran a campus magazine called *The Forge* and operated a little theater just off the campus called "The Cube." While he was still in college he married a high school friend, had a small son, and wrote his first book, *The Pedro Gorino* (Houghton). After this he was literary editor of the *Chicago Daily News* for several years. Later he became feature writer, and still later, literary editor of the *New York Post,* and then became literary editor of the *New York World Telegram and Sun.* Now he lives with his family in a house by a New Jersey waterfall, watching the deer come down to drink, and watching the birds and wild life around him. Mr. North sold his novel *So Dear to My Heart* (Doubleday) to Walt Disney. His two latest books are *Reunion on the Wabash* (Doubleday) and a juvenile called *The Birthday of Little Jesus* (Grosset).

ALFRED NOYES, poet, prose writer, teacher, and lecturer, composed his best-loved poem, "The Highwayman," when he was only twenty-four years old. Mr. Noyes was born in Staffordshire, England, and was educated at Oxford, where he rowed with his college crew. He began writing poetry as a young man, and it is to this period that "Drake," "The Barrel-Organ," and "Forty Singing Seamen" belong. He is married to an American girl, and his first visit to America was as a lecturer in Boston. From 1914 to 1923 he was a professor of English Literature at Princeton University. He and his family have lived in Maine, New Jersey, and California. Today they live on the Isle of Wight, near Tennyson's old home and very near the port where Sir Francis Drake set forth on his many voyages. A story for boys and girls, *The Secret of Pooduck Island* (Lippincott), resulted from happy times spent in Maine with his wife and children. His *Collected Poems* (Lippincott) belongs on any poetry bookshelf.

M. M. OBLINGER is a contemporary writer who is co-author with Maxine Shore of *Knight of the Wilderness: The Story of Alexander Mackenzie* (Dodd). "Alexander Mackenzie: Hero of Canada" (Volume 15:153) was taken from this book.

JACK O'BRIEN (1898–1938) was the author of *Silver Chief* (Winston) and *The Return of Silver Chief* (Winston), which won a Young Readers' Choice Award and was also a Junior Literary Guild selection. He also wrote *Valiant* (Winston) and a number of other popular out-door adventure stories. He made an eleven-hundred-mile dog-sledge trip in the Antarctic on the first Byrd expedition and his first book was called *By Dog Sled for Byrd* (Wilcox).

THOMAS C. O'DONNELL recently moved from New York State to Florida with his family. He is an author with a real sense of humor, who writes books for adults. For many years of his life he was editor of *Cartoons, Writer's Digest,* and a number of other magazines. But he is well known, too, for his plays and poems written for children. Many of these were first published in *Child Life Magazine.* Some appeared later in anthologies and in book form.

HELEN DIEHL OLDS is a contemporary writer who has sold over three hundred short stories to leading juvenile magazines. Of her seven books, two were selected for the

Junior Literary Guild, and several were reprinted in Braille. She was graduated from the University of Texas, did graduate work at Columbia, and teaches Juvenile Fiction at the Huckleberry Mountain Workshop in North Carolina. One of her recent books is *Fisherman Jody* (Messner).

JAMES OTIS (1848–1912), whose real name was James Otis Kaler, was born in Maine, worked on Boston and New York newspapers, and wrote sermons syndicated by a publishing house in Philadelphia. In his spare time he wrote stories for *Boys and Girls* and *St. Nicholas*. He even traveled once with a circus as a publicity man. Here he got his material for his most popular work, *Toby Tyler* (Harper). James Otis wrote one hundred and fifty books for young people, and during his later years he was a school superintendent in Maine, where he and his family lived.

LORENA LA BREC OUELLETTE is a contemporary poet who lives in Chicago and did much work with the Midwestern Writer's Conference.

TONY PALAZZO is a contemporary artist who has not only written and illustrated his own picture books, such as *Susie the Cat* (Viking) and *Charley the Horse* (Viking), but has illustrated a number of books by other writers. Among these illustrations are his delightful pictures for Anne White's *Serapina*.

ROBIN PALMER was the youngest in a family of six children. She spent her first ten years in New York City and then moved to Westchester County. She attended Greenwich Academy and Vassar College. In 1940 she was married to Dr. Douglas Riggs, who teaches at Harvard Medical School. Now she lives in the country near Boston and has "three children, a dog, a Persian cat, and a tame crayfish named Cora." In addition to *The Barkingtons* (Harper), she has written five books and a number of stories and articles for children's magazines. "Punch Has an Adventure" (Volume 6:52) is one of the stories in the Barkington books.

GRACE PAULL, who makes amusing and delightful pictures, was born in Cold Brook, New York, and spends most of her summers on a farm there. Here she has the opportunity to sketch animals and children, and to make fascinating lithographs. She was educated in Cold Brook and Montreal, Canada, and attended Pratt Institute, Brooklyn, and the Art Students' League and Grand Central Art School, New York. She began her career lettering labels, graduated to greeting cards, and then turned to illustrating books. This led her into writing stories for children. Her hobbies are painting and gardening.

JOSEPHINE PRESTON PEABODY (1874–1922) was an American poet and dramatist. She went to Radcliffe College and was later a teacher of English literature at Wellesley. Her *Old Greek Folk Stories* (Houghton) was one of her books that is still read by children today. Her poetic drama, *The Piper* (Houghton), written for adults, won the Stratford prize.

JEANNE PEARSON spent her early years in Oak Park, Illinois, and now lives with her husband, Richard K. Taylor, in a converted coach house on Chicago's Gold Coast. She studied art at Miami University in Ohio, the University of Arizona, and the Art Institute of Chicago. Her book designs have won awards, the most recent being in the Chicago Book Clinic's Midwest Show for Rand McNally's *Standard Atlas*. Her contribution to *The Children's Hour* has been the binding designs and the art and designs for the title pages of each volume. For relaxation she designs and hooks her own rugs.

HOWARD PEASE wrote his first short story at the age of twelve when he was attending school in Stockton, California. He has not stopped writing since. During World War I, while a sergeant stationed in France, he wrote his two nephews telling them

251

of a visit to Bluebeard's Castle. He decided then to write for children. He sold his first story to *American Boy*. His first book, *The Tattooed Man* (Doubleday), was based on his experiences during two ship voyages and a walking trip along the coast of Italy. *Jinx Ship* (Doubleday) was started while Mr. Pease was a member of the gang on a ship in the Caribbean. Other books followed, and with the publication of *The Ship without a Crew* (Doubleday) he devoted all his time to writing. He won the award of the Child Study Association for *Heart of Danger* (Doubleday). Mr. Pease divides his time between Connecticut and California. He is married and has one son.

JOSEPHINE VAN DOLZEN PEASE is a contemporary writer who has written verse for children, published in juvenile magazines. Miss Pease, formerly a Chicago writer, now lives in Michigan. *The Happy Book* (Rand), *This Is the World* (Rand), *It Seems Like Magic* (Rand), and *The Busy Book* (Rand) are four of her juvenile books.

GLADYS PECK is a contemporary artist who specializes in drawings of dogs and horses. She lives in New York.

WILLIAM ALEXANDER PERCY, a contemporary writer, is the author of many fine poems, a number of which may be found in *Collected Poems* (Knopf).

ANNE PEREZ-GUERRA is the author of *Poppy* (Rand) and of poems appearing in juvenile magazines. She is the mother of five children, two of them adopted, and her home is in California. Now that her children are grown she has the time, the room, and the urge to paint. How well she succeeded is shown by the fact that she sold eleven pictures during an exhibit at the Hollywood band shell. Her favorite medium is water color, though she has done some work with oils and charcoal.

LUCY FITCH PERKINS (1865–1937) was born in Indiana, though all her ancestors were New Englanders. When she was fourteen she moved back to her ancestral home in Massachusetts. She attended art school in Boston, and taught in the Art School of the Pratt Institute. She began illustrating books after graduating from art school, and her first children's book, *The Dutch Twins* (Houghton), grew out of some illustrations she accidentally showed a publisher. Her outstanding "Twin Series" which she both wrote and illustrated was written to emphasize the need for mutual respect and understanding between the peoples of the world. Twenty-four of these "Twin" books were published and translated into many languages. They have been so dearly loved by children everywhere that two million copies of them have been sold. Mrs. Perkins was the wife of Dwight Perkins, the architect. They lived in Evanston, Illinois, with their two children, Eleanor, who later became a distinguished lecturer, and Lawrence, an architect. "The Eskimo Twins Go Coasting" (Volume 9:20) comes from the *Eskimo Twins,* and "Kit and Kat Go Fishing" (Volume 1:75) comes from the *Dutch Twins.* You will want to read more of their adventures.

MARGERY BLAIR PERKINS lives in Evanston, and though a busy mother, she has done some excellent writing for juvenile magazines.

Jeanne Pearson   Lucy Fitch Perkins   Clay Perry

CLAY PERRY has explored caves for the past seventeen years and has had three books published about them. He also has written many magazine articles and stories. His books are *Underground New England* (Daye), *New England's Buried Treasure* (Daye), and *Underground Empire* (Daye). His forthcoming book in the "American Cave Series" is to be entitled *Spelunking in the Blue Ridge Mountains.* By a strange coincidence, two men who were lost in a cave near Franklin, West Virginia, without light for nearly three days, tried to find their way out by following the flight of bats, as the boys did in his story "Guides with Wings." Mr. Perry has visited this cave and has also visited over four hundred caves in New England, New York, Virginia, West Virginia, Maryland, and Kentucky.

HAROLD WEBSTER PERRY lives in Denver, Colorado, and is a lawyer. He is also a contemporary writer whose work appears in anthologies and textbooks.

MAUD and MISKA PETERSHAM have written and illustrated dozens of delightful children's books. They do them together in their home in Woodstock, New York. Miska Petersham is Hungarian born. His desire to paint was so strong that he walked miles each day to go to art school in Budapest. Later he studied art in London, working in the daytime to pay for his studio and his paints. After that he came to New York, where he worked in various occupations so that he could afford to paint. In New York he met his wife, Maud, and here his friend Willy Pogany persuaded him to illustrate children's books. Maud Petersham is the daughter of a minister of Kingston, New York. After graduating from Vassar, she attended the New York School of Fine and Applied Arts. It was while working with the International Art Service in New York that she met Miska Petersham. *The Rooster Crows* (Macmillan), by Maud and Miska Petersham, won the Caldecott Award in 1946.

HENRY C. PITZ's high school teacher wanted him to be a historian. Instead, he won a scholarship to the Philadelphia Museum School of Industrial Art and decided to be an artist. Since that time he has illustrated over one hundred and fifty books and has written at least four himself, among them, *Pen, Brush, and Ink* (Guptill). Many of his book illustrations are for historical tales. Mr. Pitz has long been connected with the Philadelphia Museum School of Industrial Art. He has been head of the school's illustration department for many years, has taught there, and been a notable influence in art education. Many of his students are well-known artists. He has won countless awards, including the Dana Gold Medal, the Lloyd Griscom Prize, the Obrig Prize at the National Academy, the Obst Prize at the American Water Color Society, the Pennell Memorial Medal for water colors, and a bronze medal from the French government. He has also been elected as an associate of the National Academy. He is thus eminent as painter, illustrator, teacher, author, and critic-commentator, and in Philadelphia art circles he is an energetic leader and promoter of many cultural activities. He is married, has two children, and lives in Pennsylvania.

RUTH GIPSON PLOWHEAD has lived in Idaho since she was a young girl and declares, "It is the finest state in the Union!" She wrote her first story at the age of twelve and

Maud and Miska Petersham　　　　　Henry C. Pitz　　　Ruth Gipson Plowhead

253

Edgar Allan Poe   James Ponter   Nancy Porter   Martha Lee Poston

received a check for it amounting to one dollar. She is married, has two children, and has written at least one hundred and fifty stories for leading juvenile magazines. Among her many books are *Josie and Joe* (Caxton), which was a Junior Literary Guild selection, *Lucretia Ann on the Oregon Trail* (Caxton), and *Mile High Cabin* (Caxton). "Josie's Home Run" (Volume 10:40) will be found in the book, *Josie and Joe.*

EDGAR ALLAN POE (1809–1849) was a great American poet, short-story writer, and critic. He was born in Boston, Massachusetts, but lived a good part of his life in the South. He published his first volume of poetry when he was eighteen years of age. He wrote a good deal for the *Southern Literary Messenger, The New York Quarterly Review,* and in time became associate editor of the *Gentleman's Magazine* in Philadelphia. He lived a tragic life, frequently sick and penniless. Four years before his early death he wrote his most famous poem, "The Raven." While his classic imaginative horror stories are truly great, his few poems of magic and wonder are so packed with melody and with emotion that many call them even greater. He was elected to the American Hall of Fame in 1910.

JAMES PONTER is a New Jersey artist. He resumed classes at the Pennsylvania Academy of the Fine Arts in Philadelphia after service with the U. S. Navy during World War II. He has received the Cresson award for illustration. In his studio in Glassboro, New Jersey, where he resides with his Australian wife and two sons, he works at his chosen field, illustration.

NANCY PORTER is a Chicagoan, and *The Children's Hour* is very grateful to her for all her editorial help. Her favorite hobby is horseback riding.

MARTHA LEE POSTON was born in Shanghai, China, the oldest of seven children. Her father was a medical missionary there. She writes, "Our greatest thrill was when we heard the gong of a traveling show outside our compound walls. We would call in the man with his monkey, goat, and dog, just as Bei-ling did in the story of 'The Monkey Spirit.' We were more delighted each time with the graceful tricks and pretty costumes of the monkey. We knew very well a family who lived in a house of a hundred rooms, just as Bei-ling did." Mrs. Poston went to Sweet Briar College in Virginia, and later taught school in Lynchburg, Virginia. She has two children. Three of her books are *Ching-li* (Nelson), *The Girl without a Country* (Nelson), and *The Mystery of the Eighth Horse* (Nelson).

MIRIAM CLARK POTTER was born in Minnesota. She lives in California, has three daughters, and several grandchildren, and finds time to write and illustrate stories for boys and girls. All of the stories which appeared in *The Littlebits* (Lippincott) were first told to her grandchildren and have a charming old-fashioned flavor of their own. "Mrs. Goose's Rubbers" (Volume 4:152) is one episode in the adventures of the heroine of *Mrs. Goose and the Three Ducks* (Lippincott), *Hello Mrs. Goose* (Lippincott), and *Mrs. Goose of Animaltown* (Lippincott). *Little Rabbit's Bath*

Miriam Clark Potter   Helen Prickett   Howard Pyle   Clara E. Randall

(Lippincott), *Timmy Mouse* (Lippincott), and *Animal's Train Ride* (Rand) are three of her later books. Mrs. Potter and her husband spent some time in New Delhi when he was at the American Embassy there.

HELEN PRICKETT was born in New York City but moved to Chicago when she was very young. She has lived there ever since. She received a scholarship to the Chicago Art Institute and later went in for commercial art. Now she has her own studio and is interested in painting. Her work has been exhibited in the Chicago Art Institute, the Associated Artist Galleries, and the Artist Guild of Chicago. She likes to travel—especially to Mexico.

HOWARD PYLE (1853–1911) was born just outside of Wilmington, Delaware, and when he was twenty-three Scribner's accepted some of his first sketches. He attended the Art Students' League in New York and struggled hard to sell his work. At one time he even went without food. Even after his work was in demand by leading magazines, he kept on studying at art school. He never felt he drew as well as he should. Mr. Pyle was known as a great illustrator and as a fine writer as well. Among his best-known books are *Robin Hood* (Harper), *Men of Iron* (Harper), *Twilight Land* (Harper), *Pepper and Salt* (Harper), *The Wonder Clock* (Harper), and *Howard Pyle's Book of Pirates* (Harper). (See Volume 15 for a longer biography.)

ARTHUR RACKHAM (1867–1939) was born in London and lived there all his life. He had eleven brothers and sisters and had a happy, noisy, busy boyhood, but he always had a pencil in his hand and liked imaginative books. During the matter-of-fact days of his adult life he felt that boys and girls should have an opportunity to enjoy fine, imaginative pictures and stories. Arthur Rackham's father, who was a Marshal to the British Admiralty, wanted him to be an insurance clerk. For a time, he was an insurance clerk by day, and went to art school at night. Finally, he was able to support himself as a free-lance artist. When he was thirty-six years old Mr. Rackham married a well-known portrait painter, and they had one daughter. Although he kept very busy with his drawings and paintings, he was fond of using a trapeze in his London studio. One of his friends said that he looked like a gnome or a very wise old owl with just a spark of innocent mischief. He had a country home in Sussex, with an old knotty beech tree in his garden, which he used often as a model in his pictures. During his lifetime he illustrated, in his own imaginative and decorative style, more than fifty books, and his enchanting pictures will live for many, many years to come. His drawings are now to be found in all the great galleries of Europe.

EVELINE M. RADER is a contemporary artist who lives in Chicago.

CLARA E. RANDALL has spent many happy hours writing stories and verses for her children, and now for her children's children. She feels that this is very rewarding work. Some years ago she wrote a book for boys and she also has written newspaper verse. At the present time she works for the Chicago Sunday Evening Club and does much writing for this famous religious organization.

LAURA LEE RANDALL is a contemporary Chicago writer who has published many fine poems. Some of her verse is for children and has come out in juvenile magazines. Some of her beautiful adult poems have been set to music and are sung in churches. *The Christian Science Monitor* has published still others. Her amusing light verse came out in Riq's column of the *Chicago Evening Post,* where she was his famous "Iris."

MARJORIE KINNAN RAWLINGS (1896–1953) was born in Washington, D. C. She attended the University of Wisconsin and received a LL.D. from Rollins College in Florida. She received this in recognition of her achievements in recording the life of the state's backwoods inhabitants. In her early days she wrote syndicated verse and special newspaper articles. When she settled down in Cross Creek, Hawthorne, Florida, she gave all her time to fiction. This she could not sell, but although discouraged she decided to try once more before giving up. She sold a story this time and since then her work has been most popular. *The Yearling* (Scribner) was a Pulitzer prize novel, and *Cross Creek* (Scribner), *South Moon Under* (Scribner), and *Golden Apples* (Scribner) are all well liked. Mrs. Rawlings traveled through the "piney-woods" talking to the Florida crackers and putting down her impressions slowly and carefully. "Writing," she said, "is agony. I am satisfied when I write only three pages a day." She was a member of the National Institute of Arts and Letters. "Hunting Old Slew Foot" (Volume 14:314) comes from *The Yearling.*

MARGARET THOMPSEN RAYMOND is a contemporary writer whose home for a long time was in Chicago. She has been editor of Volland's Publishing Company, and assistant editor of Beckley-Cardy. She has published a number of books. Among them are *Linnet on the Threshold* (Longmans) and *Bend in the Road* (Longmans).

FRANKLIN M. RECK is the author of popular sports stories, many of them for boys. He is a midwesterner and was educated at Iowa State University. There his only athletic activity was swimming; he was a fancy diver and swimmer on the varsity squad. After college he joined the staff of *American Boy* magazine and his sports education really began. He has spent months in Florida training camps and interviewed coaches and players of intercollegiate teams of almost every sport played throughout the United States. The incidents of his stories usually have their basis in real life, which makes them so popular and readable. Among his well-liked books are *Automobiles from Start to Finish* (Crowell), *Beyond the Call of Duty* (Crowell), *Radio from Start to Finish* (Crowell), *Romance of American Transportation* (Crowell), and *Varsity Letter* (Crowell).

ADOLPH REGLI was born in Eau Claire, Wisconsin, and graduated from the University of Wisconsin. After that he worked "along newspaperdom's ulcer trail" in New York, Florida, California, Wisconsin, and Minnesota. During the last seven years of his life he spent all his time writing books for young people. He traveled through many historical regions in order to make his backgrounds authentic. Among his many popular books are *The Mayos* (Messner), *The Real Book about the Wild West* (Garden City), *Young Readers' Cowboy Stories* (Lantern), and *Fiddling Cowboy* (McKay).

Laura Lee Randall   Franklin M. Reck   Adolph Regli

H. A. REY was born in Hamburg, Germany. During his childhood he lived near a zoo and began to draw animals. He studied at the University of Munich and Hamburg, and then went to Rio de Janeiro. Later, he and his wife went to Paris to find a publisher for some picturebooks he had done. The appearance of the Nazi armies obliged them to flee on bicycles, carrying some food and manuscripts. They made their way to Lisbon and finally reached New York, where they have lived ever since. Mr. Rey works ten hours a day in his studio, and his numerous books, that he illustrates himself, have been translated into many languages. Some of his delightful books for little children are *Curious George* (Houghton), *Where's My Baby?* (Houghton), *Pretzel* (Houghton), and *Elizabite* (Houghton). Mr. Rey's latest work is a book about the stars, a project close to his heart. It is called *The Stars* (Houghton) and is an outstanding book.

GEORGE RICHARDS is an artist whose strong, humorous illustrations are found in such books as *The Casting away of Mrs. Lecks and Mrs. Aleshine* (Appleton-Century) by Frank R. Stockton, *The Land of the Williwawas* (Houghton) by I. M. Ross, and *Dick and Tom* (Macmillan) by Mark Van Doren.

LAURA E. RICHARDS (1850-1943) was an American author who wrote over fifty books that were well loved by boys and girls everywhere. She was born in Boston and was the daughter of Julia Ward Howe, who wrote the "Battle Hymn of the Republic," and of Samuel Gridley Howe, the great humanitarian. It was he who taught Laura Bridgeman, the young girl who was blind, deaf, and dumb. Mrs. Richards lived in Gardner, Maine, and is very famous for her *Tirra Lirra* (Little), a collection of some of the most delightful nonsense verse that has ever been written. While some of her stories, such as *Captain January* (Little), are world-famous, her books for older girls are particularly well loved. These books include the "Margaret Montfort" and the "Hildegarde" series. She is also known for her biographies of famous women such as *Florence Nightingale* (Appleton-Century). Her *Stepping Westward* (Appleton-Century) is her own autobiography.

MILTON RICHARDS is a contemporary author whose work appears in leading juvenile magazines.

JAMES WHITCOMB RILEY (1849-1916) was a famous American poet from Indiana, whose poetry for children has been tremendously popular. He wrote many dialect poems for older readers and poems about the "old swimming hole" and other haunts of his own childhood. He ranks with Bret Harte as a poet who created a distinctly American literature. After Riley's own village schooldays, he traveled with a patent medicine troupe, did sign painting, wrote popular ballads, and at twenty, got into newspaper work. He was one of America's best-loved poets of the common people. School children, in his later days, marched in a procession and left flowers at his home when his birthday came around. Among his best-known books are *The Old Swimmin' Hole* (Bobbs-Merrill), *Rhymes of Childhood* (Bobbs-Merrill), *Home Folks* (Bobbs-Merrill), *An Old Sweetheart of Mine* (Bobbs-Merrill), *When the Frost Is on the*

H. A. Rey

Laura E. Richards

James Whitcomb Riley

Mabel L. Robinson   Jack Roderick   Lloyd Norman Rognan

Punkin (Bobbs-Merrill), and *Out at Old Aunt Mary's* (Bobbs-Merrill). He was a member of the American Academy of Arts and Letters.

ELIZABETH MADOX ROBERTS (1886–1941) was born near Springfield, Kentucky, educated at the University of Chicago, and lived for a while in New York. Her poems in her book *Under the Tree* (Viking) are among the most outstanding poems for children written during this century. She wrote these poems while in the University, polishing a single one for many, many weeks. Dean Robert Morss Lovett encouraged her greatly in her writing and helped her get her poems first published in the *Atlantic Monthly.* Later she wrote her famous novel, *The Time of Man* (Viking), and other adult novels that were equally outstanding.

MARY NEWLIN ROBERTS grew up on her father's estate at Fishkill-on-Hudson, New York, attended Miss Hill's School for Girls in Philadelphia, and studied music and painting in New York. After a winter in Munich, she spent five summers on a ranch at Jackson Hole, Wyoming. Then she visited Cuba and Jamaica. After her marriage to Reginald Roberts, she painted and did some writing. During a trip to Italy she furthered her study. She has contributed distinguished short stories of the lives of artists and musicians to juvenile magazines such as *Child Life, Little Folks,* and *Girls' Realm.* Among her books are *Young Masters of Music* (Crowell) and *Stories of the Youth of Artists* (Crowell).

MABEL L. ROBINSON, a consultant editor of *The Children's Hour,* is a member of the English faculty of Columbia University, where her famous seminar in juvenile story writing is unique in its field and has brought to light many talented authors. A graduate of Radcliffe College, she received her Ph.D. from Columbia. For a number of years she taught at Wellesley and at Constantinople College in Turkey. Her summers are spent at her home in Maine, where she is often found piloting her sailboat among the islands. She has written several excellent books on juvenile story writing, such as *Juvenile Story Writing* (Dutton) and *Writing for Young People* (Nelson), and has also written the well-loved "Little Lucia" series (Dutton), and such books for older boys and girls as *Bright Island* (Random), *Runner of the Mountain Tops* (Random), and *Back-Seat Driver* (Random). "False Summer" (Volume 6:314) comes from *Bright Island.*

JACK RODERICK is an Indiana artist who now lives with his wife in Grand Rapids, Michigan. His art training came after two years in the Navy. He went to the John Herron Art Institute of Indianapolis and to the American Academy of Art in Chicago. He has done many illustrations for the "American Folk Heroes" series of film strips for the Encyclopaedia Britannica Films, Inc. He has also been art director for the Informative Classroom Picture Publishers, and has recently been producing color film strips for medieval stories.

LLOYD NORMAN ROGNAN is a native Chicagoan, though he is of Norwegian descent. He studied at the American Academy of Art. During World War II he was an artist on the staff of the Army newspaper *Stars and Stripes*. After his discharge, he studied in Paris at the Academie de la Grande Chamiere for nearly two years. Then he was cover artist for the French edition of *Ellery Queen's Mystery Magazine*. For about five years he traveled in Europe, then returned to Chicago, where he specializes in illustrating religious stories.

THEODORE ROOSEVELT (1858–1918) was a great American statesman and author, and the twenty-sixth president of the United States. When he was a little boy in New York he was very delicate, but he determined to live an outdoor life and grow stronger. After graduating from Harvard, he studied law and was elected to the New York legislature. Later he was president of the Police Commission, and after that assistant secretary to the Navy. During the Spanish American War he organized his famous Rough Riders. A year after that he became governor of New York, and then vice president of the United States. Upon the death of McKinley in 1901, he became president. He won the Nobel prize for peace, was an enthusiastic hunter of big game, and was a strong believer in national preparedness. In 1912 he was the unsuccessful candidate of the Progressive Party which he organized. He wrote many books, including *The Winning of the West* (Putnam), *The Rough Riders* (Scribner's), *Oliver Cromwell* (Scribner's), *The Strenuous Life* (Century), and *The Great Adventure* (Scribner's). He was elected a member of the American Academy of Arts and Letters, and in 1923 his birthplace in New York City was opened as a permanent memorial. (See Volume 15 for a longer biography.) "Buffalo Hunting" (Volume 11:357) comes from *The Winning of the West*.

PAULINE ROSENBERG is a contemporary writer who lives in Chicago. Her early days were spent in Omaha, and she took her M.A. at the University of Michigan. She has been on the staff of Benjamin H. Sanborn and Company, Henry Holt and Company, the American College of Surgeons, and the American Medical Association. For seven years she was assistant editor of *Compton's Pictured Encyclopedia*, later was the editor of "Books to Grow On" (Consolidated). She has written a number of outstanding articles.

CHRISTINA ROSSETTI (1830–1894) lived her whole life in London. She was the sister of Dante Gabriel Rossetti, the famous Pre-Raphaelite poet and painter. Christina Rossetti was a frail child who was educated at home. Her first poem was written when she was eleven years old. Her first book of poems was published when she was seventeen. *Goblin Market* (Macmillan) and *Sing Song* (Macmillan) were two of her distinguished books. Children still love the poems she wrote for *Sing Song*.

GLEN ROUNDS had worked as a carnival barker, a sign painter, a textile designer, a hobo, a logger, and a cowboy. He had even done some drawings that had appeared in a magazine or two, but, as he put it, "he knew no more about the book business than a pig did about a schoolhouse." Born in a two-room shack on the edge of the South Dakota Badlands, he grew up loving horses and open ranges. When he began to write books in 1935 he wrote about these same horses and ranges. Among his popular

Theodore Roosevelt

Pauline Rosenberg

Glen Rounds

Rod Ruth   Ernie Rydberg   Walter R. Sabel

stories are *Old Paul* (Holiday), *The Blind Colt* (Holiday), *Whitey and the Rustlers* (Holiday), and *Whitey Takes a Trip* (Holiday). All of these are delightfully illustrated by their author. After long war service, Mr. Rounds returned to his wife and small son in Southern Pines, where he now makes his home.

MINNIE ROUSSEFF's humorous and very decorative drawings were to be found in *Child Life* for some years before her death. She was married to W. Vladimir Rousseff, who at that time taught at the Chicago Art Institute. In the summer they would do their painting in Fish Creek, Wisconsin. Two books by Paul Gilbert, *Bertram and His Funny Animals* (Rand) and *Bertram and His Fabulous Animals* (Rand), were delightfully illustrated by Minnie Rousseff.

JOHN RUSKIN (1819–1900) was a famous English author, art critic, and social reformer. He was born in London, studied at Oxford, and took a prize for poetry when he was only twenty years old. Four years later he published his first volume of *Modern Painters* in which he tried to prove that modern landscape painters, especially Turner, were better than the old masters. He was one of the Pre-Raphaelites. Among his other famous books were *The Seven Lamps of Architecture, The Stones of Venice, Sesame and Lilies,* and *The Crown of Wild Olive.* He became a professor of art at Oxford and helped increase the appreciation of the beautiful in nature and in art. His one famous book for boys and girls is still loved by them today: *The King of the Golden River.*

ROD RUTH was born in Benton Harbor, Michigan. He graduated from the Chicago Academy of Fine Arts and has been in commercial art ever since. He took time out during depression days for intermittent farm work, rough labor, sign-painting, summer camp jobs, and tramping about the country from Alaska to Yucatan—experience that he feels is invaluable to an illustrator. A lifelong outdoor enthusiast, his present outlets range from camping trips in the Rockies with his wife and three sons to watercolor sketching in the countryside near his home in Park Ridge, Illinois.

ERNIE RYDBERG was born in Nebraska and graduated from the University of Arizona, but he has spent most of his life in California. He has been a used-car dealer, a social worker, and has worked at all sorts of other jobs. Later, he turned to writing and has sold over three hundred manuscripts for juvenile, teen-age, and adult readers. He lives in San Diego, and his young daughter and her friends help him with his source material. He has had a play produced at the Pasadena Playhouse and has written a number of radio scripts. One of his books is *Bright Summer* (Longmans).

WALTER R. SABEL was born in Chicago. He had his early art training at the Chicago Art Institute and with J. H. Vanderpoel. Later he attended the American Academy. During World War I he took every opportunity to sketch the fascinating French village scenes and landscapes. Mr. Sabel is a commercial artist, and has his own studio in Chicago. He has illustrated General Motors products and has been art director of *Popular Mechanics.*

260

Ray St. Clair   J. Allen St. John   Carl Sandburg

RAY ST. CLAIR was born in California and now lives with his wife on a windy hilltop overlooking San Francisco Bay. He works for the Pullman Company, but his avocation is writing stories for children which appear in juvenile magazines and anthologies. He also writes non-fiction for adults. He has sold non-fiction to the *Saturday Evening Post* and to other magazines. One of his interests is preparing a radio version of *Robinson Crusoe* for the National Association of Educational Broadcasters Tape Network, and reading a story each week over FM station KPFA in Berkeley. He also "makes, and sometimes sells, small unclassifiable metal art objects."

ST. FRANCIS OF ASSISI (1182–1226), the founder of the Franciscan Order, was the son of a rich merchant. When Francis was twenty he joined in a fight between Assisi and a neighboring city. He was taken captive and was kept in prison for one year. While in prison he had a vision and began to think more and more about making his life a useful one. When he came out he spent his father's money so freely that he was disinherited. He went around in rags, preaching and praying, and even preached to the animals and birds. When disciples began to follow him he went to Rome and the great order of Franciscans was founded. He went on missions to foreign lands and lived a kindly, self-sacrificing, Christ-like life. After his death he was canonized a saint.

J. ALLEN ST. JOHN, America's outstanding fantasy illustrator, is best known for his fine drawings for the "Tarzan" and "Martian" books. At present, Mr. St. John is professor of life drawing and illustration at the American Academy of Art in Chicago, and for nearly twenty years he was an instructor at the Chicago Art Institute. He studied at the Art Students' League in New York, and completed his studies abroad in Belgium, Holland, and Paris. He has served as illustrator and designer for such well-known publications as the *New York Herald, Chicago Tribune, Harper's Bazaar, Red Book Magazine, Youth's Companion,* McClurg Publishing Company, and Edgar Rice Burroughs Publishing Company. He lives and works at his studio in Chicago.

FELIX SALTEN (1869–1945) was born in Austria and grew up in a poverty-stricken household. He went to school in Vienna and for a long time was bullied by his schoolmates, but one day he turned on them, and was never bullied after that. He wrote stories secretly and by the time he was eighteen he had sold several. He then contributed to leading literary journals and became a critic of standing. *Bambi* (Simon and Schuster), the life story of a buck in the Wienerwald, was his first book to be translated into English. It has become a classic and Walt Disney made a motion picture of it. In March, 1939, Mr. Salten escaped from Vienna, where he had been a notable literary figure, and took refuge in Switzerland, where he later died. Among his most famous books are *The Hound of Florence* (Simon and Schuster), *Fifteen Rabbits* (Simon and Schuster), *Bambi's Children* (Bobbs-Merrill), and *Good Comrades* (Bobbs-Merrill). "Bambi Starts To See the World" (Volume 14:27) is the first episode in *Bambi*.

CARL SANDBURG was born in Galesburg, Illinois, and was the son of a Swedish immigrant. While in his early teens he went to work and earned his own living washing hotel dishes, harvesting wheat, making bricks, and driving a milk wagon. Then came the Spanish-American War in which he served. He came back to Illinois and worked his way through Lombard College where he edited the college paper. Later, he worked on the *Chicago Daily News* and began to write his own books of verse, telling about working people and factories and quiet prairies and fog drifting over city streets. It was later that he began to write about Lincoln: *Abraham Lincoln, The Prairie Years* (Harcourt) and *Abraham Lincoln, The War Years* (Harcourt). Among his books of original, powerful, and fine poetry for adults are: *Chicago Poems* (Holt), *Cornhuskers* (Holt), *Smoke and Steel* (Harcourt), *Slabs of the Sunburnt West* (Harcourt), *Good Morning, America* (Harcourt), and *The People, Yes* (Harcourt). Among his books for boys and girls are his very original *Rootabaga Stories* (Harcourt) and *Rootabaga Pigeons* (Harcourt), *Early Moon* (Harcourt), his verse for children, and *Abe Lincoln Grows Up* (Harcourt). Mr. Sandburg at one time traveled around the country with his banjo, collecting American folk songs, which he later put into his *American Songbag* (Harcourt). He delighted audiences throughout the land when he sang the old songs to them and read some of his poems. He was awarded the Pulitzer Prize, the Gold Medal of the American Academy of Arts and Letters, and the Gold Medal of the Poetry Society of America. His autobiography *Always the Young Strangers* (Harcourt) was published on his seventy-fifth birthday. In it we find the story of his early years in Galesburg, his travels through the Kansas wheatfields, his service in the Spanish-American War, and his years as a newspaperman in Chicago.

EPES SARGENT (1813–1880) was a well-known New England writer, editor, journalist, and educator. For a while he lived in New York where he published his own journal, *Sargent's New Monthly Magazine*, but he returned to Boston and became editor of the *Boston Transcript*. Later, he left the paper and wrote plays, poetry, textbooks, and school readers.

CONSTANCE SAVERY, the eldest of five girls, was born in Wiltshire, England. Her father was a vicar who exchanged a country parish for one in the manufacturing district of Birmingham. Miss Savery was educated in King Edward's High School for Girls and Somerville College, Oxford, where she was graduated with an Honors degree. Among her friends were Margaret Kennedy and Vera Brittain. She taught until her mother died, but disliked teaching and was glad to return home and help in her father's East Anglican village parish. "Spindleberries and Pam," "The Wastwych Secret," and "The Little Dragon" are among her many delightful short stories for young people. *Enemy Brothers* (Longmans) depicts with realism and humor conditions such as prevailed in her home area which was under fire in the early days of World War II. *Moonshine in Candle Street* (Longmans) is one of her popular juveniles. "Adventure in Candle Street" (Volume 12:179) is from this book.

MATHILDA SCHIRMER, the associate editor of *The Children's Hour*, has lived all her life in Chicago, except for a short time when she attended Syracuse University in New York. She is a graduate of Northwestern University and has a certificate from the Chicago Art Institute. She has always been interested in books and children and has

Constance Savery

Mathilda Schirmer

262

worked with both. For some years she was on the staff of the Chicago Boys Club of Lawndale, and camp secretary of the Chicago Boys Clubs camp at Winona Lake, Indiana. Her experience with books has been varied, having worked for the American Library Association, American Book Company, Beckley-Cardy Company, and Consolidated Book Publishers. Among the books that she has edited are the highly recommended "Americans in Action" series (Beckley-Cardy): *Fighters for Freedom, Leaders of the Frontier, Builders for Progress,* and *Latin American Leaders.* Her *Horace* (Consolidated) is a horse story for younger readers.

HERMAN SCHNEIDER is science supervisor of the New York City elementary schools. Formerly he was lecturer in science education at the Bank Street College and consultant in science for a number of public and private schools. Although he has taught science at all levels from primary school to college, his favorite pupils ("and guinea pigs") are his own children—two boys and two girls.

JACKSON SCHOLZ was born in Buchanan, Michigan. He graduated from the School of Journalism at the University of Missouri, was ensign in Naval Aviation during World War I, and has been prominent in athletics as a sprinter, in three Olympic Games, and 200-metre winner in Paris. He has written thirteen teen-age sports books for boys. Among them are: *Batter Up* (Morrow), *Fielder from Nowhere* (Morrow), and *Gridiron Challenge* (Morrow).

JANET LAURA SCOTT had a nature-loving father who, when she was a little girl in Augusta, Wisconsin, taught her to love all outdoors. She began to draw what she saw. When she was sixteen, her father died and Janet came to Chicago to be the sole support of herself and of her mother. She got a position where she drew all the time. While making her living there, she managed to work her way through the Chicago Art Institute. The firm she worked for sent her to Munich for another year's art training. She is still working for them, making Christmas cards and illustrating their books. She now lives in Rockport, Maine, with her architect husband, Carroll Thayer Berry. She has also illustrated many magazine stories and well-known books and has painted many water colors of Maine coastal scenes. She has exhibited at the Chicago Art Institute, the Sweatt Memorial Art Gallery in Portland, and Massachusetts Workshop at Lincolnville. Among her hobbies are bird-watching, gardening, photography, and reading detective stories.

MARY LOUISE SCOTT is a contemporary writer whose verse appears in various juvenile magazines. She lives in Cambridge, Ohio.

SIR WALTER SCOTT (1771–1832), Scottish poet and novelist, was born in Edinburgh and, for a time, went to college there. He studied law at the age of fifteen, and listened to old stories about his ancestors who were border freebooters. He married and devoted himself to writing. Among his most famous poems are "The Lay of the Last Minstrel," "Marmion," and "The Lady of the Lake." He wrote many glowing historical novels which have since become classics. These include *Ivanhoe* and *Kenil-*

Jackson Scholz   Janet Laura Scott   Sir Walter Scott

263

Samuel Scoville, Jr. Augusta Huiell Seaman Kate Seredy Ernest Thompson Seton

worth. When a publishing house with which he was connected failed, Scott devoted the rest of his life to paying their liabilities. All his works rank high in the world of English literature. Several critics have placed him "second only to Shakespeare in creative and imaginative literature."

SAMUEL SCOVILLE, JR. was a lawyer by profession. He was also a versatile writer of many books for boys. His first book, *Brave Deeds of Union Soldiers* (Jacobs), was dedicated to Theodore Roosevelt, whom he greatly admired. He wrote several books on nature, but his most famous ones were *Boy Scouts in the Wilderness* (Century), *The Blue Pearl* (Century), *The Inca Emerald* (Century), and *The Red Diamond* (Century).

AUGUSTA HUIELL SEAMAN lived with her husband and daughter on the New Jersey coast in a house quite isolated among the dunes. Among her most famous mystery stories for girls were *The Riddle at Live Oaks* (Doubleday), *The House in Hidden Lane* (Doubleday), *The Charlemonte Crest* (Doubleday), and her delightful *Jacqueline of the Carrier Pigeons* (Macmillan), and *When a Cobbler Ruled a King* (Macmillan).

MARION K. SEAVEY is a contemporary writer whose poems have appeared in various juvenile magazines.

KATE SEREDY was born in Budapest, Hungary, and studied there in the Academy of Art. For two years she was a nurse in a war hospital. Shortly after that she moved to the United States, where she has lived ever since. Her first book, that she both wrote and beautifully illustrated, was *The Good Master* (Viking), in which she told about her own early life. "Easter Eggs" (Volume 9:76) and "The Round Up" (Volume 13:80) are two adventures that she tells about in this book. Later, she wrote *The Singing Tree* (Viking), *Listening* (Viking), and *The White Stag* (Viking), an epic tale of Hungary which won the Newbery Medal.

ROBERT W. SERVICE, Canadian poet and novelist, was born in England and educated in Glasgow where he worked in a bank. He then went to Vancouver Island, Canada, and later spent eight years in the Yukon. During World War I he drove an ambulance in France and was a war correspondent. Because of his vigorous rhymes he has been called "the Kipling of Canada." Among his best-known books are *The Trail of '98* (Dodd), and *Rhymes of a Red Cross Man* (Ryerson).

ERNEST THOMPSON SETON, an American naturalist, artist, author, and lecturer, was born in England and lived in the Canadian backwoods during his childhood. He was educated in Toronto, London, and Paris, and was widely known as a writer and illustrator of animal stories and also as a lecturer. He started the Woodcraft League and was one of the originators of The Boy Scouts of America. For five years he was its Chief Scout. Among his most famous books are *Wild Animals I Have Known* (Scribner), *The Trail of the Sandhill Stag* (Scribner), *Lives of the Hunted* (Scribner), and *Animal Heroes* (Scribner).

Dr. Seuss   Helen Sewell   Monica Shannon

DR. SEUSS, or Theodor Seuss Geisel, humorist, illustrator, mural painter, and cartoonist, was awarded the Legion of Merit for war film work. He is the author of such humorous favorites as *The 500 Hats of Bartholomew Cubbins* (Vanguard), *McElligot's Pool* (Random), *If I Ran the Zoo* (Random), and *Scrambled Eggs Super* (Random). He has won two Academy Awards in the motion picture field, the first for a documentary film of the history of Japan, and the second for *Gerald McBoing Boing*, voted the best motion picture cartoon of 1950. Another favorite movie is *The 5000 Fingers of Dr. T.* At present he is producing animated cartoons for television as well as more wonderful nonsense books for boys and girls.

HELEN SEWELL had circled the globe before she was eight years old. Her childhood was spent on the island of Guam, of which her father was governor. She still remembers (with no pleasure) earthquakes, tropical storms, lizards, and centipedes, and remembers (with much pleasure) Gibraltar through the mist, Arabs on camels silhouetted against the sky, an active volcano glowing in the night, a snake charmer on board her boat, and the sea streaked green and cobalt, amethyst and turquoise. After her father's death, Helen and her two sisters returned to Brooklyn, New York, for their schooling, spending long summers at Lake George or on a farm near Schenectady. At intervals, Miss Sewell has attended art school at Packer Institute, Pratt Institute, and Archipenko's Art School. She visited Brittany and England with her niece, and once her longing to see a tropical island again took her to Jamaica. Her distinguished illustrations are found in *A First Bible* (Oxford) and in a number of other children's books. She, herself, has written and illustrated *Belinda the Mouse* (Oxford), *Peggy and the Pony* (Oxford), and *Peggy and the Pup* (Oxford).

WILLIAM SHAKESPEARE (1564–1616), the greatest English dramatist, was born in Stratford-on-Avon. He was married to Ann Hathaway and had three children. He went from Stratford to London and became a great actor. He wrote most of his wonderful plays and poems there. He died in Stratford. Very little is known about Shakespeare's life, but his great plays are almost as popular today as they were when he first wrote them. Some of his most famous ones are: *Hamlet, Macbeth, King Lear, Julius Caesar, Romeo and Juliet,* and *The Tempest.* (See Volume 15 for a more complete biography.)

MONICA SHANNON is a contemporary poet and the author of a number of children's books. She was born in Ontario, Canada, and has lived in California. Among her books are *Dobry* (Viking) which won the Newbery Medal, and *California Fairy Tales* (Doubleday). "Dobry's New Year" (Volume 9:294) is an episode from her book, *Dobry.*

AGATHA SHEA is the head of the Children's Department of the Chicago Public Library. She has been in charge there since its first beginnings and has helped it in many ways in its growth. In cooperation with the Illinois Congress of Parents and Teachers she has developed reading courses for parents in the guidance of children's reading. She has worked with the book production committee and the Newbery and

Percy Bysshe Shelley

Dorothy Short

Elsie Singmaster

Caldecott award committees of the American Library Association. She has also worked with the Boy Scouts, Girl Scouts, Boys Clubs of America, and the National Conference of Christians and Jews. Her leadership in her own field and her own book reviews have also influenced the reading of Chicago's school children. For her distinguished services in the field of library work with children she has won The Children's Reading Round Table Award.

PERCY BYSSHE SHELLEY (1792–1822), the famous English poet, went to Oxford for a year. He was married twice, and when he was twenty-six he went to Italy where he remained for the rest of his short life. There he was drowned off the coast of Leghorn while sailing with a friend. Shelley wrote some of the greatest lyrics ever published, and his lyrical drama, *Prometheus Unbound*, was also very fine. Among his poems that boys and girls like best are: "To a Skylark," "The Cloud," "Indian Serenade," and "Ode to the West Wind."

ERNEST H. SHEPARD's first picture was exhibited in the Royal Academy. As a young man in London he studied at St. Paul's and Heatherley's Art School and won a scholarship at the Royal Academy School. After art school he started drawing for *Punch*. Later, he married, had two children, and during World War I was commissioned in the Royal Artillery. He served three years in France, Belgium, and Italy. Mr. Shepard will long be remembered for his delightful pictures of Christopher Robin and Pooh in *Winnie-the-Pooh* (Dutton), *House at Pooh Corner* (Dutton), *When We Were Very Young* (Dutton), and *Now We Are Six* (Dutton). He made whimsical and memorable pictures, too, for *The Wind in the Willows* (Scribner).

MAXINE SHORE is the co-author with M. M. Oblinger of *Hero of Darien: The Story of Vasco Nunez de Balboa* (Longmans) and *Knight of the Wilderness: The Story of Alexander Mackenzie* (Dodd). From this book, "Alexander Mackenzie: Hero of Canada" (Volume 15:153) was reprinted.

DOROTHY SHORT is the art editor of *The Children's Hour*. She is a native Chicagoan, and attended the Chicago Art Institute and the Chicago Academy of Fine Arts. On leaving the Art Institute she was in the commercial advertising field for a number of years, working for the Chicago Elevated Advertising Company and the William Wrigley Junior Company. For ten years before coming to *The Children's Hour*, Miss Short had her own studio.

EVELYN SICKELS is a contemporary writer who is the author of *The School Bell Rings* (Scribner).

R. LAL SINGH is a contemporary East-Indian author who wrote *Gift of the Forest* (Longmans) with Eloise Lownsbery.

ELSIE SINGMASTER is an American writer of stories with historical backgrounds. She was born in Schuylkill Haven, Pennsylvania, where her father was then preaching.

Robert Sinnott   Constance Lindsay Skinner   Janet Smalley

She grew up in Allentown, and now lives in Gettysburg. As a little girl she played with Pennsylvania·Dutch children and read Scott, Dickens, and Hawthorne. She was graduated from Radcliffe College and shortly afterwards began to write for *Scribner's* and the *Atlantic Monthly.* More than two hundred of her short stories have appeared in various magazines. Among her books are *Gettysburg* (Houghton), a series of short stories, *A Boy at Gettysburg* (Houghton), *What Everybody Wanted* (Houghton), *When Sarah Saved the Day* (Houghton), and *The Young Ravenels* (Houghton). She has also written history and biography and is considered one of Pennsylvania's outstanding writers.

ROBERT SINNOTT is a Chicago artist, one of the distinguished group, The 27 Designers, and lives in Prairie View, Illinois, "with one wife, one daughter, and one mortgage." He has worked in all parts of the country, illustrating and doing commercial art. His outstanding murals are to be found in Chicago, Baltimore, Los Angeles, Mansfield, Ohio, and Evanston, Illinois. His latest venture, with his artist wife, is an outstanding gift shop which is becoming far too popular to please him.

CONSTANCE LINDSAY SKINNER (1879–1939) was an American writer born in northwestern Canada. Her father was a member of the Legislative Assembly of British Columbia, and she was educated in the first private school in Vancouver. Miss Skinner lived many years in New York and did much of her writing there. Among her many popular books are *Beaver, Kings, and Cabins* (Macmillan), *Silent Scott* (Macmillan), *Debby Barns, Trader* (Macmillan), *Becky Landers* (Macmillan), and *Roselle of the North* (Macmillan).

JOHNNY SLOAN wrote the poem published in *The Children's Hour* when he was fourteen years old. This, we are told, began and ended his career as a poet! He is now in the Air Force.

LOUIS SLOBODKIN, illustrator and sculptor, won the Caldecott Medal in 1943 for his illustrations for James Thurber's *Many Moons.* He started drawing as a child, became a sculptor in his early teens, studied art in New York, and sculpture in Paris. His outstanding statues and friezes are found in many public buildings, museums, and private collections, the best known being the bronze statue of Abraham Lincoln in the Department of Interior building, Washington, D. C. He has also illustrated a number of books for children, including Eleanor Estes' Moffat stories.

JANET SMALLEY, a native Philadelphian, studied illustration with Henry McCarter at the Pennsylvania Academy of Fine Arts, where she received a Cresson Scholarship. Her three loves are books, children, and drawing, and she has written and illustrated several books for small children, and has delightfully illustrated many children's stories by other writers. She lives in Yeadon, Pennsylvania, and has "one daughter, a flock of nieces and nephews, and three grandchildren." She has traveled in Spain, France, and England, and claims as hobbies "gardening, stamp-collecting, and a calico cat named Mitty."

EUNICE YOUNG SMITH lives in a house on a hill in Indiana, from whose quiet and serenity she draws the inspiration for the children's books she has written and illustrated. As a child she lived in a dream world of poetry, fairy tales, and imaginary pictures. Not until after her marriage did she begin to express her poetic thoughts. She joined a poetry club and made Christmas greeting cards. A gift of oil paints from her son was the spur which sent her to Chicago to study oil painting. She ended up at a publisher's, made invaluable contacts, and returned home six months later to do her first illustrations for a children's book. Illustrating now occupies most of her time. Among her books are *The Jennifer Wish* (Bobbs-Merrill), *The Jennifer Gift* (Bobbs-Merrill), and *The Jennifer Prize* (Bobbs-Merrill). "The Prize" (Volume 10:48) comes from her book *The Jennifer Prize*.

FREDRIKA SHUMWAY SMITH was born in Chicago and grew up there, but she waited until she was a grandmother before she began publishing in juvenile magazines and in book form the stories and verse which she wrote for children. She spends much of her time in Chicago and in Lake Forest, Illinois, and in her summer home in northern Michigan. Her three popular books of very child-like poems are *The House in the Tree* (Argus), *The Magic Stairway* (Ziff-Davis), and *The Magic City* (Christopher). Mrs. Smith has also written for teen-agers and adults. Some of these books are *Rose and the Ogre* (Christopher), *The House in the Tower* (Christopher), and her popular biography of *John Greenleaf Whittier* (Christopher).

JESSIE WILCOX SMITH, who died in 1935, was a popular American artist who was born in Philadelphia. She was well known for her effective pictures of children found in various magazines and on various magazine covers, and for her delightful illustrations for juvenile books.

LOUISE DE MARIGNY SMITH wrote her first poem at the age of three, and it was published in the *Chicago Tribune*. At the age of twelve she had another poem, "Thoughts of an Unknown Soldier," published in the *Tribune*. She has also contributed to *Wee Wisdom* magazine. Now she lives in Lake Forest, Illinois, not far from her talented grandmother, Fredrika Shumway Smith, and there she attends the Bell School.

SUZIE SNIDER is a young artist who attended the American Academy of Art in Chicago. She has worked for various advertising studios and is now working in the art department of the Spencer Press. She has illustrated children's books, including *Fleurette* (Erle).

ARMSTRONG SPERRY was born in Connecticut and his forebears go back to the earliest settlers. He remembers hearing his great-grandfather tell of hair-raising adventures on the China Sea, which early awakened his interest in life at sea. He attended the Yale Art School and then joined the Navy in World War I. After that came the Art Students' League in New York, and then "a job drawing vacuum cleaners, canned soup, and blonde ladies who wore hair nets." When he could not stand this any longer he followed the trail of his great-grandfather and spent two years wandering

Eunice Young Smith   Fredrika Shumway Smith   Louise De Marigny Smith   Suzie Snider

268

Armstrong Sperry   James Stevens   Robert Louis Stevenson

through the South Seas. Here he decided that he wanted to tell stories and to illustrate them, and so his books began. Among his best-known books are *Call It Courage* (Macmillan), which won the Newbery Medal, *One Day with Jambi* (Winston), *All Sails Set* (Winston), *Lost Lagoon* (Doubleday), and *John Paul Jones* (Random). He now lives in New Hampshire. "The Forbidden Island" (Volume 9:345) is an exciting adventure from *Call It Courage* for which Mr. Sperry made a new painting, just for *The Children's Hour*. "Jambi and the Tiger" (Volume 14:184) is an episode from *One Day with Jambi*.

ANNE HIGGINSON SPICER was a Chicago poet who, during her lifetime, wrote some very beautiful verse. Some of her poems were published in book form by Ralph Fletcher Seymour.

JOHANNA SPYRI (1827–1901) was born near Zurich, Switzerland, and was educated at home. After she married she wrote books for children. Her most famous one, *Heidi*, was written in 1880 and its popularity has never diminished. In her many other popular books she also wrote about real Swiss children in their mountain homes. "Heidi's Adventures on the Mountain" (Volume 3:26) is part of her best-known, *Heidi*.

EMMA–LINDSAY SQUIER wrote a number of stories about the West, and has published many children's stories in magazines.

LEONA STAFFORD is a contemporary poet whose work appears in various magazines.

JAMES STEPHENS is a famous Irish poet. He is also a short-story writer and novelist. His best-known book for older readers is *The Crock of Gold* (Macmillan), a very humorous fantasy. While his poetry is mostly for adult readers, boys and girls like many of his poems in *The Rocky Road to Dublin* (Macmillan). Older children like his *Irish Fairy Tales* (Macmillan), which are beautifully retold.

ELEANOR ELIZABETH STEVENS has written some beautiful poetry which is published in magazine form. She is Children's Librarian at the Oberlin Public Library, Oberlin, Ohio.

JAMES STEVENS, who is much interested in American folklore, lives in Seattle, Washington. He writes a weekly column for fifty-five Pacific Northwest newspapers, and works regularly with public school educators.

WILLIAM OLIVER STEVENS is a contemporary writer interested in biography. One of his books is *Famous Women of America* (Dodd).

ROBERT LOUIS STEVENSON (1850–1894), British novelist, essayist, and poet, was born in Edinburgh. He was educated to be a lawyer but soon gave up law for literature. Stevenson was one of the best-loved writers of his time. When his health failed him he settled on the island of Samoa, where he was dearly loved by the natives whom he helped. Here he died. While his *Travels with a Donkey* (Scribner) and other books of essays are well liked, he is best known for his exciting adventure stories, *Treasure Island* (Scribner) and *Kidnapped* (Scribner). Boys and girls who read "The Man with the Belt of Gold" (Volume 12:273) will want to read more about this hero's adventures in *Kidnapped*. Children love Stevenson's famous book, *A Child's Garden of Verses* (Scribner). (See Volume 15 for a longer biography.)

LOUISE A. STINETORF was born on an Indiana farm and had eight sisters and brothers. She went to a little country school, but later got degrees from several colleges. At one time she served as a Quaker missionary in Palestine. She has traveled in various parts of the world and has spent some of her vacations in Egypt. She now lives in a red adobe house in the mountains of Santa Monica. Her juvenile stories appear in various children's anthologies.

CAROL STOAKS is a teacher of composition, color, and design at the American Academy of Art in Chicago. She is also a landscape painter in water color and oils, a fashion artist, and an illustrator. In spite of her many activities, she enjoys spending time in various parts of the United States and Alaska with her children and grandchildren. Carol Stoaks studied at Western Washington Teachers College, the University of Washington, Cornell University, the Portland (Oregon) Art Institute, and is a graduate of the Thomas School of Music and Art, and the American Academy of Art. She now has a private studio in Chicago.

FRANK R. STOCKTON (1834–1902) was a famous American humorist. He was born in Philadelphia, and when he was eighteen years old he began to earn his living as a wood engraver. Boys and girls, for many, many years, have loved his amusing fairy tales which he first published in the old *St. Nicholas*. For many years he was the assistant editor of that magazine. His fanciful stories were gathered into several volumes, such as *Old Pipes and the Dryad* (Scribner), *The Bee-Man of Orn* (Scribner), and *The Floating Prince* (Scribner). Among his books for somewhat older readers are the delightful volumes, *Rudder Grange* (Scribner) and *The Casting Away of Mrs. Lecks and Mrs. Aleshine* (Appleton). The latter you will find in Volume 4:283 of *The Children's Hour*.

ANNE STODDARD was the editor of *American Girl Magazine* for many years. At one time she was also editor of *St. Nicholas*. She now lives in East Orange, New Jersey. Her books for younger readers are delightful. One of them is *A Good Little Dog* (Appleton-Century).

PHIL STONG was born in Iowa and grew up on the family farm there. From his own boyhood memories come most of his novels, as well as his books for boys and girls. Mexico, the thinkin' burro, was Phil Stong's own; he played in that old mill where No-Sitch turned hant hound; he did all the "ornery" things that the farm boys do; and a sad moose, like Honk, was adopted by the townsfolk. When a boy, he

Louise A. Stinetorf   Carol Stoaks   Phil Stong

listened to the tales his grandfather told about the Sauk Indian boys. His grandfather had played with them as a young settler of twelve in southeastern Iowa. He, himself, roved the Des Moines River, even as Captain Kidd. Although Phil Stong lives in northern Connecticut most of the year, he owns that family farm in Iowa and goes back there frequently, with less frequent visits to New York. Among his popular books are *Captain Kidd's Cow* (Dodd), *Farm Boy* (Dodd), *Honk: the Moose* (Dodd), *No-Sitch* (Dodd), *Young Settlers* (Dodd), *Way Down Cellar* (Dodd), and *Cowhand Goes to Town* (Dodd). Part of Honk the moose's adventures you will find in "Waino and Ivar Meet Honk the Moose" (Volume 6:65).

ANNE STOSSEL lives in Wilmette, Illinois, with her two sons and her "corpulent" cat. She received her art training in Munich and Berlin and at the Art Institute of Chicago. She illustrated many stories for *Child Life,* and later she delightfully illustrated some "Bertram" books of Paul T. Gilbert (Rand). She drifted then into commercial designing and silk screen designing for textiles. Her work in these fields is very fine.

PAUL STRAYER, one of Chicago's outstanding artists, has had, through the years, the great illustrator Howard Pyle as his lodestar, his mentor, and his inspiration. Like Pyle, he, too, has been interested in historical scenes, in ships at sea, in the romance and vitality of industry, in the painting of animals and the West, in portraits, and in outdoor sporting subjects. In his early days Paul Strayer went to the Chicago Art Institute, worked in advertising, was staff artist and circulation manager of the *House Beautiful,* and did interior decorating. Then he began to do murals and his real career began. From his studio in River Forest, Illinois, which he designed himself, came some of his famous paintings such as "Christmas Cheer for the Fort," owned by the Chicago Historical Society, "The Twentieth Century's Departure from Chicago," seen at the Chicago Century of Progress, and his portrait of Paderewski, hanging in the halls of the Polish Union in Chicago. Here he illustrates many books and many magazine stories, and here he designs his dramatic magazine covers, and indulges in his favorite recreational activity—the building of very beautiful model ships.

NOEL STREATFEILD was born in England and still lives there. She has three sisters and one brother and says, "If you are going to write books for children when you grow up, there is nothing like having been one of a big family." She left school to become an actress and was trained at the Royal Academy of Dramatic Art. Her first job was touring in a Shakespearean company for two years. Later she made several overseas tours, and it was then that she decided that she wanted to write. On her return from Australia in 1930, she wrote her first novel, *The Whicharts* (Heinemann). Six years later she started to write for girls and boys, and among her popular books are *Ballet Shoes* (Random), *Circus Shoes* (Random), and *Theatre Shoes* (Random). Her hobbies are the theatre, the ballet, and the films. She is also an active gardener, and has made her garden in a bomb site on the corner of a London square.

JULIAN STREET (1879–1947), was an American novelist and essayist who was born in Chicago and educated at Ridley College Preparatory School, St. Catherines, in On-

Anne Stossel   **Paul Strayer**   **Noel Streatfeild**

271

| Ruth E. Tanner | Hascy Tarbox | Adele Jordan Tarr | Sara Teasdale |

tario, Canada. He was a reporter on the *New York Mail and Express,* and became its drama editor when he was only twenty-one. He called himself "the only critic who predicted that *Floradora* would be a flat failure!" He won the O. Henry Memorial Prize for a story, and the Chevalier's Cross of the Legion of Honor from the French government. At one time he collaborated with Booth Tarkington in writing the famous comedy, *Country Cousin.* Among his best-known books are *My Enemy the Motor* (John Lane), *The Gold Fish* (John Lane), and *Mr. Bisbee's Princess* (Doubleday).

GERTRUDE STRICKLER is a teacher of art, and lives in Wilton, Connecticut. She has done much illustration for magazines and has written and illustrated some amusing children's stories which have appeared in juvenile publications.

MARION STROBEL is a Chicago poet who has been closely connected with *Poetry Magazine.* She is a member of the Society of Midland Authors, and has published fiction as well as her books of verse. Some of her delightful children's poems appear in juvenile magazines. Several of these have been inspired by her own daughter, when she was little.

LILLIAN M. SWENSON, who lives in Minneapolis, Minnesota, is a contemporary writer whose stories for children have appeared in juvenile magazines.

RUTH E. TANNER grew up on a Colorado ranch. She loved all the animals there, from the horses in their barns to the shy quail along the creek. She loves telling stories to the school children in Gypsum, Kansas, where she now lives. She feels that she owes much of her writing ability to a grandfather who was a Texas Ranger, and to a grandmother whose family tree went back to John Alden and Priscilla.

EVA MARCH TAPPAN (1854–1930) was an American author who was born in Blackstone, Massachusetts. She liked to write biography and history for young people, and among her best-known books are *When Knights Were Bold* (Houghton), *American Heroes Stories* (Houghton), *Our European Ancestors* (Houghton), *The Story of the Greek People* (Houghton), *England's Story* (Houghton), and many others.

HASCY TARBOX was born in St. Paul, Minnesota, and he says his early years were primarily devoted to acclimating himself to his name, and that he is still doing so. He attended the Todd School for Boys in Woodstock, Illinois (as did Orson Welles), and later went to the Chicago Art Institute. For several years he was with the Art Department of *Esquire Magazine* and since then, as a sideline to being a school administrator, has been a free-lance artist. He is married and has two children and lives in Woodstock, Illinois.

ADELE JORDAN TARR was an Illinois poet who lived in Chicago. Much of her beautiful verse is found in various anthologies. She was connected with a number of literary organizations and was most helpful to younger writers. Her poems, "Song for Roberta" and "Song for Warren," were written for her grandchildren. Her humorous "Octopus" is hanging on the walls of the Shedd Aquarium in Chicago.

MARGARET W. TARRANT's father, Percy Tarrant, was an artist, and she was his only child. Her school days were spent near London, and for a time she attended an art school. When she was eighteen she began to design cards and to paint small pictures. Some of these were accepted by various publishers. Then she moved with her parents down into Surrey and remained in the same house in the country until her parents' death. After this she bought a small home which she shared with a friend, and has continued working for the same publishing company for many years. She works also for other publishers. She is now very fond of landscape work, as well as imaginative designs, and has exhibited her delicate and very beautiful paintings at the Royal Academy, the Royal Institute, and several other galleries.

CHRYSIE TAVRIDES is the daughter of A. K. Bilder, who is himself an established artist. She is a graduate of the Chicago Art Institute and has worked with her father, and, for a time, with the Spencer Press. She is married and has one child.

CHARLES TAZEWELL is a contemporary writer whose *Littlest Angel* (Childrens Press) has become a Christmas classic. Many of you have probably had the pleasure of hearing Helen Hayes read it over the radio, or have the RCA Victor record where Joan Crawford reads this story. A later book is *Littlest Stork* (Childrens Press).

SARA TEASDALE (1884–1933) came from an old American family. One of her ancestors founded Concord, Massachusetts. Both of her grandfathers were pioneers of the Middle West. Sara, born in St. Louis, had a dreamy and imaginative childhood. She was not too strong so she spent much time reading many books, and particularly loved the poems of Christina Rossetti. She was educated at a private school for girls and traveled around the world. Among her best-known volumes of poetry, filled with her beautiful lyrics, are *Rivers of the Sea* (Macmillan), *Love Songs* (Macmillan), which won the Columbia University award for the best poetry of that year, *Flame and Shadow* (Macmillan), and *Stars Tonight* (Macmillan). This last book is a selection of her simple, beautiful lyrics for boys and girls. She is also well remembered for her fine anthology for young people called *Rainbow Gold* (Macmillan).

JOHN TENNIEL (1820–1914) was an English artist who is most famous for his unforgettable illustrations for *Alice in Wonderland* and *Through the Looking Glass*. Despite his great success with these classics, Tenniel refused to illustrate another book for children. As he himself put it, "With *Through the Looking Glass*, the faculty of drawing book illustrations has departed from me, and notwithstanding all sorts of temptations I have done nothing in that line since." He did, however, draw many pages for England's humorous magazine, *Punch*, and he kept on drawing them for thirty years. As George Kerr put it, "From *Punch* he gained his bread. From *Alice*, his immortality."

ALFRED, LORD TENNYSON (1809–1892), the great English poet, lived all his life in England. He was educated at Cambridge, and at twenty-one was beginning to publish his beautiful poems. He became Poet Laureate at the time of Wordsworth's death in 1850. He was the representative poet of the Victorian Era, and in 1884 he was created Baron. Boys and girls particularly like his poems "Maud," "Idylls of the King," "Enoch Arden," "Locksley Hall," "In Memoriam," "The Princess," and "The Lady of Shallot." His *Collected Poems* (Macmillan) belong on the poetry bookshelf in every home.

ALBERT PAYSON TERHUNE (1872-1942) once lived as a member of a desert Bedouin tribe which wanted to adopt him. This was in the days when he was wandering through Egypt and Syria and doing some exploring. Before that, he grew up in

| Alfred, Lord Tennyson | Diana Thorne | Eunice Tietjens | Janet Tietjens |

Newark, New Jersey, and lived with his father, who was a clergyman, and his mother, who wrote novels and books about domestic science. It was after he was graduated from Columbia University that he traveled through Europe and the Near East. Later, in America, he was a newspaper reporter by day and a short-story writer by night. He was a great lover of dogs and finally his dog stories became famous and he was able to give up his newspaper work. Sunnybank, near Pompton Lakes, New Jersey, was his famous home. Here, surrounded by his pack of collie dogs, he tramped the hills, fished, hunted, and wrote his popular animal stories. Mr. Terhune received at Columbia a medal of excellence as "explorer, man of letters, and true interpreter of nature." Among his most famous books are *Lad, a Dog* (Dutton), *Buff, a Collie* (Dutton), *Further Adventures of Lad* (Dutton), *Treve* (Dutton), *Lad of Sunnybank* (Dutton), *The Way of a Dog* (Dutton), *A Book of Famous Dogs* (Dutton), and *Best-Loved Dog Stories* (Grosset).

ERNEST LAWRENCE THAYER wrote his famous "Casey at the Bat" years ago, and it was published in a newspaper and reprinted in many others. DeWolfe Hopper made it even more famous when he began reciting it in his own inimitable way. This humorous poem has appeared in hundreds of anthologies since that time, and is still much enjoyed today.

DANA LEE THOMAS is a contemporary writer who received his A.B. from Harvard. During World War II he was a correspondent stationed at various battlefields in Europe. He is co-author, with Henry Thomas, of the "Living Biographies" series (Garden), and "Living Adventures" series (Garden). One of his other books is *Crusaders for God*. Mr. Thomas has also contributed articles to various magazines.

HENRY THOMAS is an educator as well as an author. He has taught at Boston University and at the Fairfax Hall Preparatory School in Cambridge, Massachusetts, where he was the headmaster. As an author he has written about thirty juvenile and adult books, including *Mathematics Made Easy* (Garden), *The Complete Book of English* (Garden), *The Modern Self-Educator* (Garden), *The Wonderbook of Knowledge* (Garden), *Science Made Easy* (Garden), *The Story of the Human Race* (Garden), and the "Living Biographies" series (Garden).

DIANA THORNE was born in Winnipeg, Canada, and spent her childhood roaming the wide open spaces. She was educated in Canada and England and studied art in Germany, France, and England. William Strang, English etcher and painter, and Professor Lieberman were two of her teachers. Her paintings and etchings have been exhibited throughout the world. Her dog pictures then began to appear on magazine covers and in children's books, and many dogs of famous people sat for their portrait. Albert Payson Terhune was soon calling her "the glorifier of the American dog." Diana Thorne is married and lives in New York. Among her best-known books are *Drawing Dogs* (Studio), *The Dog Who Ran Away* (Putnam), *Your Dog and Mine* (Minton Balch), *An Album of Dogs* (Messner), *Little Fellow* (Winston) by Marguerite Henry, *101 Animals and Birds* (Sterling), and *Drawing the Dog* (Guptill).

JAMES THURBER is known to us all as a great American humorist. *Many Moons* (Harcourt) which won the Caldecott Award, and *The Great Quillow* (Harcourt) show us that he is also one of the outstanding storytellers for children. Mr. Thurber was born in Columbus, Ohio, and studied at Ohio State University. From 1918–1920 he was a code clerk with the State Department, first in Washington, then with the Embassy in Paris. It was after this that he turned to journalism, working on the *Chicago Tribune* and on the *New York Evening Post*. Since 1926 he has been a contributor to the *New Yorker*. James Thurber drew before he wrote, and in the adult field he has won great fame as a humorist. Whatever seems casual in his drawing or writing is really the result of much careful work. He is the author of a number of books for adults. These include a famous play (with Elliott Nugent), *The Male Animal* (Random), *My Life and Hard Times* (Harper), *The Thurber Carnival* (Harper), and *Thurber Country* (Harper). His *Unicorn in the Garden*, a motion picture, is a most amusing cartoon comedy.

EUNICE TIETJENS was at one time an editor of *Poetry Magazine* and was a poet of distinction. She spent much of her time in travel and lived, for some time, in the Orient, in North Africa, and in the South Seas. Her real homes were in Chicago and in Florida. She was the wife of Cloyd Head and the mother of two children. A number of her stories for children appeared first in *Child Life Magazine* and later were published in book form. Among her adult books of lovely poetry is *Leaves in Windy Weather* (Knopf). *The World at My Shoulder* (Macmillan) is her biography. Among her books for children are *Boy of the Desert* (Coward-McCann), *Boy of the South Seas* (Coward-McCann), and *Romance of Antar* (Coward-McCann). "Desert Adventure" (Volume 9:307) is one of the absorbing episodes of *Boy of the Desert*.

JANET TIETJENS (Hart) is a busy mother of several children and lives in a Chicago suburb. She is the daughter of the late Eunice Tietjens, and when she was a little girl she and her mother made up the delightful rhymes found in *The Jawbreakers Alphabet* (Boni).

JAMES TIPPETT was born on Circus Day in Memphis, Missouri, and the circus has always been one of his hobbies. He grew up on a farm and later went to Teachers College of Columbia University. For years he has taught thousands of children in many places, from California to Connecticut. At present, when he is not in New York, he lives in Scotland, Connecticut. His chief hobbies are books, gardening, and dogs. Among his best-known books of verse for children are *I Go A Traveling* (Harper), *I Live in a City* (Harper), and *I Spent the Summer* (Harper).

ENYS TREGARTHEN (1851–1923) was the author of *The Doll Who Came Alive* (Day), a Cornish fairy tale, and *Piskey Folk* (Day), a book of Cornish legends.

BEVERLY TREYBAL is a young Chicago artist who lives in Elmhurst, Illinois, a suburb of Chicago. She worked for some time in the art department of the Spencer Press and is now doing advertising work.

JOHN R. TUNIS, an American writer of sports stories for boys, was born in Boston. He was graduated from Harvard and served in France during World War I. He then became a sports writer on the *New York Evening Post*. Later he was connected with the National Broadcasting Company, covering all major tennis matches in this country and Europe. His entrance into radio happened to coincide with a major event in radio history, for he participated in the first transatlantic sports broadcast, during the Davis Cup match between Allison and Borotra in Paris in 1932. He has written for practically every magazine in the United States, from *College Humor* to the *Atlantic Monthly* and *Foreign Affairs*. Among his popular books for boys are *All-American* (Harcourt), *The Iron Duke* (Harcourt), *The Duke Decides* (Harcourt), *Yea! Wildcats* (Harcourt), *World Series* (Harcourt), and *Go Team Go* (Morrow).

"The Pass" (Volume 10:350) is from his book *All-American,* and "Two-Mile Race" (Volume 10:321) from *The Iron Duke.*

BRINTON TURKLE, an outstanding contemporary artist, was born in Alliance, Ohio, where he went to primary and high schools. Although he had always drawn pictures for as long as he could remember, he was more attracted to the theater when he was ready for college and went to the Carnegie Institute of Technology in Pittsburgh to study drama. He says that the sad discovery that there are more hungry actors than hungry artists made him decide in his Junior year to go to art school in Boston, first, the Vesper George School, and then the School of the Museum of Fine Arts. Afterwards he went to Chicago, where he was engaged in advertising and instruction at nights at the Institute of Design. The lure of the Southwest finally drew him to Santa Fe in 1948 with his wife. This was to be only a year's leave, but when he "discovered that he was able to scrape along with book illustrating commissions," he has not yet left the country to which he has become devoted. He is married and has two children, a boy and a girl. He writes: "My theater experience has stood me in good stead. Not only in my illustration, where it helps me approach a design from the dramatic point of view, and in my studies in scene, architectural and costume design which are of obvious help, but it furnishes me with a thriving hobby. I have designed sets and costumes for the Santa Fe Little Theater, as well as taught make-up, and acted. My illustrations appear in such publications as *Story Parade* and in books by Whittlesey House, Westminster Press, Doubleday, Row, Peterson, and Scott, Foresman. I am hoping to write and illustrate good books of my own some day."

NANCY BYRD TURNER is a poet of distinction. In 1930 she was awarded the New England Poetry Club's Golden Rose, and later the Lyric Award. She has published three books of poetry, a biography of the mother of Washington (in collaboration with Sidney Gunn), and fifteen books for children. She has been on the staffs of the *Youth's Companion,* Houghton Mifflin Company, and the *Atlantic Monthly.* At present she is a free-lance writer who does program work and she makes her home near Richmond, Virginia, and spends many of her summers at the MacDowell Colony in New Hampshire. It is interesting to know she was the great-great-great-great niece of Thomas Jefferson and a descendent of Pocahontas.

ELEANOR UNDERWOOD has written many verses for children, some of which have been transcribed into Braile and also set to music. She has lived for many years in Evanston, Illinois, and has worked a great deal with children.

EDITH UNNERSTAD is a Swedish author whose novels and children's books have been translated into many languages. *The Saucepan Journey* (Macmillan) was her first book to come to America. Like the Larssons of the story, Edith Unnerstad was one of a family of seven children. She was the next to the oldest, so she learned at an early age to understand children and love them, and best of all, to tell them stories. She was born in Finland, but has spent most of her life in Sweden. She lives in Stockholm with her husband and daughter. Although her novels are successful Mrs.

| James Tippett | Brinton Turkle | Nancy Byrd Turner | Nora S. Unwin |

| Hilda Van Stockum | Ruth Van Tellingen | Antoine Emile Verpilleux |

Unnerstad likes best to write her juveniles. "Nothing is too good for children," she says. She recommends writing for children as a most stimulating experience for any author. "The Singing Saucepan" (Volume 9:65) is part of *The Saucepan Journey*.

NORA S. UNWIN knew from the age of six that she wanted to be an artist. When she was eight she wrote and illustrated her first book, *The Adventures of a Blade of Grass*, and gave it to her mother for a birthday present. She lived with her four brothers and sisters in Surbiton, Surrey, England. When the photographer took a family picture, Nora, one of the twins, grew bored and began to draw. Only the top of her head showed when that photograph was developed. Her family was a happy one. They sang together and read together. When she grew older Nora went to Leon Underwood's art studio in London, then to the Kingston School of Art, and then won a scholarship to the Royal College of Art, and at nineteen she illustrated her first book, E. Nesbit's *Five of Us—and Madeline*. She grew interested in doing wood engravings, wood carving, designing, and even did some sculpture, appliqué, and embroidery. Her love for drawing figures, animals, natural and imaginative subjects, as well as lettering, soon led her to book illustrating. She has been living happily in Peterboro, New Hampshire, for several years now. She has four books of her own and has illustrated over fifty English and American books. Her wood engravings appear regularly in exhibitions in this country and abroad and have brought her wide acclaim. She is a Fellow of the Royal Society of Painter-Etchers and Engravers, and an Associate of the Royal College of Art—two great honors. Her distinguished illustrations are to be found in such books as *Round the Year* (Chatto), *Lucy and the Little Red Horse* (De la More Press), *The White Ring* (Harcourt), *Footnotes on Nature* (Doubleday), and *Mountain Born* (Coward-McCann).

MAUD E. USCHOLD who lives in Lacon, Illinois, is a contemporary author whose verse has appeared in various juvenile publications.

JUDY VAN DER VEER is a poet who lives on a ranch in California. There, amid her assortment of cows, horses, dogs, cats, a goat, and a pig, she has been writing her books, stories, and delightful poems about animals. Many of her poems appear in contemporary magazines.

HILDA VAN STOCKUM a Dutch-American miniature painter, illustrator, and author of children's books, was born in Holland. Her father was a naval officer and she did much traveling. She was graduated from the Amsterdam Academy of Art and after that married and went to New York and Washington. Later, Canada was her home. She is busy these days bringing up her six children and writing and illustrating many books for them. Among these are *The Cottage at Bantry Bay* (Viking), *Pegeen* (Viking), *Canadian Summer* (Viking), and *The Mitchells* (Viking). "A Visit with Pierre" (Volume 9:85) is part of *Canadian Summer*.

RUTH VAN TELLINGEN likes best of all to illustrate stories for boys and girls. *The Children's Treasury* (Consolidated) contains many of her chubby children and gay little brownies, and several children's magazines also use her illustrations. She lives with her husband, Victor D. Bendel, her two boys, and her German Shepherd dog, Roy, in Westmont, Illinois, not far from Chicago. After studying at Grinnell College and at the Chicago Art Institute, she did greeting cards, cut silhouettes, and designed decals and salt and pepper shakers, but now Ruth Van Tellingen keeps busy illustrating stories.

J. LILIAN VANDEVERE was born in Pennsylvania and taught there for many years. She is a musical supervisor, has taught piano, and composed a good deal. Her humorous verse has appeared in all the children's magazines and she is the author of *A Peck for Peter* (Rand).

ANNE VAUGHAN born in Worcester, Massachusetts, finished school and then went to the Boston Museum School of Fine Arts, and later to the Fontainebleau School in Fontainebleau, France. She began designing textiles in a New York studio by day and working at home on illustrations at night. She devoted all her time later to illustrating children's books and designing toys and book jackets. During World War II she took a course in engineering so that she could do designing in a defense plant. Since then she has been teaching design and illustration at the Worcester Art Museum School and illustrating a number of books, among them Bergengren's *Susan and the Butterbees* (Longmans), Carveth's *Jungle Boy* (Longmans), Lang's *Olive Fairy Book* (Longmans) and Singh and Lownsbery's *Gift of the Forest* (Longmans).

ANTOINE EMILE VERPILLEUX had an international reputation for woodcut color prints before he was thirty years old. He is the British-born son of a French father and an English mother. He studied art in England, France, Belgium, and Holland. By the end of World War I, in which he served with distinction as a captain with the Royal Flying Corps and then the Royal Air Force, his color prints were already famous and soon appeared in every major museum in the world. He has illustrated several books, notably *Robinson Crusoe* (Macmillan), and has done poster work, and his work has appeared in many magazines. His specialties now, however, are his fine landscapes, his marine paintings, and his very outstanding portraits. His work is found in leading art galleries in Europe, Asia, and America. He and his wife now live in Bermuda, where he encourages young artists and enjoys his hobbies—sailing, fencing, and gardening.

MALVIN WALD is a contemporary American author who has contributed stories to various juvenile publications.

HANS WALLEEN is a contemporary artist who has illustrated books for boys.

CAROLYN WALTHER, when she was a little girl, won a number of awards for her drawings. Later she graduated from the American Academy of Art in Chicago and then worked for a while for the Spencer Press. Now she is doing commercial art in her home town of Joliet, Illinois.

Carolyn Walther   Keith Ward   Lynd Ward   Walter Weber

278

KEITH WARD is one of the outstanding American artists of today. He lives with his wife and two children in New Canaan, Connecticut, but for many years was a very busy artist in Chicago. He did many fine covers and illustrations for *Child Life Magazine* and illustrated several books for Rand McNally & Company. He has done much art work for national advertising, and at the present time he is busy designing very humorous rubber toys for children.

LYND WARD, a distinguished artist-author, lives with his wife and two daughters in Leonia, New Jersey, where an old barn has been converted into a studio for him. Though he was born in Evanston, Illinois, he was brought up in Massachusetts and New Jersey, and graduated from Columbia Teachers College with a major in Fine Arts. After study in Leipzig, he came back to this country and began to illustrate books. His first book was for adults, a novel without words, made up entirely of woodcuts. It was called *God's Man* (Cape). Then he began to illustrate children's books and through the years has illustrated more than one hundred of them. These include Coatsworth's *The Cat Who Went to Heaven* and Forbes' *Johnny Tremain*, both Newbery winners. They also include his own book that he both wrote and illustrated, which won the Newbery Medal, *The Biggest Bear* (Houghton).

BOOKER T. WASHINGTON (1858–1915) was an American educator of the Negro, who was born in Virginia. He was the son of a mulatto slave and a white man. He graduated from Hampton Institute, Harvard, and Dartmouth. He taught at Hampton and later became the successful head of Tuskegee Institute. He was a well-known writer and speaker. Among his books were the inspiring *Up from Slavery* (Doubleday), *The Future of the American Negro* (Doubleday), and *The Negro in Business* (Doubleday). (See Volume 15:211 for a longer biography.)

WILLIAM WATSON (1858–1935), the English poet, was born in Yorkshire and educated in Liverpool. His first book was *Epigrams of Our Life and Nature*, in 1884. In time his delicate, thoughtful verse won high rank in English poetry. Among his books were *Lyric Love, The Purple East*, and *The Muse in Exile*.

WALTER WEBER was born in Chicago and was graduated from the University of Chicago, a Phi Beta Kappa. He majored in zoology and botany and specialized, when he went to art school, in drawing birds and animals. He studied at the Church School of Art, the Chicago Art Institute, and the American Academy. For the Chicago Museum of Natural History, he became a scientific illustrator. He has been on a number of scientific expeditions to paint birds and fishes in the South Seas, Bermuda, and Mexico. His bird pictures are so outstanding they have been compared to Audubon's. He has been on the National Park Service, the U. S. National Museum, and is now living in Vienna, Virginia, and is a staff artist for the National Geographic Society. He contributes many bird and animal paintings to the *National Geographic Magazine* and has done outstanding illustrations for books, including *Traveling with the Birds* (Donahue), *The Book of Birds* (Rand), *Fading Trails* (Macmillan), and *Meeting the Mammals* (Macmillan).

WINIFRED WELLES was born in Connecticut and lived there all her life. She began writing poems for her own son and her fine collection called *Skipping Along Alone* (Macmillan) made her, in recent years, one of the outstanding poets for children.

CAROLYN WELLS was an American writer and famous humorist, born in Rahway, New Jersey, who lived most of her life in the East. In 1918 she married Hadwin Houghton. She began writing at an early age, and her versatility is shown in her humorous sketches, parodies, juveniles (she wrote the "Patty Fairfield" [Dodd] books), stories, novels, and detective fiction. Some of her best children's verse is found in *The Jingle Book* (Macmillan) and *A Nonsense Anthology* (Blue Ribbon Books).

279

H. G. WELLS (1866–1952), English novelist, was born in Bromley, Kent. He graduated from London University with high honors, and for several years he taught biology. His interest in weird material, scientific knowledge, and sociological problems are all shown in his many fine adult books. Some of these are *The Time Machine* (Holt), *The Invisible Man* (Arnold), *Ann Veronica* (Harper), *Mr. Brittling Sees It Through* (Macmillan), and *Tony Bungay* (Duffield). His *Outline of History* (Macmillan) was also very popular.

PETER WELLS is a contemporary writer whose humorous verse appears in juvenile magazines. He is also the author and illustrator of *Mr. Tootwhistle's Invention* (Winston).

CHARLES WESLEY (1707–1788) was an English clergyman who wrote many hymns. He was associated with his brother, John, in the Methodist movement.

BENTON WEST is a contemporary artist who once resided in Chicago. He illustrated, among other things, *Poppy* (Rand).

ANNE H. WHITE is a contemporary writer who is the author of the delightful *Story of Serapina* (Viking). "Serapina Proves Herself" (Volume 4:166) will give you some idea of how good that book is.

WILLIAM C. WHITE is a contemporary writer, best known as the author of *Mouse-knees* (Random), a story of a West Indies colored boy. "Who Is Who" (Volume 9:253) is one episode from that book.

WALT WHITMAN (1819–1892), a great American poet, originated a new type of poetry in America. He broke with tradition by writing about the common people, and his verse lacked regularly recurring rhyme or meter, which was a departure from Tennyson and the New England poets, with their measured cadences. But it was not too long before people recognized his greatness. Whitman was born on Long Island, where he lived most of his life. He followed many different occupations before publishing his poetry. *Leaves of Grass*, his first volume, gained him a great reputation as a poet. Although a pacifist, during the War between the States he nursed wounded soldiers in Washington hospitals. He considered Lincoln one of the country's great men and two of Whitman's best poems were done in sorrow at his death: "When Lilacs Last in the Door-yard Bloomed" and "O Captain! My Captain!"

JOHN GREENLEAF WHITTIER (1807–1892) Quaker poet, newspaper editor, and antislavery agitator, was born in Massachusetts and lived most of his life there. A copy of Burns' poems, given him as a boy by his schoolmaster, made him want to write verse. Five years later his first poem, called "The Exile's Departure," was printed in Garrison's paper, the *Newburyport Free Press*. This started a lifelong friendship between Whittier and the great abolitionist. Whittier later became editor of several Eastern papers. In 1832 he devoted himself entirely to crusading for the abolitionists. The

Anne H. White   William C. White   John Greenleaf Whittier

most famous of his political poems was his denunciation of his distant relative, Daniel Webster, in "Ichabod." Ill health forced him to retire in 1842, but he continued to write. "Snow-Bound" pictures the simple rural life of his boyhood and "The Barefoot Boy" portrays the idyllic life of the New England farmer. Two of the best-known short narrative poems by John Greenleaf Whittier are "Skipper Ireson's Ride" and "Barbara Frietchie."

MARGARET WIDDEMER began to write when she was a child, and has continued doing so ever since. Her first work was poetry, and that is what she loves best. Her *The Old Road to Paradise* (Holt) won high praise. *A Tree with a Bird in It* (Harcourt) was given an award by the Poetry Society and also won the Post Literary Review prize. She has written several light-hearted novels of pure romance for adults such as *The Rose-Garden Husband* (Lippincott) and *You're Only Young Once* (Holt). One of her more serious books, *The Boardwalk* (Harcourt), is a story of a summer resort town on the Atlantic seacoast, much like the town she lived in as a little girl. Some of her delightful verse for children is found in *Little Girl and Boy Land* (Harcourt).

KURT WIESE was in China at the beginning of World War I. The British, because he was German born, sent him eventually to an Australian detention camp. To pass the time of waiting, Kurt Wiese began to draw pictures from memory—pictures of animals as he remembered them in all his travels throughout the world. When he returned to Germany, he made his first books for boys and girls. Then came a sojourn in South America, after which he came to New York. Here he married and moved to a little New Jersey farmhouse at the edge of a wood. All the children around are his friends. They come every day to watch him work, and bring him presents of animals to draw and befriend. Mr. Wiese is a fine artist and an expert craftsman, as anyone knows who looks at his pictures for *Honk: the Moose* (Dodd) by Phil Stong, *No-Sitch: the Hound* (Dodd) by Phil Stong, *Young Fu* (Winston) by Elizabeth Foreman Lewis, and *Freddy the Detective* (Knopf) by Walter Brooks, and those for many other books. He has done some books that he both wrote and illustrated, too. Among them are *The Chinese Ink Stick* (Doubleday), *Liang and Lo* (Doubleday), *Buddy the Bear* (Coward), *Kurt Wiese's Picture Book of Animals* (Coward), and *The Dog, the Fox, and the Fleas* (McKay).

KATE DOUGLAS WIGGIN (1856–1923) was born in Philadelphia. Her parents were New Englanders and her childhood was spent in Maine. She met Dickens and talked to him while traveling on a train from Hollis to Portland, Maine, when she was just a little girl. (See "A Journey with Dickens" [Volume 15:106].) This experience, she felt, always had a great influence on her life. At twenty-one she published her first story serially in *St. Nicholas*. She studied child education in Los Angeles and organized the first free kindergarten west of the Rockies. Her first book, *The Birds' Christmas Carol* (Houghton), she did for the children in her kindergarten. From that time on she continued to write stories for children. Among them are *Mother Carey's Chickens* (Houghton) and *Timothy's Quest* (Houghton). Mrs. Wiggin did much of her writing in Maine. She also lived some time in New York, where Sir Henry Irving, Ellen Terry, Mark Twain, and William Dean Howells were her friends. "Rebecca at the Brick House" (Volume 3:203) comes from *Rebecca of Sunnybrook Farm* (Houghton), one of her best-loved stories.

CAROLINE P. WILD wrote her lovely poem, "The Mountain," when she was eleven years old. It was written about Mount Monadnock in New Hampshire, and first published in *Story Parade*.

CAROLINE S. P. WILD is an Evanston, Illinois, writer who has contributed fine verse to many juvenile magazines. Her granddaughter is Caroline P. Wild, whose poetry also appears in *The Children's Hour*.

Kurt Wiese   Laura Ingalls Wilder   Barrett Willoughby

OSCAR WILDE (1856–1900), Irish dramatist, poet, and author, was born in Dublin.
His mother was a writer and Wilde was brought up in a literary world. His famous
witticisms were apparent early at Oxford, where he was a subject for caricature in
Punch and in Gilbert and Sullivan's *Patience*. He later made a lecture tour of America, carrying a sunflower and wearing silk knee breeches. In 1884, following his
marriage to Constance Lloyd, his literary career began. He first wrote fairy tales
which are loved and read even today. Among these are *The Happy Prince, The Birthday of the Infanta, The Nightingale and the Rose*, and *The Star Child*. His dramas
followed. *Lady Windemere's Fan, An Ideal Husband*, and *The Importance of Being
Earnest* are still being produced every year in various parts of the country and on
television.

LAURA INGALLS WILDER was born in the "Little House in the Big Woods." The "Big
Woods" were in Wisconsin. When she was three, her father, a trapper, hunter, and
Indian fighter, took his family West by covered wagon to the Indian Territory, where
she lived in the "Little House on the Prairie." Later, in western Minnesota, she lived
on the banks of Plum Creek. At the age of fifteen, illegally, because she was not yet
sixteen, she taught school. Three years later, she married Almanzo Wilder, the hero
of *Farmer Boy* (Harper). They moved to Mansfield, Missouri, where they bought a
dairy farm. She began her literary career by contributing special articles to newspapers and to such magazines as *Country Gentleman* and *McCall's*. This led her to
write of her own experiences for children, and many delightful books followed:
Little House in the Big Woods (Harper), *Little House on the Prairie* (Harper), *On
the Banks of Plum Creek* (Harper), *By the Shores of Silver Lake* (Harper), *The
Long Winter* (Harper), *Little Town on the Prairie* (Harper), *Farmer Boy* (Harper),
and *These Happy Golden Years* (Harper). Besides writing, she has been active in
farm women's club work through southwestern Missouri. She is still living on her
farm and her gingerbread is famous throughout the county. Rose Wilder Lane, the
novelist, is her daughter. "Christmas Horses" (Volume 11:111) is one of the adventures in *On the Banks of Plum Creek*.

DOROTHY WILDING is a well-known New York photographer whose photographs of
the Queen of England are very famous.

PERCY H. WILKINS is an Englishman, and is a writer for a number of English magazines.

BARRETT WILLOUGHBY claims the distinction of being the first native Alaskan to have
written of Alaska. She has been called "the woman Jack London." Her earliest memories are of the northern lights, Indian drums, dancing sticks, a little red blanket for
her first dress, and moccasins for her first shoes. Her first playground was the deck
of her father's trading schooner, as he sailed along the coast of Alaska in search of
gold, furs, and adventure. Thlinget chiefs tried to buy her from her parents with
sea-otter skins because of her white skin and golden hair. Later, she went with her
father into the wilderness where he opened a trading post. Here she had her first

Dixie Willson   Helen Wing

lessons in the art of fiction from listening, on long winter's nights, to adventurers from all over the world exchanging tall stories. She learned about the great seal herd and about totem-pole superstitions. She danced with "sourdoughs" and Aleuts in this Land of Always Afternoon. Today, when Barrett Willoughby has collected her material in some out-of-the-way corner of the north, she goes and lives in San Francisco, and writes her story, using a typewriter to which is tied the tiny carved ivory Eskimo fetish which has presided over her good fortunes ever since she first began to write. Among her books are such colorful Alaskan thrillers as *Alaska Holiday* (Little), *Sondra O'Moore* (Little), and *River House* (Little). "One Alaska Night" (Volume 7:297) is one of the exciting experiences she had in *Alaska Holiday*.

DIXIE WILLSON, when she was a little girl in Mason City, Iowa, wanted to ride on an elephant in a circus. Years later she joined Ringling's Circus one summer in order to get material for a circus book, and that summer she achieved her childhood ambition. One day she rode into the circus ring—and she was on an elephant's back! She had fun in Mason City as a little girl with her two brothers. One of them is Meredith Willson, the well-known musician of radio and television fame. Her first story was printed in a local paper when she was ten. After that she began writing other bits of verse and selling what she wrote. She staged a three-act musical comedy in Mason City and finally landed in New York, where she had wanted to go. She worked in a chorus on the stage there and was one of a group of specialty dancers, until Bob Davis, editor of *All Story Magazine* discovered her. She wrote twelve stories for him, many of which were selected as best short stories of the year in the O'Brien collection. After this, she began to write children's stories for Volland and poems for the *Delineator* and *Good Housekeeping*. She published her first novel, *Little Texas* (Appleton-Century), a story of circus life, and another circus story appeared in *Good Housekeeping*. At the same time she was writing stories and verses for *Child Life*. In those early days she did two movies and the Dixie Willson "Showbox," a kit which included a play, handbills, advertising posters, tickets, and costumes, so that boys and girls could put on the play themselves. To write *Hostess of the Skyways* (Dodd) she went to an air hostess school and even learned to fly.

ANTHONY C. WILSON is one of England's most popular writers for boys. His three mystery stories in *Norman Bones, Detective* (Crowell) were broadcast many times over the BBC and have been translated into several languages. Mr. Wilson is, by profession, a teacher. His hobbies include natural history, amateur dramatics, music, carpentry, and electrical work. *Norman and Henry Investigate* (Crowell) is another book about his famous young detectives. "Hunter's Moon" (Volume 7:315) is one of the exciting adventures in *Norman Bones, Detective*.

HELEN WING, in addition to contributing poems to various children's magazines and anthologies, is very much occupied running the Normandy House in Chicago. At one time she was director of radio programs on a national network, and also taught in the Chicago School of Expression. Her books include *The Lazy Lion* (Rand). Along with this she has written the lyrics and music for four operettas for children.

283

ALBERT H. WINKLER, who designed the covers for *The Children's Hour,* is well known in the field of book design and layout. He is a Chicagoan, and received his training at three Chicago art schools: The Chicago Art Institute, the Church School of Design, and the Audubon School. For a short time he was head of the latter, and also taught there. He has received honorable mention for some of his work from the Society of Typographic Art, and *The History of St. Peter's Church* (Franciscan Herald Press) that he designed, was chosen one of the Fifty Books of the Year (1953).

MARILOU WISE finds music and art are her twin vocations. She was born in Drumright, Oklahoma, and grew up in Tulsa. She majored in art at the Universities of Oklahoma and Tulsa. At the age of seventeen she was singing popular music over radio stations in Tulsa. Having decided on a career in commercial art, she came to Chicago, where she studied at the Chicago Academy, American Academy of Art, and the Art Institute. She likes to do advertising art and humorous illustrations.

FFRIDA WOLFE's delightful poems are found in many anthologies.

LOUIS WOLFE was born in Bound Brook, New Jersey. His parents were poor immigrants from Russia. At the age of ten he started working after school and during summer vacations to help with the family expenses. While at Rutgers University, he had various jobs: bucking up rivets in a steel factory, driving a truck, and selling cashew nuts from door to door. After graduation, he taught elementary school and soon was telling stories to the children. Later, he produced and conducted children's programs and wrote adventure stories and strips for comics. Louis Wolfe also had a syndicated science column in the newspaper. Following this, he specialized in writing especially for children, and was a frequent contributor to juvenile magazines. In 1950, *Young America* sent him around to the various schools in New York City to tell stories to large assemblies. He has written two Golden story books for Simon and Schuster.

CATHERINE WOOLLEY has been writing picture books and short stories for the six-to-twelve set since 1944 when *I Like Trains* (Harper) appeared. A graduate of the University of California at Los Angeles, Miss Woolley was a business woman, until she retired in 1947 to give more time to writing. She lives in Passaic, New Jersey, where she is active in civic affairs. She has been president of the League of Women Voters and now serves on the Board of Education. Among her more recent books are *David's Railroad* (Morrow), *Two Hundred Pennies* (Morrow), *Schoolroom Zoo* (Morrow), and *Railroad Cowboy* (Morrow).

WILLIAM WORDSWORTH (1770–1860) was one of the great English poets who wrote about nature. Most of his beautiful poetry belongs to older readers, but boys and girls like some of his simpler poems. Wordsworth went to Cambridge and traveled abroad a good deal. He lived with his sister for many years at Grasmere. With his wife and three children, he later made his permanent home at Rydal Mount. In his early days he and Coleridge published their famous *Lyrical Ballads*. He did not need to earn his living so he could write without thought of that. For the last thirty years

Albert H. Winkler   Marilou Wise   Louis Wolfe   Catherine Woolley

284

of his life he received a pension from the government and became Poet Laureate of England. Wordsworth insisted on writing truly and simply and with real feeling. He did much toward bringing about the revival of English poetry at the beginning of the nineteenth century. His *Complete Poems* (Macmillan) will be found in all libraries and in many homes.

KATHRYN WORTH's great-grandfather was once governor of North Carolina and it was in Wilmington, North Carolina, that she was born. Now she is married to a college professor and lives in Nashville, Tennessee. She remembers how she used to make up poems as she ran barefoot at the seashore, and how she used to write when she went to school in Switzerland and went to college at Radcliffe and Columbia. It wasn't easy, she said, to keep on sending manuscripts to editors, but finally she began to sell things. When her daughter was growing up, she began to write her books. *Poems for Josephine* (Doubleday) is a book of verse that is well liked. *They Love To Laugh* (Doubleday), *The Middle Button* (Doubleday), *Sea Change* (Doubleday), and *New World's for Josie* (Doubleday) were written later. They are novels for young people, and her own daughter told her what she wanted to find in her books. "Have at least one death, preferably two; have at least one wild animal or dangerous snake; include a lot of animals of the tame kind; make part of the story funny; and if possible have a cataclysm near the end." She says she has tried to follow Josephine's directions.

LILLIAN WUERFEL is a contemporary artist who lives in Elmhurst, Illinois, close to Chicago. She was graduated from the Chicago Art Institute, married a fellow student, and has three children. Now she is a happy grandmother. She has been art editor of the Merrill Publishing Company in Chicago, art editor of the *Children's Treasury* (Consolidated), art editor for the children's records brought out by the Regensteiner Corporation, art editor for the Spencer Press, and is now art editor of *Children's Activities.*

EDGAR WYATT lives in Tucson, Arizona. He has written numerous articles and short stories about the Indian wars in our Southwest. His *Geronimo* (Whittlesey) is a fictional biography of the great Apache war chief. His *Cochise* (Whittlesey) is a selection of the Junior Literary Guild.

EDITH FRANKLIN WYATT is a well-known Chicago poet whose lovely poems have appeared in a number of magazines. Miss Wyatt was one of the founders of *Poetry Magazine* and of The Society of Midland Authors. She was born in Tomah, Wisconsin, and went to Bryn Mawr, later working on *McClure's Magazine* in New York. Among her books are *Great Companions* (Appleton), *The Wind in the Corn* (Appleton), and *The Satyr's Children* (Argus). Miss Wyatt still lives in Chicago and loves to garden. She spends her winters in Florida.

N. C. WYETH (1882–1945) was an American artist, born in Needham, Massachusetts, and was known for his vivid colorful pictures found in many children's classics.

Kathryn Worth   Edgar Wyatt   Edith Franklin Wyatt   William Butler Yeats

285

He also did many fine murals, among them panels in the Missouri state capitol and in the Hubbard Memorial Building in Washington, D. C.

ANNETTE WYNNE was born in Brooklyn and educated at New York University and the University of California. Although her first job was on a Portland, Oregon, newspaper, she did not do much newspaper work. Instead, she went to teach in Alaska, where she learned to speak an Indian language. She later returned to Brooklyn and to New York, where she went on teaching. She had been writing rhymes from childhood days, but most of her later poems appearing in *For Days and Days* (Lippincott) and *All through the Year* (Lippincott) were written for her own students and for the children in a settlement house club in New York, which she directed.

WILLIAM BUTLER YEATS (1865–1939) was a great poet, essayist, and playwright. He was born near Dublin, Ireland. His father and brother were artists, and he studied painting for three years. As a boy, after his parents moved to London, he spent much of his time on the west coast of Ireland with his shipowner grandfather. He was educated at Godolphin School, London, and Erasmus Smith School, Dublin. At the age of twenty-one, he turned to literature, reading Gaelic, listening to folk tales, and writing poetry. At thirty-five he helped Lady Gregory found the Abbey Theater, for which he wrote plays in verse. This made him the acknowledged leader of the Irish Movement. He lived with his wife and two children in an old tower on the western coast of Ireland. From 1922 to 1928 he served as senator of the Irish Free State. His *Collected Poems* (Macmillan) and *Collected Plays* (Macmillan) show how outstanding his work really was.

BARBARA YOUNG's book *Christopher O* (McKay) is filled with many of the delightful poems she writes for children.

ELLA YOUNG is a famous Irish poet. She is also an authority on Irish literature and folklore. She is a graduate of the Royal University, Dublin, with honors in history, jurisprudence and political economy. But she has devoted herself to the field of mythology and folklore, and earned distinction in it. She has spent many years in research work in Celtic mythology, and has pieced out the old Celtic Myth of Creation—a myth of most noble conception. She has written and published many books— books of fairy tales and folklore and books of her own poetry. Some of these are *The Wonder-Smith and His Son* (Longmans), and *Celtic Wonder Tales* (Longmans). She has long been a favorite lecturer in Ireland and in America as well. In her lecture on "Celtic Ireland and the Story-tellers," she tells stories that have been handed down in Gaelic-speaking families for generations. They have been told to her in peasant huts, in fishing boats, and on mountainsides. They are living stories, still real in the lives of the simple people who relate them. She herself says, "If I have anything to interest an American audience, it will be because I have lived in wild places amongst a primitive unspoiled people, and have heard by turf fires in little mountain cabins stories a thousand years old, and tales of faery creatures that happen amongst such people even now—and because I have myself a heart that loves such stories and such adventures." In "Poets I Have Known," she gives her own vivid impressions of the Irish poets. She gives humorous and picturesque descriptions of them and their doings and then makes their poetry alive to us. She came to America as a lecturer in 1925. Later, in California, she was a lecturer on Celtic Mythology and Literature in the University of California at Berkeley. She is now living near the great dunes at Oceano and believes her writing has gained something from the rhythm of the Pacific and the weird beauty of the Mojave desert.

ANN ZELENKA is a contemporary poet who, when she was just a child, wrote some very beautiful poetry. Her poems have been appearing in various anthologies and in children's magazines since her early teens. She is married now, lives in Detroit, and has one child.

CONSULTANT EDITORS FOR THE CHILDREN'S HOUR

CAROL RYRIE BRINK, who is a consultant editor of *The Children's Hour,* began writing stories 'or her two children when they were young and later these stories grew into books. Two of them, *Anything Can Happen on the River* (Macmillan) and *Lad with a Whistle* (Macmillan), were inspired while living in France and Scotland. One of her most famous books, *Caddie Woodlawn* (Macmillan), which won a Newbery award, is based on stories of her grandmother's childhood. She and her family live in Minnesota where her husband is a professor at the University. Her *Family Grandstand* (Viking) depicts just such a family. "Caddie's Silver Dollar" (Volume 11:127) is one adventure you will find in *Caddie Woodlawn,* and "The Willow Basket" (Volume 11:93) comes from her book *Magical Melons.* These are both fine books you will want to read.

JULIA M. H. CARSON, who is a consultant editor for *The Children's Hour,* is a writer of outstanding biographies. She was admitted to the Connecticut bar and to the United States Supreme Court bar shortly after graduating from Yale. She has always been interested in government functions on both the local and national levels, and has worked closely with the League of Women Voters. She chose Patrick Henry to write about (Volume 15:337) as he was one of the brilliant leaders when our government was being organized. Her book about him is called *Son of Thunder* (Longmans).

FLEUR CONKLING, wife of William Heyliger, has been teacher, writer, poet, critic, and lecturer. Trained to be a kindergarten and primary teacher, she has always been interested in children. She served as educational director of *Cue Magazine* in New York and has been on the staffs of Silver Burdett & Co., Dell Publishing Co., and Walt Disney Publications. A frequent contributor to children's magazines, her poetry has also appeared in the *Saturday Evening Post, Saturday Review of Literature,* and other publications. Among her children's books are: *The Bingity Bang School Bus* (Westminster), *The Brave Little Duck* (Westminster), *Billy Between* (Westminster), and *Mr. Grumpy and the Kitten* (Winston), a Junior Literary Guild selection. Fleur Conkling greatly helped her husband with his work as consultant editor of *The Children's Hour.*

IRVING CRUMP, a well-loved editor of *Boys' Life,* and consultant editor for *The Children's Hour,* learned to like the out-of-doors as a child. It was at this time, too, that he first decided to write stories for boys when he grew up. Before he was able to do this, however, he worked as a reporter for six years and then wrote several adult tales. In addition to his magazine work he has done many books, some of which are: *Boys' Book of Cowboys* (Dodd), *Our Firemen* (Dodd), and *Our Airliners* (Dodd). He has also written radio shows and motion pictures, and has been associated with both the Local and National Council of the Boy Scouts of America.

Carol Ryrie Brink   Julia M. H. Carson   Fleur Conkling   Irving Crump

Helen Dean Fish   Wilhelmina Harper   William Heyliger   Siddie Joe Johnson

HELEN DEAN FISH, editor of juvenile books at Lippincott, died a short time ago. She was a distinguished and well-loved children's book editor. Among the books she discovered, two won the Newbery Medal and one the Caldecott Award. She herself was the author or editor of ten juvenile books, including her famous *The Boys' Book of Verse*. She had made ten trips to Europe and wrote two books for adults about these trips. They were *Invitation to Travel* (Ives Washburn) and *Invitation to England* (Ives Washburn). Miss Fish at one time was president of the Association of Children's Book Editors and was most active in the Children's Book Council. Among her most famous discoveries were Hugh Lofting's *Dr. Dolittle* books.

WILHELMINA HARPER is the famous librarian at Redwood City, California. She has done outstanding work as a compiler of at least twenty highly recommended anthologies for children. At one time she was connected with the New York Public Library. She has contributed to magazines on children's literature. *Merry Christmas to You* (Dutton), *Ghosts and Goblins* (Dutton), *For Love of Country* (Dutton), *Yankee Yarns* (Dutton), and *The Harvest Feast* (Dutton) are among her well-loved books.

WILLIAM HEYLIGER, a consultant editor of *The Children's Hour*, was born in New Jersey and was educated in the public schools there. When he was just a boy he was captivated by the stories of Richard Harding Davis and wanted to be a writer, too. His first story was promptly rejected. He had sent it, written in longhand and tied with blue ribbons, to the *Saturday Evening Post*. As he grew older he went into the mercantile business and then did newspaper work. After this he began to write popular sports stories for boys. Mr. Heyliger is the father of three boys (he has eight children). He has camped with boys, talked to schoolboys in ten states, and has written books for them continuously. He and his wife, Fleur Conkling, the writer, live at Drexel Hill, Pennsylvania. Among the forty-five books that he has published are *S O S Radio Patrol* (Dodd), *High Benton* (Appleton-Century), *Backfield Comet* (Appleton-Century), *The County Pennant* (Appleton-Century), and *The Macklin Brothers* (Appleton-Century).

SIDDIE JOE JOHNSON spent her childhood roaming the countryside of southern Texas. She started writing poems when she went to school but considered them to be "very bad." At Texas Christian University she was the campus poet. Since graduating from college she has done library work with children. She is children's librarian at the Dallas Public Library, has a radio program for boys and girls, and teaches children's literature at Southern Methodist University. She is a consultant editor of *The Children's Hour*. Her first book for boys and girls, *Debby* (Longmans), was about herself as a child. *Texas: The Land of the Tejas* (Random), *Cathy* (Longmans), and *Susan's Year* (Longmans) followed. "The Story Hour" (Volume 6:95) comes from *Susan's Year*.

CORNELIA MEIGS, consultant editor for *The Children's Hour*, was born in Rock Island, Illinois, a descendant of a family which has supplied illustrious names to United States history. She began writing in the days when she was teaching school. She tried out her stories on all her pupils and on her twelve nieces and nephews, some of whom

288

Cornelia Meigs   Norma Rathbun   Mabel L. Robinson   Margaret Jones Williams

lived with her. The criticisms of her child audience were carefully heeded. Later, Miss Meigs was an outstanding professor of English at Bryn Mawr College and spent her summers at her lovely Vermont farm, "Green Pastures," where she now does much of her writing. Her books have brought her outstanding recognition among those seeking the highest standards in children's literature. *Trade Wind* (Little) received the Beacon Hill Book Shelf prize and *Invincible Louisa* (Little) was awarded the Newbery Medal. Her short story, "Fox and Geese," won the *Child Life* prize story contest. Other well-liked books of hers are *Wind in the Chimney* (Macmillan), *Rain on the Roof* (Macmillan), *The Pool of Stars* (Macmillan), *The Wonderful Locomotive* (Macmillan), and *As the Crow Flies* (Macmillan). From *Invincible Louisa* was taken "Early Days with Invincible Louisa" (Volume 15:130).

NORMA RATHBUN was born in Reedsburg, Wisconsin, but spent her childhood in Madison, where she later attended the University of Wisconsin. Her interest in books and children led her to specialize in library work with children and young people, and she received her M.A. from Western Reserve University in this field. After graduation, she was children's librarian in libraries in Rochester, New York, New Rochelle, New York, and Wheaton, Illinois. She also taught children's literature at State Teachers College, Willimantic, Connecticut, where she was college librarian. For seven years she has been Chief of Children's Work at the Milwaukee Public Library, Milwaukee, Wisconsin. For six years she has had a radio program, "Young Moderns and Authors Talk Books." She also has a television program, "Your Library Story." Besides these activities, Norma Rathbun is part-time instructor in children's literature at Marquette University in Milwaukee. Her hobbies are "books, children, and gardening."

MABEL L. ROBINSON, a consultant editor of *The Children's Hour,* is a member of the English faculty of Columbia University, where her famous seminar in juvenile story writing is unique in its field and has brought to light many talented authors. A graduate of Radcliffe College, she received her Ph.D. from Columbia. For a number of years she taught at Wellesley and at Constantinople College in Turkey. Her summers are spent at her home in Maine, where she is often found piloting her sailboat among the islands. She has written several excellent books on juvenile story writing, such as *Juvenile Story Writing* (Dutton) and *Writing for Young People* (Nelson), and has also written the well-loved "Little Lucia" series (Dutton), and such books for older boys and girls as *Bright Island* (Random), *Runner of the Mountain Tops* (Random), and *Back-Seat Driver* (Random). "False Summer" (Volume 6:314) comes from *Bright Island.*

MARGARET JONES WILLIAMS is an educator who has specialized in work for younger children. She graduated from the National College of Education and she received her M.A. at Northwestern University. Among the various positions that she has held is Director of Elementary Education, Cornell College, Iowa. At the present time she is holding the same position at Hiram College, Hiram, Ohio.

AUTHOR — TITLE INDEX

Tentative age group: Ⓐ younger readers and read-aloud group, Ⓑ 7–12 years, Ⓒ older readers, Ⓓ all ages

ABOU BEN ADHEM, Leigh Hunt, 5:328Ⓒ

ABOUT CHRISTMAS, Adelaide Love, 5:76Ⓑ

ABRAHAM LINCOLN'S BOYHOOD, Helen Nicolay, 15:25Ⓑ

ABRAHAM LINCOLN WALKS AT MIDNIGHT, Vachel Lindsay, 5:346Ⓒ

ACORNS, Edith King, 5:34Ⓑ

ADAM TO THE RESCUE, Elizabeth Janet Gray, 12:240Ⓒ

ADAMS, BESS PORTER, Child's Personal Library, The, 16:153

ADMIRAL'S GHOST, THE, Alfred Noyes, 5:338Ⓒ

ADOLFUSS, Fredricka Shumway Smith, 5:135Ⓐ

ADVENTURE AT THE TOLL BRIDGE, THE, Howard Pease, 7:279Ⓒ

ADVENTURE IN A CHIMNEY, Florence Choate, 12:14Ⓒ

ADVENTURE IN CANDLE STREET, Constance Savery, 12:179Ⓒ

ADVENTURES OF A BROWNIE, Dinah Maria Mulock, 1:163Ⓐ

ADVENTURE OF THE BLUE CARBUNCLE, THE, A. Conan Doyle, 7:254Ⓒ

ADVENTURE ON MARS, Richard M. Elam, Jr., 16:21Ⓑ

AFTERNOON, Polly Chase, 5:181Ⓑ

AIR MAIL, Gordon Hillman, 5:40Ⓑ

ALBERT SCHWEITZER: THE DOCTOR IN THE JUNGLE, Mathilda Schirmer, 15:256Ⓒ

ALCOTT, LOUISA MAY, Jo Meets Laurie, 3:138; Tabby's Tablecloth, 11:264; Unexpected Christmas, An, 3:113

ALDIS, DOROTHY, Clown, The, 5:17; Creature Brontosaurus, The, 5:128; Grasshoppers, The, 5:94; Harper's Farm, The, 5:30; I Caught a Fish, 5:68; Ironing, 5:16; It Was, 5:68; Little, 5:13; Looking In, 5:16; Rolling Down a Hill, 5:8; Secret Place, The, 5:17; What I Would Do, 5:9

ALEXANDER, CECIL FRANCIS, All Things Beautiful, 5:268

ALEXANDER MACKENZIE: HERO OF CANADA, Maxine Shore and M. M. Oblinger, 15:153Ⓒ

ALL MUTT, Helen Train Hilles, 6:126Ⓑ

290

ALL THINGS BEAUTIFUL, Cecil Francis Alexander, **5**:268Ⓓ

ALL THROUGH THE NIGHT, Author Unknown, **5**:268Ⓓ

ALL THROUGH THE NIGHT, Rachel Field, **1**:360Ⓓ

ALLEN, MARGARET FORD, Lewis Carroll, **15**:8; When Mark Twain Was a Boy, **15**:43

ALLIGATOR UP THE BAYOU, Steve Benedict, **13**:60Ⓑ

ALONE?, New York Sun Editorial, **15**:255ⒸC

ALPHORN, THE, Roger Duvoisin, **8**:47Ⓑ

ALT, JESS DOBSON, Little Susan Zebra, **5**:219

ALTSHELER, JOSEPH A., With the Forest Runners, **11**:295

AMERICA THE BEAUTIFUL, FROM, Katharine Lee Bates, **9**:201Ⓓ

ANDERSEN, HANS CHRISTIAN, Emperor's New Clothes, The, **2**:258; Fir Tree, The, **1**:339; Nightingale, The, **2**:358; Ugly Duckling, The, **2**:149

ANDERSON, C. W., Blaze and the Forest Fire, **14**:1

ANDERSON, MARJORIE ALLEN, At the Zoo, **5**:49; Fairy and I, **5**:156; New Friend, A, **5**:32; Swinging, **5**:32; Thank You, Lord, **5**:265

ANDERSON, MILDRED LEIGH, I Can Be a Tiger, **5**:24

ANGUS AND THE DUCKS, Marjorie Flack, **1**:49Ⓐ

ANIMAL CRACKERS, Aileen Fisher, **5**:217Ⓑ

ANIMAL STORE, THE, Rachel Field, **5**:98Ⓑ

ANIMALS' FAIR, THE, Carolyn Wells, **5**:204Ⓓ

ANSWERING THE CHALLENGE, Irving Crump, **14**:227ⒸC

ANTONIO VAN DYKE AND HIS MASTER RUBENS, Mary Newlin Roberts, **15**:88Ⓑ

ANYBODY CAN SKI, B. J. Chute, **10**:95ⒸC

APACHE WARPATH, Edgar Wyatt, **11**:338ⒸC

APPLE BLOSSOMS, Helen Wing, **1**:301Ⓐ

APPLES OF IDUNA, THE, Dorothy Hosford, **8**:226ⒸC

APPLE RHYME, THE, Madeleine Nightingale, **5**:172Ⓑ

APRIL, Eunice Tietjens, **5**:179Ⓑ

APRIL RAIN, Robert Loveman, **5**:178Ⓓ

ARCHIE AND THE APRIL FOOLS, B. J. Chute, **6**:267Ⓑ

ARDAN'S POOKA, Ella Young, **2**:89Ⓑ

ARISTOCRAT, THE, Carl S. Junge, **5**:227Ⓓ

ARMSTRONG, EDITH M., Mason Children on the Roof, The, **6**:137

ARMSTRONG, MILDRED BOWERS, Boredom, **5**:149; City Fairies, **2**:224; Garden Fancy, **5**:33; Great Craftsman, The, **5**:193; Little Girl Next Door, **5**:57; Offer, **5**:142; Rain Toys, The, **5**:190; Song for a Summer Evening, **2**:33; Spring Signs, **5**:50; Squirrel, The, **5**:113; Tree House, **5**:163; Wind, **5**:177

ASHES THAT MADE TREES BLOOM, THE, William Elliot Griffis, **8**:80Ⓑ

ASQUITH, HERBERT, Skating, **5**:65

AT NIGHT, Elizabeth-Ellen Long, **5**:187Ⓓ

AT THE AQUARIUM, Max Eastman, **13**:353Ⓓ

291

AT THE BOAR HUNT, Edna Becker, 12:61Ⓑ

AT THE FALL OF POMPEII, Jennie Hall, 12:301Ⓑ

AT THE ZOO, Marjorie Allen Anderson, 5:49Ⓐ

ATTIC TRUNK, Polly Chase, 5:36Ⓑ

ATWATER, FLORENCE and RICHARD, Mr. Popper and Captain Cook, 4:30

ATWATER, MONTGOMERY, Chisel Chin, 14:112; Trail-Makers, 14:301

AUGUSTA GOOSE, Ruth Dixon, 1:67Ⓐ

AUSTIN, MARY, Brown Bear, The, 5:112; Rocky Mountain Sheep, The, 14:371; Sandhill Crane, The, 14:54; Texas Trains and Trails, 5:26

AUTUMN, Emily Dickinson, 5:189Ⓓ

AUTUMN SONG, Elizabeth-Ellen Long, 5:194Ⓓ

AWAY WE GO, Aileen Fisher, 5:69Ⓐ

BABY, THE, Marchette Chute, 5:13Ⓑ

BACMEISTER, RHODA W., Galoshes, 5:14

BAD KITTENS, THE, Elizabeth Coatsworth, 5:41Ⓓ

BAEDEKER BOY, THE, Helen Coale Crew, 9:116Ⓑ

BAILEY, CAROLYN SHERWIN, Boy Who Loved Birds, The, 15:51; Boy Who Loved Puppets, The, 15:69; Helen Keller, 15:81; King's Daughter, 15:33

BAKER, MARGARET, Lost Merbaby, The, 1:272

BAKER, MARGARET and MARY, Patsy and the Leprechaun, 2:109

BAKER, MARGARET J., Fairy Who Didn't Believe in Children, The, 2:128

BALDWIN, FAITH, Boiling the Billy, 9:281; In Grandmother's Garden, 5:180

BALLAD OF THE OYSTERMAN, Oliver Wendell Holmes, 5:282Ⓓ

BALLOON, Ruth Dixon, 5:62Ⓐ

BALLOR'S SON GOES RIDING, Ella Young, 2:280Ⓑ

BAMBI STARTS TO SEE THE WORLD, Felix Salten, 14:27Ⓑ

BANGS, JANET NORRIS, Coalie, 5:130; Playing at the Waterfall, 5:160; Snowfall, 6:326

BANGS, JOHN KENDRICK, Little Elf, The, 2:19

BARBER, THE, J. G. Francis, 1:311Ⓓ

BARBOUR, RALPH HENRY, "Hoot!", Said the Owl, 10:110

BARRETT, KATHERINE ELLIS, Corn in the Shocks, 5:191

BARRIE, JAMES, Peter Pan and Captain Hook, 2:225

BARROWS, MARJORIE, Belinda, 5:208; Cocky, 1:150; Cricket, The, 5:114; Deep Sea Song, 5:150; Fairy School, The, 2:148; Long-Ago Doll, The, 5:37; Muggins Mouse at the Seashore, 1:240; Pigeon, The, 5:52; Pine Tree Song, 5:73; Purple-Eyed Pirate, The, 5:202; Star, The, 5:6

292

BARROWS, WALTER RANSOM, Leonardo da Vinci, **15**:325; Robert Louis Stevenson, **15**:206

BARTER, Sara Teasdale, **5**:351ⓒ

BASKETBALL MYSTERY, THE, Helen Diehl Olds, **10**:32Ⓑ

BATES, KATHARINE LEE, America the Beautiful, From, **9**:201

BAXENDALE, AUDREY, Secret of Rainbow Ridge, The, **7**:69

BEARS OF BLUE RIVER, THE, Charles Major, **11**:306Ⓑ

BEAST I LIKE, A, Carolyn Wells, **5**:213Ⓓ

BEAUTY, Sir William Watson, **15**:99Ⓓ

BEAUTY'S SISTER, Owen Johnson, **10**:125ⓒ

BECKER, EDNA, At the Boar Hunt, **12**:61

BEDTIME FOR A BABY BROOK, Ruth Crary, **5**:193Ⓓ

BEDTIME STORY, Rowena Bennett, **5**:202Ⓓ

BEIMFOHR, MARY, Circus, The, **5**:48

BEING A GYPSY, Barbara Young, **5**:5Ⓑ

BELINDA, Marjorie Barrows, **5**:208Ⓑ

BELLEROPHON, Padraic Colum, **8**:93Ⓑ

BELLOC, HILAIRE, Big Baboon, The, **4**:234; Gnu, The, **4**:234; Yak, The, **4**:235

BELLS, THE, Edgar Allan Poe, **5**:284ⓒ

BELONGINGS, Marchette Chute, **5**:53Ⓑ

BENEDICT, STEVE, Alligator up the Bayou, **13**:60

BENÉT, LAURA, Box a Bee Crept In, The, **12**:52; Climb High, **13**:8; Henry Wadsworth Longfellow, **15**:237; Horseshoe Nails, **11**:197

BENÉT, ROSEMARY and STEPHEN, Western Wagons, **11**:82

BENÉT, STEPHEN VINCENT, Daniel Webster, **15**:367

BEN FRANKLIN'S FIRST ADVENTURES, Andre Maurois, **15**:164ⓒ

BENJAMIN JONES AND HIS DOGS, Aileen Fisher, **5**:238Ⓑ

BENJY GOES TO THE CIRCUS, Aileen Fisher, **5**:239Ⓑ

BENNETT, JOHN, A Gift from the Queen, **12**:69

BENNETT, ROWENA, Bedtime Story, **5**:202; Can a Mouse Keep House?, **5**:223; Deep Sea Adventure, A, **5**:151; Dryad, The, **5**:152; Garden Hat Shop, The, **5**:157; Geography Lesson, **5**:203; Goblin Gadgets, **5**:88; God Is Like This, **5**:269; Hannibal, the Cannibal, **5**:224; Lady Slipper, The, **5**:161; Over the Chimney-Tops, **5**:159; Parade of the Animal Crackers, **5**:157; Remembering the Winter, **5**:195; Second-Hand Shop, The, **5**:147; Witch Cat, **5**:87; Witch of Willoughby Wood, The, **5**:162

BENNY AND THE CAT'S TAIL, Elsie Singmaster, **15**:62Ⓑ

BERTRAM AND THE LION, Paul T. Gilbert, **4**:102Ⓓ

BERTRAM AND THE MUSICAL CROCODILE, Paul T. Gilbert, **4**:197Ⓓ

BEST RIDE OF ALL, THE, Adelaide Love, **6**:276Ⓑ

BIANCO, MARGERY WILLIAMS, Dolly Joins the Circus, **6**:193; Mr. Murdle's Large Heart, **1**:250; Velveteen Rabbit, The **1**:1; Winterbound Adventure, A, **6**:327

BIG BABOON, THE, Hilaire Belloc, **4**:234Ⓓ

BIG MOMENT, Elizabeth Janet Gray, **10**:185ⓒ

BIG MUSIC, Margaret Prescott Montague, **8**:338ⓒ

293

BIM'S GIFT FROM THE FOREST, R. Lal Singh and Eloise Lownsbery, 9:150Ⓑ

BIOGRAPHIES BRING NEW COMPANIONS, Marchette Chute, 16:151

BIRD'S NEST, THE, John Drinkwater, 5:134Ⓑ

BIRTHDAY OF OUR LAND, THE, Nancy Byrd Turner, 5:84Ⓑ

BIRTHDAYS, Marchette Chute, 5:55Ⓐ

BLACK PIRATE OF THE PEAKS, Willis G. Craig, 14:202Ⓑ

BLACK PITS OF LUNA, THE, Robert A. Heinlein, 16:115Ⓑ

BLACK STALLION'S RACE, THE, Walter Farley, 14:162Ⓑ

BLAKE, WILLIAM, Night, 5:38

BLAZE AND THE FOREST FIRE, C. W. Anderson, 14:1Ⓑ

BLUEBELLS, Walter de la Mare, 2:186Ⓓ

BLUEBIRD, A, Helen Coale Crew, 2:39Ⓑ

BOAT, THE, Rose Fyleman, 5:25Ⓑ

BOBO, Elizabeth Orton Jones, 14:13Ⓑ

BOGGS, RALPH STEELE and MARY GOULD DAVIS, Three Golden Oranges, 8:188

BOILING THE BILLY, Faith Baldwin, 9:281Ⓑ

BOLTON, IVY, King's Cygnet, The, 12:99

BOND, NELSON, Lancelot Biggs: Spaceman, 16:70

BOOT AND SADDLE, Robert Browning, 5:319Ⓒ

BOOZER, Lysbeth Boyd Borie, 5:132Ⓐ

BOREDOM, Mildred Bowers Armstrong, 5:149Ⓑ

BORIE, LYSBETH BOYD, Boozer, 5:132

BOWERS, BEE, Rainy Day, 5:133

BOX A BEE CREPT IN, THE, Laura Benét, 12:52Ⓑ

BOY WHO LIKED PUPPETS, THE, Carolyn Sherwin Bailey, 15:69Ⓑ

BOY WHO LOVED BIRDS, THE, Carolyn Sherwin Bailey, 15:51Ⓑ

BOY WHO OWNED AN ELEPHANT, THE, Malvin Wald, 1:285Ⓐ

BOY WHO VOTED FOR ABE LINCOLN, THE, Milton Richards, 11:83Ⓑ

BRADLEY, MARY HASTINGS, Gorillas and Lions!, 13:158

BRALEY, BERTON, Naturally Enough, 5:164

BREATHES THERE A MAN WITH SOUL SO DEAD, Sir Walter Scott, 5:281Ⓒ

BRECK, VIVIAN, Touch of Arab, A, 13:178

BRIDGET ON FORTUNE'S TRAIL, Berta and Elmer Hader, 14:55Ⓑ

BRIER, HOWARD M., Fools Walk In, 13:302; Yogi's Dark Horse, 10:361

BRINK, CAROL RYRIE, Caddie's Silver Dollar, 11:127; Farmer of Paimpol, 9:7; Goody O'Grumpity, 1:223; Willow Basket, The, 11:93

BRISLEY, JOYCE L., If I Were Otherwise, 5:52; Which?, 5:52

BROCK, EMMA, In a Covered Wagon, 11:72

BROKEN NOTE, THE, Eric P. Kelly, 8:294Ⓒ

BROOKS, WALTER, Freddy the Detective Solves a Mystery, 4:71

BROUGHAM, PATRICIA, Cuckoo in the Nest, The, 12:1

294

BROWN BEAR, THE, Mary Austin, 5:112Ⓑ

BROWN, BEATRICE CURTIS, Jonathan Bing, 4:134; Jonathan Bing Dances for Spring, 5:200; More about Jonathan Bing, 5:246; New Song to Sing about Jonathan Bing, A, 5:247

BROWN, BILL, Star Ducks, The, 16:36

BROWNIE'S RIDE, Dinah Maria Mulock, 2:102Ⓐ

BROWNING, ROBERT, Boot and Saddle, 5:319; Home-Thoughts, from Abroad, 5:274; How They Brought the Good News from Ghent to Aix, 5:320; Pied Piper of Hamelin, The, 5:294; Year's at the Spring, The, 5:271

BROWNY, THE, Nancy Clinton, 2:93Ⓐ

BRYAN, DOROTHY and MARGUE-RITE, Pixie, Dixie, Trixie, and Nixie, 1:206; There Was Tammie!, 1:145

BUCCA BOO'S LITTLE MERRY MEN, Enys Tregarthen, 8:1Ⓑ

BUCHANAN, FANNIE R., Good Morning, 5:1

BUCK, PEARL S., Little Red, 13:68

BUFFALO HUNTING, Theodore Roosevelt, 11:357Ⓒ

BUG AND BEETLE CIRCUS, THE, Carolyn Forsyth, 5:124Ⓑ

BUGLE SONG, Alfred Tennyson, 5:318Ⓓ

BUNNY, THE, Adelaide Love, 5:196Ⓐ

BUNNY, THE, Eleanor Underwood, 1:239Ⓐ

BURNETT, CONSTANCE, Marion Anderson: A Voice in a Hundred Years, 15:293

BURNETT, FRANCES HODGSON, Sara Crewe, or What Happened at Miss Minchin's, 3:325

BURNS, ROBERT, Sweet Afton, 5:278

BURRO BELLS IN THE MOONLIGHT, Glenn Ward Dresbach, 14:115Ⓑ

BUTTERBEAN TENT, THE, Elizabeth Madox Roberts, 5:11Ⓑ

BUTTS, MARY F., Roses, 5:161

BYRON, LORD, Ye Stars, 5:277

CADDIE'S SILVER DOLLAR, Carol Ryrie Brink, 11:127Ⓑ

CAKE AT MIDNIGHT, Norma Bicknell Mansfield, 9:269Ⓒ

CAKE FOR COMPANY DINNER, Miriam E. Mason, 4:185Ⓑ

CALLOWAY'S CODE, O. Henry, 7:245Ⓒ

CAMEL, THE, Carolyn Wells, 5:217Ⓓ

CAMEL, THE, Clara E. Randall, 5:132Ⓑ

CAMEL AND THE CACHELOT, THE, Laurence McKinney, 5:228Ⓓ

CAMEL IS A MAMMAL, THE, Peter Wells, 4:145Ⓓ

CAMEL'S COMPLAINT, THE, Charles Edward Carryl, 5:218Ⓑ

CAN A MOUSE KEEP HOUSE?, Rowena Bennett, 5:223Ⓑ

CANADIAN BOAT-SONG, Thomas Moore, 5:278Ⓓ

CANDLEBRIGHT, CANDLELIGHT!, Ivy O. Eastwick, 5:172Ⓑ

CANFIELD, DOROTHY, Down in the Wolf Pit, **13**:38

CANNERY BEAR, THE, Ray St. Clair, **4**:94Ⓑ

CANTICLE OF THE SUN, St. Francis of Assisi, **5**:354Ⓒ

CAPTURE OF THE SHEN, Arthur Bowie Chrisman, **8**:300Ⓒ

CARAVAN, THE, Madeleine Nightingale, **5**:54Ⓑ

CARCA, George Cory Franklin, **14**:136Ⓒ

CARICATURE, Ernie Rydberg, **10**:212Ⓒ

CARLEY, PEARL B., My Hummingbirds, **14**:42

CARPENTER, FRANCES, Son of the South Wind, **8**:86; White Horse of Volendam, The, **13**:198

CARPENTER, RUSSELL, You Never Saw Such an Egg, **4**:270

CARR, MARY JANE, Feather of the Northman, The, **11**:64

CARROLL, LEWIS, Father William, **5**:240; Lobster Quadrille, The, **4**:93; Melancholy Pig, The, **5**:223; Walrus and the Carpenter, The, **4**:206

CARRYL, CHARLES EDWARD, Camel's Complaint, The, **5**:218; Nautical Ballad, A, **4**:164; Robinson Crusoe's Story, **4**:236; Sir Peter Bombazoo, **4**:358

CARSON, JULIA, Patrick Henry Enters Public Life, **15**:337

CARTER, RUSSELL GORDON, Old Sly Eye, **11**:173; Three-Cornered Hat, The, **11**:189

CASE OF THE COSMIC COMIC, THE, Robert McCloskey, **4**:238Ⓑ

CASE OF THE SENSATIONAL SCENT, THE, Robert McCloskey, **7**:30Ⓑ

CASEY AT THE BAT, Ernest Lawrence Thayer, **5**:332Ⓒ

CAT, Mary Britton Miller, **5**:103Ⓓ

CATALOGUE, Rosalie Moore, **14**:160Ⓓ.

CATASTROPHE!!, Malcolm Douglas, **5**:206Ⓓ

CATCH ME CADDY, Leroy F. Jackson, **5**:243Ⓐ

CAVE, THE, Glenn Ward Dresbach, **5**:10Ⓑ

CELESTIAL SURGEON, THE, Robert Louis Stevenson, **15**:210Ⓒ

CHALMERS, ANN, Lizard, The, **5**:115

CHAMBERED NAUTILUS, THE, Oliver Wendell Holmes, **5**:287Ⓒ

CHANT OF THE CHIPMUNK, Arthur Guiterman, **5**:135Ⓐ

CHARLES DICKENS: THE BOY OF THE LONDON STREETS, Rupert S. Holland, **15**:100Ⓒ

CHASE, POLLY, Afternoon, **5**:181; Attic Trunk, **5**:36; Explorer, **5**:16; I Stare at the Cow, **5**:136; Mud, **5**:14; Santa Fe, New Mexico, **5**:45; Self-Control, **5**:61; Tidy Turtle, **5**:47

CHILD AND THE FAIRIES, THE, Author Unknown, **5**:175Ⓑ

CHILDREN'S INTERESTS IN READING, Miriam Blanton Huber, **16**:176

CHILDREN OF THE WOLF, THE, Eleanor Farjeon, **8**:34Ⓑ

CHILD'S PERSONAL LIBRARY, THE, Bess Porter Adams, **16**:153

CHILD'S PRAYER, Elizabeth-Ellen Long, **5**:266Ⓑ

CHILD'S PRAYER FOR OTHER CHILDREN, Elizabeth-Ellen Long, **5**:270Ⓑ

CHIMNEY, THE, Mildred Plew Meigs, **1**:246Ⓐ

CHISEL CHIN, Montgomery Atwater, **14**:112Ⓑ

CHOATE, FLORENCE, Adventure in a Chimney, **12**:14

CHOOSING SHOES, Ffrida Wolfe, **5**:18Ⓑ

CHRISMAN, ARTHUR BOWIE, Capture of the Shen, **8**:300

CHRISTMAS CALF, THE, Judy Van der Veer, **5**:126Ⓑ

CHRISTMAS EVE, Ruth Dixon, **5**:75Ⓑ

CHRISTMAS EVE AT REGINALD'S, Elizabeth Rhodes Jackson, **6**:359Ⓑ

CHRISTMAS GIFTS, Ruth Dixon, **5**:74Ⓑ

CHRISTMAS HORSES, Laura Ingalls Wilder, **11**:111Ⓑ

CHRISTMAS IN THE WOODS, Frances Frost, **5**:77Ⓓ

CHRISTMAS MORNING, Elizabeth Madox Roberts, **5**:70Ⓓ

CHRISTMAS PATH, THE, Anne Higginson Spicer, **6**:16Ⓓ

CHRISTMAS SONG, Eleanor Underwood, **11**:126Ⓑ

CHRISTMAS SONG, Elizabeth-Ellen Long, **5**:76Ⓑ

CHUMS, Arthur Guiterman, **5**:102Ⓑ

CHUTE, B. J., Anybody Can Ski, **10**:95; Archie and the April Fools, **6** :267; Denny Puts in His Oar, **10**:332; Master Mind, **10**:220

CHUTE, MARCHETTE, Baby, The, **5**:13; Belongings, **5**:53; Biographies Bring New Companions, **16**:151; Birthdays, **5**:55; Farmers, **5**:15; Horses, **5**:105; Life of William Shakespeare, A, **15**:222; My Dog, **5**:63; My Plan, **5**:15; Principal Exports, **5**:12; Spring Rain, **5**:14

CINDERELLA, Jane McHenry, **2**:165Ⓑ

CIRCUS, THE, Mary Beimfohr, **5**:48Ⓑ

CIRCUS, Eleanor Farjeon, **5**:22Ⓑ

CIRCUS, THE, Elizabeth Madox Roberts, **5**:23Ⓑ

CIRCUS DRUMS, THE, Adelaide Love, **6**:201Ⓑ

CIRCUS ELEPHANT, Kathryn Worth, **14**:80Ⓑ

CITY FAIRIES, Mildred Bowers Armstrong, **2**:224Ⓑ

CLARINDA, 1869, Elizabeth Enright, **6**:297Ⓑ

CLARK, MARGERY, Picnic Basket, The, **1**:158

CLEARY, BEVERLY, Ellen's Secret, **6**:177; Gallons of Guppies, **6**:17

CLEMENS, SAMUEL, Cub Pilot on the River, **11**:321; Glorious Whitewasher and His Friends, The, **3**:1; Tom and Becky in the Cave, **3**:308

CLIMB HIGH, Laura Benét, **13**:8Ⓒ

CLINTON, NANCY, Browny, The, **2**:93; Guppies Are Best, **6**:29

CLOUGH, ARTHUR HUGH, Struggle, The, **15**:273

CLOWN, THE, Dorothy Aldis, **5**:17Ⓑ

CLUTCH MAN, William Heyliger, **10**:251Ⓒ

COALIE, Janet Norris Bangs, **5**:130Ⓑ

COALY–BAY, THE OUTLAW HORSE, Ernest Thompson Seton, **14**:305Ⓒ

COATSWORTH, ELIZABETH, Bad Kittens, The, **5**:41; Forgotten Island, **7**:1; In from the Sea, **5**:192; In the Garden, **5**:183; Kangaroo, The, **5**:129; Mary Silver, **11**:159; Pioneer Wedding, A, **11**:314; Sea Gull, The, **5**:108; Sleigh Bells at Night, **5**:64; Song for Summer, **2**:50; Song of Grandfather Thomas' Parrot, **5**:108; Song of the Rabbits Outside the Tavern, **5**:96; Sun Is First to Rise, The, **5**:179; Still It Is Wilderness, **14**:256

COCKY, Marjorie Barrows, **1**:150Ⓐ

COFFIN, ROBERT P. TRISTRAM, Country Church, **5**:353; Eyes Are Lit Up, **5**:92; Strange Holiness, **5**:350

COLBY, RUTH H., Horse Mackerel, **10**:79

COLERIDGE, SAMUEL TAYLOR, He Prayeth Best, **5**:266; Kubla Khan, From, **12**:330

COLUM, PADRAIC, Bellerophon, **8**:93; First Harp, The, **8**:44; Man with the Bag, The, **2**:171; Phaeton, **8**:144; Poetry and Childhood, **16**:147; White Blackbird, The, **2**:34; Imagination and Children's Literature, **16**:173

COLUMBUS, Joaquin Miller, **5**:84Ⓒ

COLUMBUS DISCOVERS AMERICA, Roger Duvoisin, **15**:12Ⓑ

CONKLING, FLEUR, My New Roller Skates, **5**:47; Sea Horse, The, **5**:24

CONKLING, HILDA, Fairies, **5**:166; Morning, **5**:177

CONSOLATION, Rose Fyleman, **5**:149Ⓑ

COOL, Elizabeth-Ellen Long, **5**:183Ⓑ

COOMBS, CHARLES, Frisbie Cures the Doctor, **6**:71

CORN IN THE SHOCKS, Katherine Ellis Barrett, **5**:191Ⓑ

COTTLER, JOSEPH and HAYM JAFFE, Guglielmo Marconi, **15**:189; Wright Brothers, The, **15**:158

COUNTRY CHURCH, Robert P. Tristram Coffin, **5**:353Ⓓ

COURLANDER, HAROLD and GEORGE HERZOG, One You Don't See Coming, The, **8**:56; Talk, **8**:17

COW GOLDEN HORN, THE, Dhan Gopal Mukerji, **8**:39Ⓑ

COX, G. W., Roland and His Horn, **8**:355

CRADLE HYMN, Martin Luther, **5**:255Ⓓ

CRADLE SONG, Elizabeth-Ellen Long, **5**:252Ⓑ

CRAIG, WILLIS G., Black Pirate of the Peaks, **14**:202

CRARY, RUTH, Bedtime for a Baby Brook, **5**:193; Morning Exercises, **5**:33; To a Very Young Cloud, **5**:179

CRATCHITS' CHRISTMAS DINNER, THE, Charles Dickens, **12**:292Ⓒ

CRAZY STORY OF DIZZY LIZZIE, Hugh Lofting, **4**:118Ⓓ

CREAM–COLORED PONY, THE, Chesley Kahmann, **6**:242Ⓑ

CREATURE BRONTOSAURUS, THE, Dorothy Aldis, **5**:128Ⓑ

CREDLE, ELLIS, Down, Down the Mountain, **1**:108

CREMATION OF SAM McGEE, THE, Robert W. Service, **5**:329Ⓒ

CREW, FLEMING and ALICE CREW GALL, Nanook, **14**:64; Song of the Little Donkey, The, **1**:214; Tungwa, **9**:180

CREW, HELEN COALE, Baedeker Boy, The, **9**:116; Bluebird, A, **2**:39; In the Garden, **1**:161; MacDonald Plaid, The, **9**:202; That Boy!, **9**:96

CRICKET, THE, Marjorie Barrows, **5**:114Ⓑ

CRIMSON DAWN, THE, Percy Bysshe Shelley, **5**:277Ⓒ

CROSS–STITCH SAMPLER, Marion Strobel, **5**:57Ⓑ

CRUMP, IRVING, Answering the Challenge, **14**:227; Little Guy, The, **10**:286

CUB PILOT ON THE RIVER, Samuel Clemens, **11**:321Ⓒ

CUBBY, David M. Newell, **14**:45Ⓐ

CUCHULAIN'S ADVENTURES IN SHADOW-LAND, Eleanor Hull, 8:329©

CUCKOO IN THE NEST, THE, Patricia Brougham, 12:1Ⓑ

CUNNINGHAM, ALLAN, Sea Song, A, 5:273

CURIOUS GEORGE, H. A. Rey, 1:53Ⓐ

CURSE OF KAING, THE, Willis Lindquist, 9:320©

CUTTER RACE, THE, Stephen Meader, 10:302©

D IS FOR DIPLODOCUS, Eunice and Janet Tietjens, 5:225Ⓑ

DAFFODILS, William Wordsworth, 5:272Ⓓ

DALGLIESH, ALICE, Letters from the Sea, 1:264; Rusty—Movie Star, 6:89; Story of Dobbin, The, 1:244

DANCER IN THE SUN, Scharmel Iris, 5:257Ⓑ

DANIEL BOONE, Arthur Guiterman, 11:369©

DANIEL WEBSTER, Stephen Vincent Benét, 15:367©

DANTÈS' ESCAPE FROM THE CHÂTEAU D'IF, Alexander Dumas, 13:291©

DASENT, GEORGE WEBBE, Gudbrand on the Hillside, 2:160; Lad Who Went to the North Wind, The, 2:264

DAUGHERTY, JAMES, Saving of Boonesborough, The, 11:181

DAUGHERTY, SONIA, Thomas Jefferson, 15:274

DAVIES, MARY CAROLYN, Tree-Children, 5:9

DAVIS, JULIA, Rivers and Beasts Betray, 11:277

DAVIS, L. R., Stalactite Surprise, 7:61; Why Bother with Ladders?, 13:134

DAVIS, MARY GOULD and RALPH STEELE BOGGS, Three Golden Oranges, 8:188

DE ANGELI, MARGUERITE, Robin Finds a Way, 12:26

DE BRUNHOFF, JEAN, Story of Babar, The, 1:100

DE LA MARE, WALTER, Bluebells, 2:186; Dream-Song, 5:261; Listeners, The, 5:344; Silver, 5:38; Ship of Rio, The, 4:70

DE LAMARTER, JEANNE, Happiness, 5:3; Sing Ho!, 5:196

DE LA RAMÉE, LOUISE, Nurenberg Stove, The, 9:36

DE WITT, JOHANNA, Littlest Reindeer, The, 1:58

DEAN, AGNES LOUISE, Fires, 5:76; Galantry Bower, 5:46; North Country, 5:39; Rainy Day, 5:188

DEAR LAND OF ALL MY LOVE, Sidney Lanier, 5:277©

DEARMER, GEOFFREY, Whale, 5:117

DECKER, DUANE, Marshall at Bat, 10:313

DEEP SEA ADVENTURE, A, Rowena Bennett, 5:151Ⓑ

DEEP SEA SONG, Marjorie Barrows, 5:150Ⓐ

DEER AT NIGHT, Elizabeth-Ellen Long, 14:41Ⓓ

DEFOE, DANIEL, Robinson Crusoe Is Shipwrecked, 3:153

DENNY PUTS IN HIS OAR, B. J. Chute, 10:332Ⓒ

DESERT ADVENTURE, Eunice Tietjens, 9:307Ⓑ

DESIRABLE SHAWL, THE, Grace Moon, 9:14Ⓑ

DEVLIN, EDWARD WADE, Dippy, The, 2:94; King's Wish, The, 4:24

DICKENS, CHARLES, Cratchit's Christmas Dinner, The, 12:292; Magic Fishbone, 4:38

DICKINSON, EMILY, Autumn, 5:189; I Never Saw a Moor, 5:182

DINNER HORSES, Lucy Sprague Mitchell, 5:130Ⓑ

DINOSAUR, THE, Carl S. Junge, 5:119Ⓓ

DINOSAUR, THE, Clara E. Randall, 5:129Ⓑ

DINTY—A HUSKY'S STORY, Jack O'Brien, 14:176Ⓒ

DIPPY, THE, Edward Wade Devlin, 2:94Ⓑ

DISCOMFORT, Carolyn Wells, 5:217Ⓑ

DISPERSE, YE REBELS, Esther Forbes, 11:238Ⓒ

DIXON, RUTH, Augusta Goose, 1:67; Balloon, 5:62; Christmas Eve, 5:75; Christmas Gifts, 5:74; Enchanted Garden, The, 2:357; Fidgity Fairy, The, 5:163; Goose, 5:47; May Morning, 5:180; Morning, 5:80; My Friend Lu, 5:19; On the Train, 5:50; Our America, 5:83; Pale Pink Tea, The, 5:242; Radio Wish, 5:38; Sammy Snowman, 5:64; Snowflake Fun, 5:170; Spell, The, 5:166; Teddy Bear Dance, 5:158; Wind Elves, The, 5:171

DOBRY'S NEW YEAR, Monica Shannon, 9:294Ⓒ

DODGE, MARY MAPES, Mystery—and the Race, 3:261

DOG, A, Aileen Fisher, 5:123Ⓑ

DOGS AND WEATHER, Winifred Welles, 5:104Ⓑ

DOG'S DOG, Jim Kjelgaard, 14:86Ⓒ

DOLLY JOINS THE CIRCUS, Margery Williams Bianco, 6:193Ⓑ

DON, THE STORY OF A LION DOG, Zane Grey, 14:330Ⓒ

DONAHEY, MARY DICKERSON, Mr. Dooley Disgraces His Family, 6:202

DONAHEY, WILLIAM, Teenie Weenie Picnic, The, 1:132; Uppity Orioles, 1:137

DOUGLAS, MALCOLM, Catastrophe, 5:206

DOWN, DOWN THE MOUNTAIN, Ellis Credle, 1:108Ⓐ

DOWN IN DAVY JONES'S LOCKER, Margaret Norris, 13:334Ⓒ

DOWN IN THE WOLF PIT, Dorothy Canfield, 13:38Ⓑ

DOYLE, A. CONAN, Adventure of the Blue Carbuncle, The, 7:254; Red-Headed League, The, 7:346

DR. DOLITTLE AND THE PUSHMI-PULLYU, Hugh Lofting, 4:158Ⓑ

DR. DOLITTLE MEETS A LONDONER IN PARIS, Hugh Lofting, 4:210Ⓑ

DREAM—SONG, Walter De La Mare, 5:261Ⓓ

DRESBACH, GLENN WARD, Cave, The, 5:10; Burro Bells in the Moonlight, 14:115

DRINKWATER, JOHN, Bird's Nest, The, 5:134

DRYAD, THE, Rowena Bennett, 5:152Ⓑ

DU BOIS, WILLIAM PENE, Otta at Sea, 1:181

DUCK AND THE KANGAROO, THE, Edward Lear, 5:244Ⓓ

DUEL, THE, Eugene Field, 5:219Ⓓ

DUMAS, ALEXANDER, Dantès' Escape from the Château D'If, 13:291

DUNGEON DEEP, Phillis Garrard, 12:108Ⓒ

DUNSING, DEE, Tooth of the Great One, 11:346

DUVOISIN, ROGER, Alphorn, The, 8:47; Columbus Discovers America, 15:12

EAGLE, THE, Alfred Tennyson, 5:304Ⓓ

EARLY DAYS WITH INVINCIBLE LOUISA, Cornelia Meigs, 15:130Ⓒ

EASTER BUNNY, THE, Louise de Marigny Smith, 5:56Ⓐ

EASTER EGGS, Kate Seredy, 9:76Ⓑ

EASTER IN THE WOODS, Frances Frost, 5:141Ⓓ

EASTMAN, MAX, At the Aquarium, 13:353

EASTWICK, IVY O., Candlebright, Candlelight!, 5:172; Nightingale Made up a Tune, The, 5:6; Sea-Shell, 2:251

EBERLE, IRMENGARDE, Henri Fabre: A Place of His Own, 15:308

EDEY, MARION and DOROTHY GRIDER, The Little Fox, 14:300

EDMUNDS–HEMINGWAY, CLARA, Fairy Phone, The, 5:160

ELAM, RICHARD M., JR., Adventure on Mars, 16:21; What Time Is It?, 16:1

ELEPHANT IN THE CINNAMON TREE, THE, Leroy F. Jackson, 5:206Ⓐ

ELEPHANT'S CHILD, THE, Rudyard Kipling, 4:4Ⓐ

ELETELEPHONY, Laura E. Richards, 4:14Ⓓ

ELF, THE, Janet Lewis, 2:127Ⓑ

ELF AND THE DORMOUSE, THE, Oliver Herford, 5:148Ⓐ

ELIZABETH ELIZA'S PIANO, ABOUT, Lucretia P. Hale, 4:135Ⓒ

ELLEN'S SECRET, Beverly Cleary, 6:177Ⓑ

ELVES AND THE SHOEMAKER, THE, Jacob and Wilhelm Grimm, 2:40Ⓑ

EMERSON, RALPH WALDO, Rhodora, The, 5:276

EMPEROR'S NEW CLOTHES, THE, Hans Christian Andersen, 2:258Ⓑ

ENCHANTED GARDEN, THE, Ruth Dixon, 2:357Ⓑ

ENRIGHT, ELIZABETH, Clarinda, 1869, 6:297; Oliver at the Circus, 13:26; Randy at the Art Gallery, 6:211

ESKIL, RAGNA, Jacques Cartier, 15:315; Montcalm, 15:332

ESKIMO TWINS GO COASTING, THE, Lucy Fitch Perkins, 9:20Ⓐ

ESTES, ELEANOR, First Day of School, The, 4:146; Ginger on the Fire Escape, 10:1; Middle Bear, The, 6:144

EVANS, HUBERT, Trust Fulfilled, A, **13**:125

EVER SEE A RHEA?, Carl S. Junge, **5**:242Ⓑ

EVER VERY NEAR, Author Unknown, **5**:75Ⓓ

EVERS, HELEN and ALF, Happy Hen, The, **1**:162; House the Pecks Built, The, **4**:18; Little Lamb, A, **1**:97; Mr. Scrunch, **4**:52; This Little Pig, **1**:72

EXPLORER, Polly Chase, **5**:16Ⓑ

EYES ARE LIT UP, Robert P. Tristram Coffin, **5**:92Ⓓ

FAERY RIDERS, Ella Young, **5**:155Ⓒ

FAIRIES, Hilda Conkling, **5**:166Ⓑ

FAIRY AND I, Marjorie Allen Anderson, **5**:156Ⓐ

FAIRY LORE, Rose Fyleman, **5**:166Ⓐ

FAIRY PHONE, THE, Clara Edmunds-Hemingway, **5**:160Ⓑ

FAIRY SCHOOL, THE, Marjorie Barrows, **2**:148Ⓑ

FAIRY TALES AND THE SPIRIT, Bertha E. Mahony, **16**:144

FAIRY WHO DIDN'T BELIEVE IN CHILDREN, THE, Margaret J. Baker, **2**:128Ⓑ

FALSE SUMMER, Mabel Robinson, **6**:314Ⓒ

FAMILIAR FRIENDS, James S. Tippett, **5**:133Ⓐ

FAMILY DRAGON, THE, Margaret Widdemer, **5**:7Ⓑ

FAREWELL TO THE FARM, Robert Louis Stevenson, **5**:28Ⓑ

FARJEON, ELEANOR, Children of the Wolf, The, **8**:34; Circus, **5**:22; Kitten, A, **5**:122; Night Will Never Stay, The, **5**:185; Over the Garden Wall, **5**:2

FARLEY, WALTER, Black Stallion's Race, The, **14**:162

FARMER OF PAIMPOL, Carol Ryrie Brink, **9**:7Ⓑ

FARMERS, Marchette Chute, **5**:15Ⓑ

FARMERS, William Alexander Percy, **5**:126Ⓒ

FATHER WILLIAM, Lewis Carroll, **5**:240Ⓓ

FAULKNER, GEORGENE, Most Wonderful Thing in the World, The, **10**:69

FAWN'S FIRST JOURNEY, Maud E. Uschold, **5**:110Ⓓ

FEATHER OF THE NORTHMAN, THE, Mary Jane Carr, **11**:64Ⓒ

FERN TIKI, THE, Phillis Garrard, **9**:332Ⓒ

FIDGITY FAIRY, THE, Ruth Dixon, **5**:163Ⓐ

FIELD, EUGENE, Duel, The, **5**:219; Jest 'Fore Christmas, **5**:312; Lady Button-Eyes, **5**:248; Little Blue Pigeon, **5**:256; Rock-a-by Lady, **5**:255; Wynken, Blynken, and Nod, **5**:262

FIELD, RACHEL, All through the Night, **1**:360; Animal Store, The, **5**:98; General Store, **5**:61; Grandmother's Brook, **5**:2; Hitty's Shipwreck, **12**:81; I'd Like to Be a Lighthouse, **5**:29; If Once You Have Slept on an Island, **5**:188; Old Coach Road, The, **6**:313; Playhouse Key, The, **5**:35; Roads, **5**:51; Snow by Night, **5**:21; Something Told the Wild Geese, **5**:187; Song for a Blue Roadster, **5**:27; My First Book Friends, **16**:170

FIELD FLOWERS, Eleanor Jewett, 5:192ⓒ

FIELD MOUSE, Emilie Fendall Johnson, 5:139Ⓐ

FINGER, CHARLES J., Tale of the Lazy People, The, 8:129; Tale of Three Tails, A, 8:241

FINGER CHURCH, THE, Eleanor Jewett, 5:12Ⓐ

FIR TREE, THE, Hans Christian Andersen, 1:339Ⓑ

FIRES, Agnes Louise Dean, 5:76Ⓑ

FIRST CHRISTMAS TREE, THE, Rose Fyleman, 2:51Ⓑ

FIRST DAY OF SCHOOL, THE, Eleanor Estes, 4:146Ⓑ

FIRST HARP, THE, Padraic Colum, 8:44Ⓑ

FIRST LAMB, THE, Louise A. Stinetorf, 9:49Ⓑ

FIRST NIGHT, THE, Louise Ayres Garnett, 5:75Ⓓ

FIRST SNOWFALL, Elizabeth-Ellen Long, 5:199Ⓑ

FIRST THANKSGIVING OF ALL, Nancy Byrd Turner, 5:89Ⓑ

FISCHER, MARJORIE, Rococo Skates, 6:30

FISHER, AILEEN, Animal Crackers, 5:217; Away We Go, 5:69; Benjamin Jones and His Dogs, 5:238; Benji Goes to the Circus, 5:239; Dog, A, 5:123; Hilly Little Town, A, 5:4; How to Get to Italy, 5:206; Rabbit Tracks, 5:138; Sandpile Town, 5:4; Silver Trees, 5:191; Wise, 5:176

FISHERMAN AND HIS WIFE, THE, Jacob and Wilhelm Grimm, 2:133Ⓑ

FISHERMAN'S LUCK, Margaret Leighton, 12:348ⓒ

500 HATS OF BARTHOLOMEW CUBBINS, THE, Dr. Seuss, 1:16Ⓐ

FIVE LITTLE BEARS HAVE THEIR PICTURES TAKEN, THE, Sterling North, 1:269Ⓐ

FLACK, MARJORIE, Angus and the Ducks, 1:49

FLAME, Willis Lindquist, 14:251ⓒ

FLAMINGO, THE, Carolyn Wells, 5:212Ⓑ

FLANIGAN'S FIELD, Leroy F. Jackson, 5:221Ⓐ

FLOWER-FED BUFFALOES, THE, Vachel Lindsay, 14:75Ⓓ

FOG, Carl Sandburg, 5:193Ⓓ

FOLLOW THE GLEAM, Alfred Tennyson, 8:293ⓒ

FOLLOW YOUR LEADER, S. T. James, 13:315ⓒ

FOOLS WALK IN, Howard M. Brier, 13:302ⓒ

FORBES, ESTHER, Disperse, Ye Rebels, 11:238

FORBIDDEN ISLAND, THE, Armstrong Sperry, 9:345ⓒ

FOREST LULLABY, Leona Stafford, 5:259Ⓐ

FORGOTTEN ISLAND, Elizabeth Coatsworth, 7:1Ⓑ

FORSYTH, CAROLYN, Bug and Beetle Circus, The, 5:124; Headlights, 5:27; Home-Made Ship, The, 5:58; King Quiet, 5:196

FOR THE LOVE OF A MAN, Jack London, 14:275ⓒ

FORTY SINGING SEAMEN, Alfred Noyes, 5:334ⓒ

FOWLER, ELSIE MELCHERT, Thanksgiving Is Coming, 5:91

FOX AND GEESE, Cornelia Meigs, 11:10Ⓑ

FOX FERRY, THE, Ray St. Clair, 2:218Ⓑ

FRANCIS, J. G., Barber, The, 1:311; Genial Grimalkin, The, 1:311; Juggler, The, 4:196

FRANKLIN, GEORGE CORY, Carca, 14:136; White Flag, 14:239

FREDDY THE DETECTIVE SOLVES A MYSTERY, Walter Brooks, 4:73Ⓑ

FRIENDLY PUP, THE, Arthur Guiterman, 5:63Ⓑ

FRISBIE CURES THE DOCTOR, Charles Coombs, 6:71Ⓑ

FRISKEY, MARGARET, Johnny and the Monarch, 1:260

FROG, THE, Marion K. Seavey, 5:110Ⓑ

FROGS, Helen Wing, 5:132Ⓐ

FRONTIER BLOCKADE BUSTER, Harry Edward Neal, 11:229Ⓒ

FROST, FRANCES, Christmas in the Woods, 5:77; Easter in the Woods, 5:141; Inquisitive Barn, 5:197; Musical Mice, The, 5:134; New Snow, 5:197; Night of Wind, 14:111; Sniff, 5:60; Snowy Morning, 5:195; Trains at Night, 5:40; Woodchuck Hill, 5:96

FROST, ROBERT, Pasture, The, 5:136; Runaway, The, 5:131; Stopping by Woods on a Snowy Evening, 5:357

FUN, Leroy F. Jackson, 4:13Ⓑ

FUNNY THING, THE, Wanda Gág, 1:90Ⓐ

FYLEMAN, ROSE, Boat, The, 5:25; Consolation, 5:149; Fairy Lore, 5:166; First Christmas Tree, The, 2:51; If Only . . ., 5:25; Mice, 5:95; Mrs. Brown, 5:29; Please, 5:149

GÁG, WANDA, Funny Thing, The, 1:90

GALL, ALICE and FLEMING CREW Nanook, 14:64; Song of the Little Donkey, The, 1:214; Tungwa, 9:180

GALLANTRY BOWER, Agnes Louise Dean, 5:46Ⓑ

GALILEO, Rolf Klep, 15:74Ⓒ

GALLONS OF GUPPIES, Beverly Cleary, 6:17Ⓑ

GALOSHES, Rhoda W. Bacmeister, 5:14Ⓑ

GANG'S ALL THERE, THE, Chesley Kahmann, 6:115Ⓑ

GARDEN FANCY, Mildred Bowers Armstrong, 5:33Ⓑ

GARDEN HAT SHOP, THE, Rowena Bennett, 5:157Ⓑ

GARNETT, LOUISE AYRES, First Night, The, 5:75

GARRARD, PHILLIS, Dungeon Deep, 12:108; Fern Tiki, The, 9:332

GARTHWAITE, JIMMY, Policemen on Parade, 5:53

GAWK, THE, Franklin M. Reck, 10:168Ⓒ

GENERAL STORE, Rachel Field, 5:61Ⓑ

GENIAL GRIMALKIN, THE, J. G. Francis, 1:311Ⓓ

GENTLE JESUS, MEEK AND MILD, Charles Wesley, 5:267Ⓓ

GEOGRAPHY LESSON, Rowena Bennett, 5:203Ⓑ

GEORG HANDEL AND THE DUKE, Mary Newlin Roberts, 15:76Ⓑ

GEORGE WASHINGTON CARVER, Mabelle E. Martin, 15:269Ⓑ

GIFT FROM THE QUEEN, A, John Bennett, 12:69Ⓑ

GILBERT, ETTA F., Little Woodchuck's Fright, 5:99

GILBERT, KENNETH, Koyo, the Singer, 14:98

GILBERT, NAN, House of the Singing Windows, 9:191

GILBERT, PAUL T., Bertram and the Lion, 4:102; Bertram and the Musical Crocodile, 4:197

GINGER ON THE FIRE ESCAPE, Eleanor Estes, 10:1Ⓑ

GIRAFFE, THE, Arthur Kramer, 1:213Ⓐ

GLASS HILL, THE, Jane McHenry, 2:44Ⓑ

GLORIOUS WHITEWASHER AND HIS FRIENDS, THE, Samuel Clemens, 3:1Ⓓ

GLOVE AND THE LIONS, THE, Leigh Hunt, 12:347Ⓓ

GNU, THE, Hilaire Belloc, 4:234Ⓑ

GOBLIN GADGETS, Rowena Bennett, 5:88Ⓑ

GOD IS LIKE THIS, Rowena Bennett, 5:269Ⓓ

GODDARD, KATE COX, Ranger Wishes, 5:45

GODE, MARGUERITE, Guests, 5:40; Little Cats, 5:135; Merry-Go-Round, 5:34; Puppies, 5:127

GOD'S WORLD, Edna St. Vincent Millay, 5:343Ⓒ

GOING UP!, Helen Train Hilles, 9:215Ⓑ

GOLD BUG, THE, Edgar Allan Poe, 7:201Ⓒ

GOLDEN CUP OF KASIMIR, THE, Eric P. Kelly, 12:259Ⓑ

GOLDEN FLEECE, THE, Nathaniel Hawthorne, 8:148Ⓒ

GOLDEN TOUCH, THE, Nathaniel Hawthorne, 8:62Ⓒ

GOOD LITTLE DOG, A, Anne Stoddard, 1:178Ⓐ

GOOD MORNING, Fannie R. Buchanan, 5:1Ⓐ

GOODY O'GRUMPITY, Carol Ryrie Brink, 1:223Ⓐ

GOOSE, Ruth Dixon, 5:47Ⓐ

GOOSIE GRAY, Leroy F. Jackson, 1:74Ⓐ

GORDON, MARJORIE, Ludwig van Beethoven, 15:328

GORILLAS AND LIONS!, Mary Hastings Bradley, 13:158Ⓒ

GOULED, VIVIAN G., Where Does Music Come From?, 5:181

GRAFE, FRANCES BARBARA, Miranda, 5:123

GRAHAME, KENNETH, Open Road, The, 2:20

GRAMATKY, HARDIE, Hercules, 1:200

GRANDMOTHER'S BROOK, Rachel Field, 5:2Ⓑ

GRASSHOPPERS, THE, Dorothy Aldis, 5:94Ⓐ

GRATITUDE, Mary Louise Scott, 5:120Ⓑ

305

GRAY, ELIZABETH JANET, Adam to the Rescue, **12**:240; Big Moment, **10**:185

GREAT CRAFTSMAN, THE, Mildred Bowers Armstrong, **5**:193Ⓑ

GREAT HUNTER OF THE WOODS, THE, James Stevens, **8**:103Ⓒ

GREAT QUILLOW, THE, James Thurber, **2**:195Ⓑ

GREAT STONE FACE, THE, Nathaniel Hawthorne, **8**:271Ⓒ

GREGORY GRIGGS, Laura E. Richards, **1**:118Ⓐ

GREGUTT, HELEN, Jam Session at Abbie's, **10**:86

GREY, ZANE, Don, the Story of a Lion Dog, **14**:330

GRIDER, DOROTHY AND MARION EDEY, The Little Fox, **14**:300

GRIFFIS, WILLIAM ELLIOT, Ashes that Made Trees Bloom, The, **8**:80

GRIMM, JACOB AND WILHELM, Elves and the Shoemaker, The, **2**:40; Fisherman and His Wife, The, **2**:133; Little Snow-White, **2**:269; Rumpelstiltskin, **2**:252; Sleeping Beauty, The, **2**:289

GUDBRAND ON THE HILLSIDE, George Webbe Dasent, **2**:160Ⓑ

GUESTS, Marguerite Gode, **5**:40Ⓐ

GUGLIELMO MARCONI, Joseph Cottler and Haym Jaffe, **15**:189Ⓑ

GUIDES WITH WINGS, Clay Perry, **13**:228Ⓑ

GUITERMAN, ARTHUR, Chant of the Chipmunk, **5**:135; Chums, **5**:102; Daniel Boone, **11**:369; Friendly Pup, The, **5**:63; Pet Show, **5**:102

GUPPIES ARE BEST, Nancy Clinton, **6**:29Ⓑ

HADER, BERTA and ELMER, Bridget on Fortune's Trail, **14**:55

HALE, LUCRETIA P., About Elizabeth Eliza's Piano, **4**:135; Lady Who Put Salt in Her Coffee, The, **4**:262

HALL, JENNIE, At the Fall of Pompeii, **12**:301

HALLOWEEN, Helen Wing, **5**:88Ⓑ

HANDSOME IS, Helen Train Hilles, **6**:234Ⓑ

HANNIBAL, THE CANNIBAL, Rowena Bennett, **5**:224Ⓓ

HAPPILY EVER AFTER, Adelaide Love, **5**:39Ⓑ

HAPPINESS, Jeanne De Lamarter, **5**:3Ⓑ

HAPPY DAY, Betty Jump, **5**:32Ⓑ

HAPPY HEN, THE, Helen and Alf Evers, **1**:162Ⓐ

HAPPY PRINCE, THE, Oscar Wilde, **2**:346Ⓒ

HARBOR OF HUSHABY HO, THE, Mildred Plew Meigs, **5**:254Ⓐ

HARK! HARK! THE LARK!, William Shakespeare, **5**:272Ⓓ

HARPERS' FARM, THE, Dorothy Aldis, **5**:30Ⓑ

HARRIS, JOEL CHANDLER, Uncle Remus and the Tar-Baby, **8**:20

HARRISON, HENRY SYDNOR, Miss Hinch, 7:179

HASTY PUDDING, Cornelia Meigs, 11:36Ⓑ

HAWTHORNE, NATHANIEL, Golden Fleece, The, 8:148; Golden Touch, The, 8:62; Great Stone Face, The, 8:271

HAYES, MARJORIE H., Ride with Tom Thumb, A, 11:56; World Secrets, 5:3

HE PRAYETH BEST, Samuel Taylor Coleridge, 5:266Ⓓ

HE WHOM A DREAM HATH POS-SESSED, Shaemus O'Sheel, 5:352Ⓒ

HEADLIGHTS, Carolyn Forsyth, 5:27Ⓑ

HEIDI'S ADVENTURES ON THE MOUNTAIN, Johanna Spyri, 3:26Ⓑ

HEINLEIN, ROBERT A., Black Pits of Luna, The, 16:115

HELEN KELLER, Carolyn Sherwin Bailey, 15:81Ⓒ

HENRI FABRE: A PLACE OF HIS OWN, Irmengarde Eberle, 15:308Ⓒ

HENRY, MARGUERITE, King of the Wind and the Queen's Plate, 14:123

HENRY, O., Calloway's Code, 7:245; Ransom of Red Chief, The, 4:248

HENRY WADSWORTH LONGFEL-LOW, Laura Benét, 15:237Ⓑ

HERCULES, Hardie Gramatky, 1:200Ⓐ

HERFORD, OLIVER, Elf and the Dormouse, The, 5:148; Unfortunate Giraffe, The, 5:243

HEROISM, Helen Wing, 5:104Ⓐ

HERON, Ella Young, 5:109Ⓑ

HERZOG,- GEORGE and HAROLD COURLANDER, One You Don't See Coming, The, 8:56; Talk, 8:17

HERZOG, MAURICE, The Third of June on Annapurna, 13:322

HEYERDAHL, THOR, Kon-Tiki Adventure, A, 13:354

HEYLIGER, WILLIAM, Clutch Man, 10:251; Hit or Error?, 10:143; Steelman's Nerve, 13:144

HIAWATHA'S CHILDHOOD, Henry Wadsworth Longfellow, 5:305Ⓓ

HIE AWAY, HIE AWAY, Sir Walter Scott, 5:271Ⓓ

HIGH FLIGHT, John Gillespie Magee, Jr., 5:352Ⓒ

HIGHWAYMAN, THE, Alfred Noyes, 5:289Ⓒ

HILLES, HELEN TRAIN, All Mutt, 6:126; Living Christmas, 6:164; Going Up!, 9:215; Handsome Is, 6:234

HILLMAN, GORDON, Air Mail, 5:40

HILLY LITTLE TOWN, A, Aileen Fisher, 5:4Ⓑ

HILSABECK, EMILY, Slide, The, 1:295

HIT OR ERROR?, William Heyliger, 10:143Ⓒ

HITTY'S SHIPWRECK, Rachel Field, 12:81Ⓑ

HOGAN, INEZ, Twin Seals, 1:84

HOK-HWA OF THE WATERFRONT, Elizabeth Foreman Lewis, 9:58Ⓑ

HOLIDAY CUP, THE, Elizabeth Rhodes Jackson, 10:18Ⓑ

HOLLAND, MARION, Smoky, 6:104

HOLLAND, RUPERT S., Charles Dickens: The Boy of the London Streets, 15:100

HOLLOW TREE HOUSE, THE, Margaret Widdemer, 5:59Ⓑ

HOLMES, OLIVER WENDELL, Ballad of the Oysterman, 5:282; Chambered Nautilus, The, 5:287

307

HOME–MADE SHIP, THE, Carolyn Forsyth, 5:58Ⓑ

HOMER PRICE AND THE DOUGH-NUTS, Robert McCloskey, 4:360Ⓑ

HOME–THOUGHTS, FROM ABROAD, Robert Browning, 5:274Ⓓ

HONNESS, ELIZABETH, School for Sandpipers, 5:109

HOOP HOKUM, Jackson V. Scholz, 10:236Ⓒ

"HOOT!", SAID THE OWL, Ralph Henry Barbour, 10:110Ⓒ

HOPPITY TOAD, THE, Ruth Stephens Porter, 5:124Ⓐ

HORNBILL FAMILY, THE, Carl S. Junge, 5:118Ⓓ

HORSE MACKEREL, Ruth H. Colby, 10:79Ⓑ

HORSE WHO LIVED UPSTAIRS, THE, Phyllis McGinley, 1:173Ⓐ

HORSES, Marchette Chute, 5:105Ⓑ

HORSESHOE NAILS, Laura Benét, 11:197Ⓑ

HOSFORD, DOROTHY, Apples of Iduna, The, 8:226; How Beowulf Rules the Geats, 8:97

HOUSE CAT, THE, Annette Wynne, 5:136Ⓐ

HOUSE OF THE MOUSE, THE, Lucy Sprague Mitchell, 5:138Ⓐ

HOUSE OF THE SINGING WINDOWS, Nan Gilbert, 9:191Ⓑ

HOUSE THE PECKS BUILT, THE, Helen and Alf Evers, 4:18Ⓐ

HOUSMAN, A. E., Loveliest of Trees, 5:357

HOUSMAN, LAURENCE, Rocking-Horse Land, 1:302

HOWARD PYLE: GREAT AMERICAN ILLUSTRATOR, Mathilda Schirmer, 15:348Ⓒ

HOW BEOWULF RULES THE GEATS, Dorothy Hosford, 8:97Ⓒ

HOW BIRGIT DANCED IN HER RED SHOES, Eleanor F. Lattimore, 9:1Ⓑ

HOW KARI SAVED OUR LIVES IN THE JUNGLE, Dhan Gopal Mukerji, 14:76Ⓑ

HOW THEY BROUGHT THE GOOD NEWS FROM GHENT TO AIX, Robert Browning, 5:320Ⓒ

HOW TO GET TO ITALY, Aileen Fisher, 5:206Ⓑ

HOW TO TELL WILD ANIMALS, Carolyn Wells, 4:162Ⓓ

HUBER, MIRIAM BLANTON, Children's Interest in Reading, 16:176

HUCKABUCK FAMILY, THE, Carl Sandburg, 4:47Ⓓ

HUGHES, RICHARD, Magic Glass, The, 4:65

HULL, ELEANOR, Cuchulain in Shadow-Land, 8:329

HUNT, LEIGH, Abou Ben Adhem, 5:328; Glove and the Lions, The, 12:347

HUNT, MABEL LEIGH, Johnny Appleseed's Coat, 11:47; Tomorrow Will Be Bright, 11:26

HUNTER'S MOON, Anthony C. Wilson, 7:315Ⓒ

HUNTING OLD SLEW FOOT, Marjorie Kinnan Rawlings, 14:314Ⓒ

HUNTING SONG, Sir Walter Scott, 12:258Ⓓ

HUT, THE, Hilda van Stockum, 5:66Ⓑ

I CAN BE A TIGER, Mildred Leigh Anderson, 5:24Ⓐ

I CAUGHT A FISH, Dorothy Aldis, 5:68Ⓐ

I HEAR AMERICA SINGING, Walt Whitman, 5:281Ⓒ

I HEAR PAUL BUNYAN, Louise Leighton, 8:197Ⓒ

I IS FOR ICHTHYOSAURUS, Eunice and Janet Tietjens, 5:225Ⓓ

I KEEP THREE WISHES READY, Annette Wynne, 5:153Ⓑ

I NEVER SAW A MOOR, Emily Dickinson, 5:182Ⓓ

I STARE AT THE COW, Polly Chase, 5:136Ⓐ

I WISH I LIVED IN ELFLAND, Anne Pérez-Guerra, 5:152Ⓑ

ICEBOAT RACE, THE, Olive Burns Kirby, 10:60Ⓑ

ICHTHYOSAURUS, THE, Author Unknown, 5:227Ⓓ

I'D LIKE TO BE A LIGHTHOUSE, Rachel Field, 5:29Ⓑ

IF I WERE A ONE-LEGGED PIRATE, Mildred Plew Meigs, 5:214Ⓑ

IF I WERE OTHERWISE, Joyce L. Brisley, 5:52Ⓐ

IF I WERE THUMBELINA, Anne Pérez-Guerra, 2:88Ⓐ

IF ONCE YOU HAVE SLEPT ON AN ISLAND, Rachel Field, 5:188Ⓓ

IF ONLY . . ., Rose Fyleman, 5:25Ⓑ

IMAGINATION AND CHILDREN'S LITERATURE, Padraic Colum, 16:173

I'M WISHING THE WHOLE WORLD CHRISTMAS, Annette Wynne, 5:73Ⓑ

IN A COVERED WAGON, Emma Brock, 11:72Ⓑ

IN CHURCH, Clara E. Randall, 5:266Ⓐ

INDEPENDENCE DAY FOR DAVY, Margaret Leighton, 6:42Ⓑ

INDIAN BOY, Johnny Sloan, 5:56Ⓑ

INDIAN CHILDREN LONG AGO, Nancy Byrd Turner, 5:90Ⓑ

INDIAN SONG, Elizabeth-Ellen Long, 5:258Ⓓ

IN FROM THE SEA, Elizabeth Coatsworth, 5:192Ⓓ

IN GRANDMOTHER'S GARDEN, Faith Baldwin, 5:180Ⓑ

INQUISITIVE BARN, Frances Frost, 5:197Ⓑ

IN THE GARDEN, Elizabeth Coatsworth, 5:183Ⓓ

IN THE GARDEN, Helen Coale Crew, 1:161Ⓑ

IN WHICH EEYORE HAS A BIRTH-DAY AND GETS TWO PRESENTS, A. A. Milne, 1:186Ⓐ

IRIS, SCHARMEL, Dancer in the Sun, 5:257

IRONING, Dorothy Aldis, 5:16Ⓑ

IRVING, WASHINGTON, Rip Van Winkle, 8:252

IRWIN, WALLACE, Nautical Extravaganza, A, 4:267

IS THERE LIFE ON THE MOON?, Percy H. Wilkins, 16:132Ⓒ

ISLAND CHRISTMAS, AN, Louise Andrews Kent, **6**:277ⓒ

IT WAS, Dorothy Aldis, **5**:68Ⓐ

IT'S SNOWING!, Adelaide Love, **5**:199Ⓐ

JACKSON, ELIZABETH RHODES, Christmas Eve at Reginald's, **6**:359; Holiday Cup, **10**:18; Old Houses, **7**:89; Rule of Three, **6**:156; Street of Memories, **6**:1

JACKSON, LEROY F., Catch Me Caddy, **5**:243; Elephant in the Cinnamon Tree, The, **5**:206; Flanigan's Field, **5**:221; Fun, **4**:13; Goosie Gray, **1**:74; Peaceful Pirate, The, **1**:172

JACOBS, JOSEPH, Three Sillies, The, **2**:139

JACQUES CARTIER, Ragna Eskel, **15**:315ⓒ

JAFFE, HAYM and JOSEPH COTTLER, Guglielmo Marconi, **15**:189; Wright Brothers, The, **15**:158

JAM SESSION AT ABBIE'S, Helen Gregutt, **10**:86ⓒ

JAMBI AND THE TIGER, Armstrong Sperry, **14**:184ⓒ

JAMES, BERTHA TEN EYCK, Magic Screen, The, **5**:41; Stephen Wants a Mouse, **5**:99

JAMES, S. T., Follow Your Leader, **13**:315

JAMES, WILL, Squeak of Leather, The, **14**:211

JANE ADDAMS, William Oliver Stevens, **15**:320ⓒ

JANIE'S WISH, Mildred Lawrence, **1**:296Ⓐ

JAQUES, FLORENCE PAGE, Piping on Christmas Eve, The, **2**:187; Runaway Bus, The, **1**:312; There Once Was a Puffin, **5**:226; Thoughts about Grasshoppers, **1**:43

JEST 'FORE CHRISTMAS, Eugene Field, **5**:312Ⓓ

JEWETT, ELEANOR, Field Flowers, **5**:192; Finger Church, The, **5**:12; Present, The, **5**:19; Puddle, The, **5**:180

JO MEETS LAURIE, Louisa May Alcott, **3**:138ⓒ

JOHN HENRY, MIGHTY RAILROADER, Louis Wolfe, **8**:26ⓒ

JOHNNY AND THE MONARCH, Margaret Friskey, **1**:260Ⓐ

JOHNNY APPLESEED'S COAT, Mabel Leigh Hunt, **11**:47Ⓑ

JOHNNY APPLESEED VISITS LICKING CREEK, Meridel Le Sueur, **11**:146Ⓑ

JOHNNY FIFE AND JOHNNY'S WIFE, Mildred Plew Meigs, **5**:222Ⓑ

JOHNSON, EMILIE FENDALL, Field Mouse, **5**:139; Mexican Palm, **5**:46

JOHNSON, OWEN, Beauty's Sister, **10**:125; Third Round, The, **10**:199

JOHNSON, SIDDIE JOE, Pirate, The, **5**:54; Story Hour, **6**:95

JONATHAN BING, Beatrice Curtis Brown, **4**:134Ⓓ

JONATHAN BING DANCES FOR SPRING, Beatrice Curtis Brown, **5**:200Ⓓ

JONES, ELIZABETH, Ten Little Pussycats **1**:71

JONES, ELIZABETH ORTON, Bobo, **14**:13

JONES, ELIZABETH ORTON and TOM, Minnie the Mermaid, 1:35

JOSIE'S HOME RUN, Ruth Gipson Plowhead, 10:40Ⓑ

JOSLYN, CLAIRE, On Our Way to Dreamland, 5:253

JOURNEY WITH DICKENS, A, Kate Douglas Wiggin, 15:106Ⓒ

JUGGLER, THE, J. G. Francis, 4:196Ⓓ

JUMP, BETTY, Happy Day, 5:32

JUNGE, CARL S., Aristocrat, The, 5:227; Dinosaur, The, 5:119; Ever See a Rhea?, 5:242; Hornbill Family, The, 5:118; Strange Beast, A, 5:119

KAHMANN, CHESLEY, Cream-Colored Pony, The, 6:242; Gang's All There, The, 6:115

KANGAROO, THE, Elizabeth Coatsworth, 5:129Ⓑ

KEATS, JOHN, Thing of Beauty, A, 8:270

KELLY, ERIC P., Broken Note, The, 8:294; Golden Cup of Kasimir, The, 12:259

KELSEY, ALICE GEER, Skeleton Windmill, The, 9:127

KENT, LOUISE ANDREWS, An Island Christmas, 6:277; On Kublai Khan's Service, 12:313

KEY, ALEXANDER, Strangers in the Wilderness, 11:150

KILMER, JOYCE, Trees, 5:356

KING, EDITH, Acorns, 5:34

KING, KENNETH M., Mystery of the Bay, The, 13:190

KING OF THE GOLDEN RIVER, THE, John Ruskin, 3:231Ⓑ

KING OF THE WIND AND THE QUEEN'S PLATE, Marguerite Henry, 14:123Ⓑ

KING QUIET, Carolyn Forsyth, 5:196Ⓑ

KING'S BREAKFAST, THE, A. A. Milne, 1:44Ⓐ

KING'S CYGNET, THE, Ivy Bolton, 12:99Ⓑ

KING'S DAUGHTER, Carolyn Sherwin Bailey, 15:33Ⓑ

KING'S WISH, THE, Edward Wade Devlin, 4:24Ⓑ

KIPLING, RUDYARD, Elephant's Child, The, 4:4; Recessional, 5:288; Rikki-Tikki-Tavi, 14:257; Sea Lullaby, 5:258

KIRBY, OLIVE BURNS, Ice Boat Race, The, 10:60

KIT AND KAT GO FISHING, Lucy Fitch Perkins, 1:75Ⓐ

KITTEN, A, Eleanor Farjeon, 5:122Ⓑ

KJELGAARD, JIM, Dog's Dog, 14:86

KLEP, ROLF, Galileo, 15:74

KNIGHTS OF THE RED ROSE, Franklin M. Reck, 10:269Ⓒ

KNIPE, EMILE BENSON and ALDEN ARTHUR, Six Bells, 12:152

KON-TIKI ADVENTURE, A, Thor Heyerdahl, 13:354Ⓒ

KOYO, THE SINGER, Kenneth Gilbert, 14:98Ⓒ

KRAMER, ARTHUR, Giraffe, The, 1:213

KUBLA KHAN, FROM, Samuel Taylor Coleridge, 12:330©

KUDU, THE, Clara E. Randall, 5:227Ⓑ

LAD WHO WENT TO THE NORTH WIND, THE, George Webbe Dasent, 2:264Ⓑ

LADY BUTTON-EYES, Eugene Field, 5:248Ⓓ

LADY CLARE, Alfred Tennyson, 5:322©

LADY SLIPPER, THE, Rowena Bennett, 5:161Ⓑ

LADY WHO PUT SALT IN HER COFFEE, THE, Lucretia P. Hale, 4:262Ⓑ

LAKE ISLE OF INNISFREE, THE, William Butler Yeats, 5:355Ⓓ

LANCELOT BIGGS ON THE SATURN, Nelson Bond, 16:70©

LANIER, SIDNEY, Dear Land of All My Love, 5:277

LAST OF THE DRAGONS, THE, E. Nesbit, 2:11Ⓑ

LATHROP, DOROTHY P., Who Goes There?, 14:17

LATTIMORE, ELEANOR F., How Birgit Danced in Her Red Shoes, 9:1

LAWRENCE, MILDRED, Janie's Wish, 1:296

LEAR, EDWARD, Duck and the Kangaroo, The, 5:244; Nonsense Limericks, 4:266; Owl and the Pussy Cat, The, 5:232; Young Lady's Eyes, The, 4:117

LEE, AGNES, Shakespeare, 15:236

LEE, MELICENT HUMASON, Secret Staircase, The, 9:29

LEGACY OF CANYON JOHN, THE, Margaret Leighton, 7:98Ⓑ

LEGEND OF LAKE OKEFINOKEE, Laura E. Richards, 4:71Ⓓ

LEIGHTON, LOUISE, I Hear Paul Bunyan, 8:197

LEIGHTON, MARGARET, Fisherman's Luck, 12:348; Independence Day for Davy, 6:42; Legacy of Canyon John, The, 7:98; Parchment Door, The, 12:140

LEONARDO DA VINCI, Walter Ransom Barrows, 15:325©

LESEMANN, MAURICE, Mockingbird, The, 5:107

LE SUEUR, MERIDEL, Johnny Appleseed Visits Licking Creek, 11:146

LETTERS FROM THE SEA, Alice Dalgliesh, 1:264Ⓐ

LEWIS CARROLL, Margaret Ford Allen, 15:8Ⓑ

LEWIS, ELIZABETH FOREMAN, Hok-Hwa of the Waterfront, 9:58

LEWIS, GLADYS FRANCIS, Wild-Horse Roundup, 14:194

LEWIS, JANET, Elf, The, 2:127

LEYSON, BURR W., Trail to the Stars, 16:134

LIFE OF WILLIAM SHAKESPEARE, A, Marchette Chute, 15:222©

LIFE ON THE OCEAN WAVE, A, Epes Sargent, 12:272Ⓓ

LIGHT-HEARTED FAIRY, THE, Author Unknown, 5:170Ⓐ

LINCOLN, Nancy Byrd Turner, 5:80Ⓑ

LINDBERGH, CHARLES A., New York to Paris, **15**:246

LINDBERGH FLIES ALONE, **15**:255ⓒ

LINDERMAN, FRANK B., Why the Chipmunk's Back Is Striped, **8**:50

LINDGREN, ASTRID, Pippi Acts as a Lifesaver, **13**:94

LINDQUIST, WILLIS, Curse of Kaing, The, **9**:320; Flame, **14**:251; Storm Tide, **13**:51; Yukon Trail, **13**:1

LINDSAY, MAUD, Mrs. Tabby Gray, **1**:210

LINDSAY, VACHEL, Abraham Lincoln Walks at Midnight, **5**:346; Little Turtle, The, **5**:95; Mysterious Cat, The, **5**:97; Flower-Fed Buffaloes, The, **14**:75

LISTENERS, THE, Walter de la Mare, **5**:344ⓒ

LITTLE, Dorothy Aldis, **5**:13Ⓑ

LITTLE BEAR TAKES HIS NAP, Catherine Woolley, **1**:224Ⓐ

LITTLE BLUE PIGEON, Eugene Field, **5**:256Ⓐ

LITTLE CATS, Marguerite Gode, **5**:135Ⓐ

LITTLE DOG STAR, THE, Cornelia Meigs, **11**:102Ⓑ

LITTLE DRAGON, THE, Constance Savery, **2**:142Ⓐ

LITTLE ELF, THE, John Kendrick Bangs, **2**:19Ⓐ

LITTLE FOLKS IN THE GRASS, Annette Wynne, **5**:114Ⓐ

LITTLE FOX, THE, Marion Edey and Dorothy Grider, **14**:300Ⓑ

LITTLE GIRL NEXT DOOR, Mildred Bowers Armstrong, **5**:57Ⓑ

LITTLE GNOME, THE, Laura E. Richards, **5**:168Ⓑ

LITTLE GUY, THE, Irving Crump, **10**:286ⓒ

LITTLE JOHN BOTTLEJOHN, Laura E. Richards, **5**:234Ⓓ

LITTLE LAMB, A, Helen and Alf Evers, **1**:97Ⓐ

LITTLE ORPHANT ANNIE, James Whitcomb Riley, **5**:310Ⓓ

LITTLE RED, Pearl S. Buck, **13**:68ⓒ

LITTLE SNOW-WHITE, Jacob and Wilhelm Grimm, **2**:269Ⓑ

LITTLE STEAM ENGINE, THE, Author Unknown, **1**:247Ⓐ

LITTLE SUSAN ZEBRA, Jess Dobson Alt, **5**:219Ⓐ

LITTLE TOY LAND OF THE DUTCH, THE, Author Unknown, **9**:306Ⓑ

LITTLE TURTLE, THE, Vachel Lindsay, **5**:95Ⓐ

LITTLE WOODCHUCK'S FRIGHT, Etta F. Gilbert, **5**:99Ⓑ

LITTLEST ANGEL, THE, Charles Tazewell, **1**:350Ⓐ

LITTLEST REINDEER, THE, Johanna De Witt, **1**:58Ⓐ

LIVING CHRISTMAS, Helen Train Hilles, **6**:164Ⓑ

LIZARD, THE, Ann Chalmers, **5**:115Ⓑ

LOBSTER QUADRILLE, THE, Lewis Carroll, **4**:93Ⓓ

LOCHINVAR, Sir Walter Scott, **5**:316ⓒ

LOFTING, HUGH, Crazy Story of Dizzy Lizzie, **4**:118; Dr. Dolittle and the Pushmi-Pullyu, **4**:158; Dr. Dolittle Meets a Londoner in Paris, **4**:210; Story of Mrs. Tubbs, The, **1**:119

LONDON, JACK, For the Love of Man, **14**:275

313

LONG, ELIZABETH-ELLEN, At Night, 5:187; Autumn Song, 5:194; Child's Prayer, 5:266; Child's Prayer for Other Children, 5:270; Christmas Song, 5:76; Cool, 5:183; Cradle Song, 5:252; Deer at Night, 14:41; First Snowfall, 5:199; Indian Song, 5:258; Night Prayer for Wild Things, 5:125; Night Song, 14:183; Nocturne, 5:182; Song for a Country Night, 5:125; Song for Summer, 5:182; Song of Gray Things, 5:184; Summer, 5:185; White, 5:184

LONG-AGO DOLL, THE, Marjorie Barrows, 5:37Ⓑ

LONGFELLOW, HENRY WADS-WORTH, Hiawatha's Childhood, 5:305; Santa Filomena, 15:244; Village Blacksmith, The, 5:315

LONG, LONG AGO, Author Unknown, 5:71Ⓓ

LOOK AT THE GRAND CHAMP, A, Harold Webster Perry, 14:148Ⓑ

LOOKING IN, Dorothy Aldis, 5:16Ⓒ

LOST MERBABY, THE, Margaret Baker, 1:272Ⓐ

LOUIS AGASSIZ, Mabel L. Robinson, 15:354Ⓒ

LOVE, ADELAIDE, About Christmas, 5:76; Best Ride of All, The, 6:276; Bunny, The, 5:196; Circus Drums, The, 6:201; Happily Ever After, 5:39; It's Snowing!, 5:199; My House, 5:42; Packages, 5:18; Polite Penguins, The, 5:116

LOVELIEST OF TREES, A. E. Housman, 5:357Ⓓ

LOVEMAN, ROBERT, April Rain, 5:178

LOWELL, JAMES RUSSELL, Vision of Sir Launfal, From The, 5:274

LOWNSBERY, ELOISE, Bim's Gift from the Forest, 9:150; Might of a Song, The, 12:331

LUCKY SNAIL, THE, Winifred Welles, 5:124Ⓑ

LUDWIG VAN BEETHOVEN, Marjorie Gordon, 15:328Ⓒ

LUTHER, MARTIN, Cradle Hymn, 5:255

MABIE, HAMILTON WRIGHT, Thor's Wonderful Journey, 8:230

MacDONALD, BETTY, Won't-Pick-Up-Toys Cure, The, 4:136

MACDONALD PLAID, THE, Helen Coale Crew, 9:202Ⓑ

MacGREGOR, ELLEN, Miss Pickerell Goes to Mars, 16:47

MADAME CURIE: DISCOVERER OF HIDDEN TREASURE, Nicholas Nirgiotis, 15:264Ⓒ

MAGEE, JOHN GILLESPIE, JR., High Flight, 5:352

MAGIC FISHBONE, Charles Dickens, 4:38Ⓑ

MAGIC GLASS, THE, Richard Hughes, 4:65Ⓑ

MAGIC SCREEN, THE, Bertha Ten Eyck James, 5:41Ⓑ

MAHOGANY FOX, THE, Samuel Scoville, Jr., 14:290Ⓒ

MAHONY, BERTHA E., Fairy Tales and the Spirit, 16:144

MAID OF TIMBUCTOO, THE, Laura E. Richards, 5:207Ⓓ

MAJOR, CHARLES, Bears of Blue River, The, 11:306

MALCOLMSON, ANNE, Pecos Bill and His Bouncing Bride, 8:115

MALKUS, ALIDA, Silver Llama, The, 9:171

MANNING, JOHN, Neighborly Gnu, The, 5:236; Odorous Owl, The, 5:237; Playful Puma, The, 5:236; Tickly Ostrich, The, 5:236; Turbulent Tiger, The, 5:237; Tyrannical Toad, The, 5:237

MANSFIELD, NORMA BICKNELL, Cake at Midnight, 9:269

MAN WITH THE BAG, THE, Padraic Colum, 2:171Ⓑ

MAN WITH THE BELT OF GOLD, THE, Robert Louis Stevenson, 12:273Ⓒ

MANY MOONS, James Thurber, 2:1Ⓐ

MARION ANDERSON: A VOICE IN A HUNDRED YEARS, Constance Burnett, 15:293Ⓒ

MARSHALL AT BAT, Duane Decker, 10:313Ⓒ

MARTIN, BETTY, Tommy the Tugboat, 1:228

MARTIN, MABELLE E., George Washington Carver, 15:269

MARY SILVER, Elizabeth Coatsworth, 11:159Ⓑ

MASEFIELD, JOHN, Sea-Fever, 5:358; West Wind, The, 5:345

MASON CHILDREN ON THE ROOF, THE, Edith M. Armstrong, 6:137Ⓑ

MASON, MIRIAM E., Cake for Company Dinner, 4:185

MASTER MIND, B. J. Chute, 10:220Ⓒ

MASTER'S FOOTSTOOL, THE, Evelyn Sickels, 11:20Ⓑ

MAUROIS, ANDRE, Ben Franklin's First Adventures, 15:164

MAYBE, Mildred Plew Meigs, 4:261Ⓓ

MAY MORNING, Ruth Dixon, 5:180Ⓑ

McCLOSKEY, ROBERT, Case of the Cosmic Comic, The, 4:238; Case of the Sensational Scent, The, 7:30; Homer Price and the Doughnuts, 4:360

McDONALD, ELLIS ATKINSON, My Puppy, 1:259

McELLIGOT'S POOL, Dr. Seuss, 1:323Ⓐ

McGINLEY, PHYLLIS, Horse Who Lived Upstairs, The, 1:173

McHENRY, JANE, Cinderella, 2:165; Glass Hill, The, 2:44

McKEE, JOHN DUKES, Tillyheehee, The, 4:51

McKINNEY, LAURENCE, Camel and the Cachalot, The, 5:228

McLAVERTY, MICHAEL, Wild Duck's Nest, The, 14:81

McSWIGAN, MARIE, Secret in the Snow, 13:101

MEADER, STEPHEN, Cutter Race, The, 10:301

MEADOWCROFT, ENID LA MONTE, On the Mayflower, 11:1

MEIGS, CORNELIA, Early Days with Invincible Louisa, 15:130; Fox and Geese, 11:10; Hasty Pudding, 11:36; Little Dog Star, The, 11:102; Tale of Sir Gareth, The, 8:309

MEIGS, MILDRED PLEW, Chimney, The, 1:246; Harbor of Hushaby Ho, The, 5:254; If I Were a One-Legged Pirate, 5:214; Johnny Fife and Johnny's Wife, 5:222; Maybe, 4:261; Moon Song, 5:250; Organ Grinder's Garden, The, 5:174; Pirate Don Durk of Dowdee, 5:230; Road to Raffydiddle, The, 5:144; Sandpipers, The, 6:37; Shepherd Left Behind, The, 5:72; Silver Ships, 5:67

MELANCHOLY PIG, THE, Lewis Carroll, 5:223Ⓓ

MERMAIDENS, THE, Laura E. Richards, 5:167Ⓐ

MERRY–GO–ROUND, Marguerite Gode, 5:34Ⓑ

MESSAGE FOR WASHINGTON, A, Eleanor Sickels, 11:255Ⓑ

MEXICAN PALM, Emilie Fendall Johnson, 5:46Ⓑ

MICE, Rose Fyleman, 5:95Ⓐ

MICHELANGELO AND THE SNOW MAN, Mary Newlin Roberts, 15:1Ⓑ

MIDDLE BEAR, THE, Eleanor Estes, 6:144Ⓑ

MIGHT OF A SONG, THE, Eloise Lownsbery, 12:331Ⓒ

MILLAY, EDNA ST. VINCENT, God's World, 5:343; Travel, 5:356

MILLER, JOAQUIN, Columbus, 5:84

MILLER, MARY BRITTON, Cat, 5:103

MILNE, A. A., In Which Eeyore Has a Birthday and Gets Two Presents, 1:186; King's Breakfast, The, 1:44

MINNIE THE MERMAID, Tom and Elizabeth Orton Jones, 1:35Ⓐ

MIRACLES, FROM, Walt Whitman, 15:195Ⓒ

MIRANDA, Frances Barbara Grafe, 5:123Ⓑ

MISHAPS OF GENTLE JANE, THE, Carolyn Wells, 5:216Ⓓ

MISS HINCH, Henry Sydnor Harrison, 7:179Ⓒ

MISS PICKERELL GOES TO MARS, Ellen MacGregor, 16:47Ⓑ

MIST AND ALL, THE, Dixie Willson, 5:194Ⓓ

MITCHELL, LUCY SPRAGUE, Dinner Horses, 5:130; House of the Mouse, The, 5:138

MOCKINGBIRD, THE, Maurice Lesemann, 5:107Ⓓ

MODEL FOR ME, Tom Robinson, 5:137Ⓑ

MOLLOY, ANNE, Penny Walk, The, 6:59

MONKEY SPIRIT, THE, Martha Lee Poston, 9:140Ⓑ

MONROE, HARRIET, Power-Plant, A, 13:143

MONTAGUE, MARGARET PRESCOTT, Big Music, 8:338

MONTCALM, Ragna Eskil, 15:332Ⓒ

MOON, CARL, Silver Belt, The, 9:110

MOON, GRACE, Desirable Shawl, The, 9:14

MOON SONG, Mildred Plew Meigs, 5:250Ⓓ

MOORE, ROSALIE, Catalogue, 14:161

MOORE, THOMAS, Canadian Boat-Song, 5:278

MORE ABOUT JONATHAN BING, Beatrice Curtis Brown, 5:246Ⓓ

MORNING, Ruth Dixon, 5:180Ⓐ

MORNING, Hilda Conkling, 5:177Ⓑ

MORNING EXERCISES, Ruth Crary, 5:33Ⓑ

MOST WONDERFUL THING IN THE WORLD, THE, Georgene Faulkner, 10:69Ⓑ

MOUNTAIN, THE, Caroline P. Wild, 5:56Ⓑ

MOVING, Eunice Tietjens, 5:44Ⓑ

MR. DOOLEY DISGRACES HIS FAMILY, Mary Dickerson Donahey, 6:202Ⓑ

MR. MURDLE'S LARGE HEART, Margery Williams Bianco, **1**:250Ⓐ

MR. POPPER AND CAPTAIN COOK, Richard and Florence Atwater, **4**:30Ⓑ

MR. RABBIT, Dixie Willson, **1**:96Ⓐ

MR. SCRUNCH, Helen and Alf Evers, **4**:52Ⓐ

MRS. BROWN, Rose Fyleman, **5**:29Ⓑ

MRS. GOOSE'S RUBBERS, Miriam Clark Potter, **4**:15Ⓐ

MRS. LECKS AND MRS. ALESHINE ARE SHIPWRECKED, Frank R. Stockton, **4**:283Ⓒ

MRS. TABBY GRAY, Maud Lindsay, **1**:210Ⓐ

MUD, Polly Chase, **5**:14Ⓑ

MUGGINS MOUSE AT THE SEASHORE, Marjorie Barrows, **1**:240Ⓐ

MUKERJI, DHAN GOPAL, Cow Golden Horn, The, **8**:39; How Kari Saved Our Lives in the Jungle, **14**:76

MULOCK, DINAH MARIA, Adventures of a Brownie, **1**:163; Brownie's Ride, **2**:102

MUMPS, THE, Elizabeth Madox Roberts, **5**:49Ⓑ

MUSICAL MICE, THE, Frances Frost, **5**:134Ⓑ

MY CROOKED OLD HOUSE, Lorena La Brec Ouellette, **5**:48Ⓑ

MY DOG, Marchette Chute, **5**:63Ⓐ

MY DOG, Tom Robinson, **5**:111Ⓑ

MY DOG, James S. Tippett, **5**:120Ⓑ

MY FIRST BOOK FRIENDS, Rachel Field, **16**:170

MY FRIEND LU, Ruth Dixon, **5**:19Ⓐ

MY GIFT, Christina Rossetti, **5**:74Ⓓ

MY HOUSE, Adelaide Love, **5**:42Ⓑ

MY HUMMINGBIRDS, Pearl B. Carley, **14**:42Ⓑ

MY NEW ROLLER SKATES, Fleur Conkling, **5**:47Ⓑ

MY PLAN, Marchette Chute, **5**:15Ⓑ

MY PUPPY, Ellis Atkinson McDonald, **1**:259Ⓐ

MY STRUGGLE FOR AN EDUCATION, Booker T. Washington, **15**:211Ⓒ

MY TEDDY BEAR, Louise de Marigny Smith, **5**:33Ⓐ

MYSTERIOUS CAT, THE, Vachel Lindsay, **5**:97Ⓓ

MYSTERY—AND THE RACE, Mary Mapes Dodge, **3**:261Ⓑ

MYSTERY OF NO. 30, THE, L. M. Swenson, **7**:42Ⓑ

MYSTERY OF THE BAY, THE, Kenneth M. King, **13**:190Ⓒ

NANOOK, Alice Gall and Fleming Crew, **14**:64Ⓒ

NASH, OGDEN, Panther, The, **4**:111; Rhinoceros, The, **4**:111; Tale of Custard the Dragon, The, **4**:1

NATURALLY ENOUGH, Berton Braley, **5**:164Ⓓ

NAUTICAL BALLAD, A, Charles Edward Carryl, **4**:164Ⓓ

317

NAUTICAL EXTRAVAGANZA, A, Wallace Irwin, 4:267Ⓓ

NEAL, HARRY EDWARD, Frontier Blockade Buster, 11:229

NEIGHBORLY GNU, THE, John Manning, 5:236Ⓓ

NEIKIRK, MABEL E., Oscar, the Trained Seal, 4:58

NESBIT, E., Last of the Dragons, The, 2:11

NEW FRIEND, A, Marjorie Allen Anderson, 5:32Ⓐ

NEW SNOW, Frances Frost, 5:197Ⓑ

NEW SONG TO SING ABOUT JONATHAN BING, A, Beatrice Curtis Brown, 5:247Ⓓ

NEW YORK TO PARIS, Charles Lindbergh, 15:246Ⓒ

NEWELL, DAVID M., Cubby, 14:45

NICOLAY, HELEN, Abraham Lincoln's Boyhood, 15:25

NIGHT, William Blake, 5:38Ⓓ

NIGHT, Sara Teasdale, 5:354Ⓓ

NIGHT OF WIND, Frances M. Frost, 14:111Ⓓ

NIGHT PRAYER FOR WILD THINGS, Elizabeth-Ellen Long, 5:139Ⓓ

NIGHT SONG, Elizabeth-Ellen Long, 14:183Ⓑ

NIGHT WILL NEVER STAY, THE, Eleanor Farjeon, 5:185Ⓓ

NIGHTINGALE, MADELEINE, Apple Rhyme, The, 5:172; Caravan, The, 5:54

NIGHTINGALE, THE, Hans Andersen, 2:358Ⓒ

NIGHTINGALE, THE, Ivy O. Eastwick, 5:6Ⓑ

NINE RABBITS AND ANOTHER ONE, Miriam Clark Potter, 1:234Ⓐ

NIRGIOTIS, NICHOLAS, Madame Curie: Discoverer of Hidden Treasure, 15:264

NOCTURNE, Elizabeth-Ellen Long, 5:182Ⓑ

NONSENSE LIMERICKS, Edward Lear, 4:266Ⓓ

NORDHOFF, CHARLES, Pearl Diver, The, 13:347

NORRIS, MARGARET, Down in Davy Jones's Locker, 13:334

NORTH COUNTRY, Agnes Louise Dean, 5:39Ⓑ

NORTH, STERLING, Five Little Bears Have Their Pictures Taken, The, 1:269

NOYES, ALFRED, Admiral's Ghost, The, 5:338; Forty Singing Seamen, 5:334; Highwayman, The, 5:289; Song of Sherwood, A, 5:348

NURENBERG STOVE, THE, Louise De La Ramée, 9:36Ⓑ

OBLINGER, M. M., and MAXINE SHORE, Alexander MacKenzie: Hero of Canada, 15:153

O'BRIEN, JACK, Dinty—A Husky's Story, 14:176

OCELOT, Clara E. Randall, 5:203Ⓑ

318

OCTOPUS, Adele Jordan Tarr, **5**:208Ⓓ

O'DONNELL, THOMAS C., Pink Giraffe, The, **4**:111

ODOROUS OWL, THE, John Manning, **5**:237Ⓓ

OFFER, Mildred Bowers Armstrong, **5**:142Ⓑ

OLD COACH ROAD, THE, Rachel Field, **6**:313Ⓑ

OLD COUNTRY, THE, Ann Zelenka, **5**:5Ⓑ

OLD GOOSE, THE, Helen Wing, **1**:52Ⓐ

OLD HOUSES, Elizabeth Rhodes Jackson, **7**:89Ⓑ

OLD SLY EYE, Russell Gordon Carter, **11**:173Ⓒ

OLD WOMAN AND THE TRAMP, THE, **4**:112Ⓑ

OLDS, HELEN DIEHL, Basketball Mystery, The, **10**:32

OLIVER AT THE CIRCUS, Elizabeth Enright, **13**:26Ⓑ

ONCE WHEN YOU WERE WALKING, Annette Wynne, **2**:120Ⓑ

ONE ALASKA NIGHT, Barrett Willoughby, **7**:297Ⓒ

ONE MINUTE LONGER, Albert Payson Terhune, **14**:358Ⓒ

ONE YOU DON'T SEE COMING, THE, Harold Courlander and George Herzog, **8**:56Ⓑ

ON KUBLAI KHAN'S SERVICE, Louise Andrews Kent, **12**:313Ⓒ

ON OUR WAY TO DREAMLAND, Clare Joslyn, **5**:253Ⓓ

ON THE FARM, Anne Pérez-Guerra, **5**:28Ⓑ

ON THE MAYFLOWER, Enid La Monte Meadowcroft, **11**:1Ⓑ

ON THE TRAIN, Ruth Dixon, **5**:50Ⓑ

OPEN ROAD, THE, Kenneth Grahame, **2**:20Ⓐ

ORGAN GRINDERS' GARDEN, THE, Mildred Plew Meigs, **5**:174Ⓐ

OSCAR, THE TRAINED SEAL, Mabel E. Neikirk, **4**:58Ⓑ

O'SHEEL, SHAEMUS, He Whom a Dream Hath Possessed, **5**:352

OTIS, JAMES, Toby Tyler and Mr. Stubbs, **3**:93

OTTO AT SEA, William Pène du Bois, **1**:181Ⓐ

OUELLETTE, LORENA LA BREC, My Crooked Old House, **5**:48

OUR AMERICA, Ruth Dixon, **5**:83Ⓒ

OUR BURRO, Clara E. Randall, **5**:115Ⓓ

OUR DONKEY, Tom Robinson, **5**:104Ⓓ

OUR STREET, Gertrude Strickler, **5**:31Ⓓ

OUT OF DEFEAT, Constance Lindsay Skinner, **12**:359Ⓒ

OVER THE CHIMNEY-TOPS, Rowena Bennett, **5**:159Ⓑ

OVER THE GARDEN WALL, Eleanor Farjeon, **5**:2Ⓑ

OWL, THE, Alfred Tennyson, **5**:279Ⓓ

OWL AND THE PUSSY CAT, THE, Edward Lear, **5**:232Ⓓ

319

PACKAGES, Adelaide Love, 5:18Ⓑ

PACK RAT, THE, Emma-Lindsay Squier, 14:50Ⓑ

PALE PINK TEA, THE, Ruth Dixon, 5:242Ⓑ

PALMER, ROBIN, Punch Has an Adventure, 6:52

PANTHER, THE, Ogden Nash, 4:111Ⓓ

PARADE OF THE ANIMAL CRACKERS, Rowena Bennett, 5:157Ⓐ

PARCHMENT DOOR, THE, Margaret Leighton, 12:140Ⓑ

PASS, THE, John R. Tunis, 10:350Ⓒ

PASTURE, THE, Robert Frost, 5:136Ⓓ

PATHFINDERS: LEWIS AND CLARK, THE, Eva March Tappan, 11:289Ⓒ

PATHS, Josephine Van Dolzen Pease, 5:189Ⓑ

PATRICK HENRY ENTERS PUBLIC LIFE, Julia Carson, 15:337Ⓒ

PATSY AND. THE LEPRECHAUN, Margaret and Mary Baker, 2:109Ⓑ

PEABODY, JOSEPHINE PRESTON, Wooden Horse and the Fall of Troy, The, 12:355

PEACEFUL PIRATE, THE, Leroy F. Jackson, 1:172Ⓑ

PEARL DIVER, THE, Charles Nordhoff, 13:347Ⓒ

PEASE, HOWARD, Adventure at the Toll Bridge, The, 7:279

PEASE, JOSEPHINE VAN DOLZEN, Paths, 5:189

PECOS BILL AND HIS BOUNCING BRIDE, Anne Malcolmson, 8:115Ⓒ

PENGUIN SUMMER, Kathryn Worth, 5:116Ⓑ

PENNY WALK, THE, Anne Molloy, 6:59Ⓐ

PERCY, WILLIAM ALEXANDER, Farmers, 5:126

PÉREZ–GUERRA, ANNE, I Wish I Lived in Elfland, 5:152; If I were Thumbelina, 2:88; On the Farm, 5:28; Poppy, 2:54

PERKINS, LUCY FITCH, Eskimo Twins Go Coasting, The, 9:20; Kit and Kat Go Fishing, 1:75

PERKINS, MARGERY BLAIR, Stranger in the Wood, The, 12:169

PERRY, CLAY, Guides with Wings, 13:228

PERRY, HAROLD WEBSTER, Look at the Grand Champ, A, 14:148

PETER PAN AND CAPTAIN HOOK, James Barrie, 2:225Ⓑ

PET SHOW, Arthur Guiterman, 5:102Ⓑ

PHAETON, Padraic Colum, 8:144Ⓑ

PICNIC BASKET, THE, Margery Clark, 1:158Ⓐ

PIED PIPER OF HAMELIN, THE, Robert Browning, 5:294Ⓓ

PIGEON, THE, Marjorie Barrows, 5:52Ⓑ

PINE TREE SONG, Marjorie Barrows, 5:73Ⓑ

PINK GIRAFFE, THE, Thomas C. O'Donnell, 4:111Ⓑ

PIONEER WEDDING, A, Elizabeth Coatsworth, 11:314Ⓑ

PIPING ON CHRISTMAS EVE, THE, Florence Page Jaques, 2:187Ⓑ

PIPPI ACTS AS A LIFESAVER, Astrid Lindgren, 13:94Ⓑ

PIRATE, THE, Siddie Joe Johnson, 5:54Ⓑ

PIRATE DON DURK OF DOWDEE, Mildred Plew Meigs, 5:230Ⓓ

PIXIE, DIXIE, TRIXIE, AND NIXIE, Dorothy and Marguerite Bryan, 1:206Ⓐ

PLANTING A TREE, Nancy Byrd Turner, 5:82Ⓑ

PLAYFUL PUMA, THE, John Manning, 5:236Ⓓ

PLAYHOUSE KEY, THE, Rachel Field, 5:35Ⓓ

PLAYING AT THE WATERFALL, Janet Norris Bangs, 5:160Ⓓ

PLEASE, Rose Fyleman, 5:149Ⓓ

PLOWHEAD, RUTH GIPSON, Josie's Home Run, 10:40

POE, EDGAR ALLAN, Bells, The, 5:284; Gold Bug, The, 7:201

POETRY AND CHILDHOOD, Padraic Colum, 16:147

POLICEMEN ON PARADE, Jimmy Garthwaite, 5:53Ⓐ

POLITELY, Dixie Willson, 1:107Ⓐ

POLITE PENGUINS, THE, Adelaide Love, 5:116Ⓑ

POOKA, Ella Young, 5:173Ⓒ

POPPY, Anne Pérez-Guerra, 2:54Ⓐ

PORTER, RUTH STEPHENS, Hoppity Toad, The, 5:124

POSTON, MARTHA LEE, Monkey Spirit, The, 9:140

POTTER, MIRIAM CLARK, Mrs. Goose's Rubbers, 4:15; Nine Rabbits and Another One, 1:234

POWER–PLANT, A, Harriet Monroe, 13:143Ⓒ

PRESENT, THE, Eleanor Jewett, 5:19Ⓐ

PRINCIPAL EXPORTS, Marchette Chute, 5:12Ⓑ

PRIZE, THE, Eunice Young Smith, 10:48Ⓑ

PUCK'S SONG, William Shakespeare, 2:43Ⓓ

PUDDLE, THE, Eleanor Jewett, 5:180Ⓐ

PUNCH HAS AN ADVENTURE, Robin Palmer, 6:52Ⓑ

PUPPIES, Marguerite Gode, 5:127Ⓐ

PUPPY WHO WANTED A BOY, THE, Catherine Woolley, 1:332Ⓐ

PURPLE-EYED PIRATE, THE, Marjorie Barrows, 5:202Ⓑ

PYLE, HOWARD, Robin Hood and the Shooting Match, 12:227; Robin Hood turns Beggar, 8:205; Swan Maiden, The, 2:178; Tom Chist and the Treasure Box, 13:247; Trial by Battle, 13:278

QUEEN OF THE ORKNEY ISLANDS, THE, Laura E. Richards, 4:100Ⓓ

QUEER ONE, THE, Carolyn Wells, 5:213Ⓓ

QUESTIONS, Laura Lee Randall, 5:158Ⓐ

RABBIT TRACKS, Aileen Fisher, 5:138Ⓑ

RADIO WISH, Ruth Dixon, 5:38Ⓑ

RAGGEDY MAN, THE, James Whitcomb Riley, 5:311Ⓓ

RAIN, Ella Young, 5:190Ⓑ

RAIN TOYS, THE, Mildred Bowers Armstrong, 5:190Ⓑ

RAINY DAY, Bee Bowers, 5:133Ⓐ

RAINY DAY, Agnes Louise Dean, 5:188Ⓑ

RANDALL, CLARA E., Camel, The, 5:132; Dinosaur, The, 5:129; In Church, 5:266; Kudu, The, 5:227; Ocelot, 5:203; Our Burro, 5:115; We Give Our Thanks, 5:265; Whizz, 1:83

RANDALL, LAURA LEE, Questions, 5:158

RANDY AT THE ART GALLERY, Elizabeth Enright, 6:211Ⓑ

RANGER WISHES, Kate Cox Goddard, 5:45Ⓑ

RANSOM OF RED CHIEF, THE, O. Henry, 4:248Ⓒ

RAWLINGS, MARJORIE KINNAN, Hunting Old Slew Foot, 14:314

RAYMOND, MARGARET, Robert E. Lee, 15:176

REBECCA AT THE BRICK HOUSE, Kate Douglas Wiggin, 3:203Ⓑ

RECESSIONAL, Rudyard Kipling, 5:288Ⓒ

RECK, FRANKLIN M., Gawk, The, 10:168; Knights of the Red Rose, 10:269

RED-HEADED LEAGUE, THE, A. Conan Doyle, 7:346Ⓒ

REFLECTION, Eunice Tietjens, 5:43Ⓑ

REFORMED PIRATE, THE, Frank R. Stockton, 2:322Ⓒ

REGLI, ADOLPH, Willie the Moose, 14:7

REMEMBERING THE WINTER, Rowena Bennett, 5:195Ⓑ

REY, H. A., Curious George, 1:53

RHINOCEROS, THE, Ogden Nash, 4:111Ⓓ

RHODORA, THE, Ralph Waldo Emerson, 5:276Ⓒ

RICHARDS, LAURA E., Eletelephony, 4:14; Gregory Griggs, 1:118; Legend of Lake Okefinokee, 4:71; Little Gnome, The, 5:168; Little John Bottlejohn, 5:234; Maid of Timbuctoo, The, 5:207; Mermaidens, The, 5:167; Queen of the Orkney Islands, The, 4:100; Shark, The 5:210

RICHARDS, MILTON, Boy Who Voted for Abe Lincoln, The, 11:83

RIDE WITH TOM THUMB, A, Marjorie Hayes, 11:56Ⓑ

RIKKI-TIKKI-TAVI, Rudyard Kipling, 14:257Ⓒ

RILEY, JAMES WHITCOMB, Little Orphant Annie, 5:310; Raggedy Man, The, 5:311

RIP VAN WINKLE, Washington Irving, 8:252Ⓒ

RIVER AND BEASTS BETRAY, Julia Davis, 11:277Ⓒ

ROAD TO RAFFYDIDDLE, THE, Mildred Plew Meigs, 5:144Ⓓ

ROADS, Rachel Field, 5:51Ⓓ

ROBERT E. LEE, Margaret Raymond, 15:176Ⓒ

ROBERT LOUIS STEVENSON, Walter Ransom Barrows, 15:206Ⓒ

ROBERTS, ELIZABETH MADOX, Butterbean Tent, The, 5:11; Christmas Morning, 5:70; Circus, The, 5:23; Mumps, The, 5:49; Woodpecker, The, 5:10

ROBERTS, MARY NEWLIN, Antonio Van Dyke and his Master Reubens, 15:88; Georg Handel and the Duke, 15:76; Michelangelo and the Snow Man, 15:1; Titian's First Picture, 15:56; Wolfgang Mozart, 15:94

ROBIN FINDS A WAY, Marguerite de Angeli, **12**:26Ⓑ

ROBIN HOOD AND ALLEN–A–DALE, Author Unknown, **5**:325ⓒ

ROBIN HOOD AND THE SHOOTING MATCH, Howard Pyle, **12**:227ⓒ

ROBIN HOOD TURNS BEGGAR, Howard Pyle, **8**:205ⓒ

ROBINSON CRUSOE IS SHIP-WRECKED, Daniel Defoe, **3**:153ⓒ

ROBINSON CRUSOE'S STORY, Charles Edward Carryl, **4**:236Ⓑ

ROBINSON, MABEL L., False Summer, **6**:314; Louis Agassiz, **15**:354

ROBINSON, TOM, Model for Me, **5**:137; My Dog, **5**:111; Our Donkey, **5**:104

ROCK–A–BY LADY, THE, Eugene Field, **5**:255Ⓐ

ROCKING–HORSE LAND, Laurence Housman, **1**:302Ⓐ

ROCKY MOUNTAIN SHEEP, THE, Mary Austin, **14**:371Ⓑ

ROCOCO SKATES, Marjorie Fischer, **6**:30Ⓑ

ROLAND AND HIS HORN, G. W. Cox, **8**:355ⓒ

ROLLING DOWN A HILL, Dorothy Aldis, **5**:8Ⓐ

ROOSEVELT, THEODORE, Buffalo Hunting, **11**:357

ROSENBERG, PAULINE, Three Wishes, The, **2**:99

ROSES, Mary F. Butts, **5**:161Ⓑ

ROSSETTI, CHRISTINA, My Gift, **5**:74; Who Has Seen the Wind, **5**:275

ROUND THE MAYPOLE NOW WE DANCE, Nancy Byrd Turner, **5**:83Ⓑ

ROUNDS, GLEN, Whitey and the Rustlers, **13**:16

ROUND UP, THE, Kate Seredy, **13**:80Ⓑ

RUGGLESES' CHRISTMAS DINNER, THE, Kate Douglas Wiggin, **4**:217Ⓑ

RULE OF THREE, Elizabeth Rhodes Jackson, **6**:156Ⓑ

RUMPELSTILTSKIN, Jacob and Wilhelm Grimm, **2**:252Ⓑ

RUNAWAY, THE, Robert Frost, **5**:131Ⓓ

RUNAWAY BUS, THE, Florence Page Jaques, **1**:312Ⓐ

RUSKIN, JOHN, King of the Golden River, The, **3**:231

RUSTY–MOVIE STAR, Alice Dalgliesh, **6**:89Ⓑ

RYDBERG, ERNIE, Caricature, **10**:212

ST. CLAIR, RAY, Cannery Bear, The, **4**:94; Fox Ferry, The, **2**:218

ST. FRANCIS OF ASSISI, Canticle of the Sun, **5**:354

SAID THE SANDMAN, Helen Wing, **1**:338Ⓐ

SALTEN, FELIX, Bambi Starts To See the World, **14**:27

SAMMY SNOWMAN, Ruth Dixon, **5**:64Ⓐ

SANDBURG, CARL, Fog, **5**:193; Huckabuck Family, The, **4**:47; Small Homes, **5**:115; Splinter, **5**:191

SANDHILL CRANE, THE, Mary Austin, **14**:54Ⓓ

SANDPILE TOWN, Aileen Fisher, 5:4Ⓑ

SANDPIPERS, THE, Cornelia Meigs, 6:37Ⓑ

SANTA FE, NEW MEXICO, Polly Chase, 5:45Ⓑ

SANTA FILOMENA, Henry Wadsworth Longfellow, 15:244Ⓒ

SARA CREWE, OR WHAT HAPPENED AT MISS MINCHIN'S, Frances Hodgson Burnett, 3:325Ⓑ

SARGENT, EPES, Life on the Ocean Wave, A, 12:272

SAVERY, CONSTANCE, Adventure in Candle Street, 12:179; Little Dragon, The, 2:142; Spindleberries and Pam, 6:78; Wastwych Secret, The, 7:49

SAVING OF BOONESBOROUGH, THE, James Daugherty, 11:181Ⓒ

SCHIRMER, MATHILDA, Albert Schweitzer: The Doctor in the Jungle, 15:256; Howard Pyle: Great American Illustrator, 15:348

SCHNEIDER, HERMAN, What Is a Good Science Book?, 16:162

SCHOLZ, JACKSON V., Hoop Hokum, 10:236

SCHOOL FOR SANDPIPERS, Elizabeth Honness, 5:109Ⓑ

SCOTT, MARIE LOUISE, Gratitude, 5:120

SCOTT, SIR WALTER, Breathes There the Man with Soul So Dead, 5:281; Hie Away, Hie Away, 5:271; Hunting Song, 12:258; Lochinvar, 5:316

SCOVILLE, SAMUEL, JR., Mahogany Fox, The, 14:290

SEA CHILD, Nancy Byrd Turner, 5:167Ⓑ

SEA-FEVER, John Masefield, 5:358Ⓓ

SEA GULL, THE, Elizabeth Coatsworth, 5:108Ⓑ

SEA HORSE, THE, Fleur Conkling, 5:24Ⓑ

SEA-SHELL, Ivy O. Eastwick, 2:251Ⓑ

SEA SONG, A, Allan Cunningham, 5:273Ⓓ

SEAL LULLABY, Rudyard Kipling, 5:258Ⓓ

SEAMAN, AUGUSTA HUIELL, Strange Pettingill Puzzle, The, 7:108

SEASHORE GOSSIP, J. Lilian Vandevere, 5:117Ⓑ

SEAVEY, MARION K., Frog, The, 5:110

SECOND-HAND SHOP, THE, Rowena Bennett, 5:147Ⓑ

SECRET CAVERN, THE, Margaret Widdemer, 5:66Ⓑ

SECRET IN THE SNOW, Marie McSwigan, 13:101Ⓑ

SECRET OF RAINBOW RIDGE, THE, Audrey Baxendale, 7:69Ⓑ

SECRET PLACE, THE, Dorothy Aldis, 5:17Ⓑ

SECRET STAIRCASE, THE, Meliċent Humason Lee, 9:29Ⓑ

SELF-CONTROL, Polly Chase, 5:61Ⓑ

SELFISH GIANT, THE, Oscar Wilde, 2:316Ⓒ

SENSIBLE LOBSTER, THE, Helen Wing, 5:208Ⓑ

SERAPINA PROVES HERSELF, Anne H. White, 4:166Ⓑ

SEREDY, KATE, Easter Eggs, 9:76; Round Up, The, 13:80

SERVICE, ROBERT W., Cremation of Sam McGee, The, 5:329

SETON, ERNEST THOMPSON, Coaly-Bay, the Outlaw Horse, 14:305

324

SEUSS, DR., 500 Hats of Bartholomew Cubbins, The, 1:16; McElligot's Pool, 1:323

SHAKESPEARE, Agnes Lee, 15:236©

SHAKESPEARE, WILLIAM, Hark! Hark! The Lark, 5:272; Puck's Song, 2:43

SHANNON, MONICA, Dobry's New Year, 9:294

SHARES, Judy Van der Veer, 5:100®

SHARK, THE, Laura E. Richards, 5:210®

SHEA, AGATHA L., Your Child and World Neighborliness, 16:159

SHELLEY, PERCY BYSSHE, Crimson Dawn, The, 5:277

SHEPHERD LEFT BEHIND, THE, Mildred Plew Meigs, 5:72®

SHINE, STAR, Nancy Byrd Turner, 5:79®

SHIP OF RIO, THE, Walter de la Mare, 4:70®

SHORE, MAXINE and M. M. OB-LINGER, Alexander MacKenzie: Hero of Canada, 15:153

SICKELS, EVELYN, Master's Footstool, The, 11:20; Message for Washington, A, 11:255

SILVER, Walter de la Mare, 5:38®

SILVER BELT, THE, Carl Moon, 9:110®

SILVER LLAMA, THE, Alida Malkus, 9:171®

SILVER SHIPS, Mildred Plew Meigs, 5:67®

SILVER TREES, Aileen Fisher, 5:191®

SING HO!, Jeanne De Lamarter, 5:196®

SING, WORLD, SING!, Nancy Byrd Turner, 5:82®

SINGH, R. LAL, Bim's Gift from the Forest, 9:150

SINGING SAUCEPAN, THE, Edith Unnerstad, 9:65®

SINGMASTER, ELSIE, Benny and the Cat's Tail, 15:62

SIR PETER BOMBAZOO, Charles Edward Carryl, 4:358®

SIX BELLS, Emilie Benson Knipe and Alden Arthur Knipe, 12:152®

SKATING, Herbert Asquith, 5:65®

SKELETON WINDMILL, THE, Alice Geer Kelsey, 9:127®

SKINNER, CONSTANCE LINDSAY, Out of Defeat, 12:359

SLEEP, BABY, SLEEP, Author Unknown, 5:267®

SLEEPING BEAUTY, THE, Grimm and Perrault, 2:289®

SLEIGH BELLS AT NIGHT, Elizabeth Coatsworth, 5:64®

SLIDE, THE, Emily Hilsabeck, 1:295®

SLOAN, JOHNNY, Indian Boy, 5:56

SMALL HOMES, Carl Sandburg, 5:115®

SMITH, EUNICE YOUNG, Prize, The, 10:48

SMITH, FREDRIKA SHUMWAY, Adolfuss, 5:135; Spectacles, The, 5:42

SMITH, LOUISE DE MARIGNY, Easter Bunny, The, 5:56; My Teddy Bear, 5:33

SMOKY, Marion Holland, 6:104®

SNIFF, Frances Frost, 5:60®

SNOW BY NIGHT, Rachel Field, 5:21®

SNOWBOUND, John Greenleaf Whittier, 5:308®

325

SNOWFALL, Janet Norris Bangs, 6:326Ⓑ

SNOWFLAKE FUN, Ruth Dixon, 5:170Ⓐ

SNOWY MORNING, Frances Frost, 5:195Ⓑ

SOLITARY REAPER, THE, William Wordsworth, 5:280Ⓒ

SOMETHING TOLD THE WILD GEESE, Rachel Field, 5:187Ⓓ

SON OF THE SOUTH WIND, Frances Carpenter, 8:86Ⓑ

SONG AT DUSK, Nancy Byrd Turner, 5:252Ⓐ

SONG FOR A BLUE ROADSTER, Rachel Field, 5:27Ⓑ

SONG FOR A COUNTRY NIGHT, Elizabeth-Ellen Long, 5:125Ⓑ

SONG FOR A SUMMER EVENING, Mildred Bowers Armstrong, 2:33Ⓑ

SONG FOR ROBERTA, Adele Jordan Tarr, 5:256Ⓑ

SONG FOR SUMMER, Elizabeth Coatsworth, 2:50Ⓑ

SONG FOR SUMMER, Elizabeth-Ellen Long, 5:182Ⓑ

SONG FOR SUPPER, J. Lilian Vandevere, 5:43Ⓐ

SONG FOR WARREN, Adele Jordan Tarr, 5:110Ⓑ

SONG OF GRANDFATHER THOMAS' PARROT, Elizabeth Coatsworth, 5:108Ⓓ

SONG OF GRAY THINGS, Elizabeth-Ellen Long, 5:184Ⓑ

SONG OF KING ARTHUR'S KNIGHTS, Alfred Tennyson, 8:328Ⓓ

SONG OF SHERWOOD, A, Alfred Noyes, 5:348Ⓓ

SONG OF THE HERD, Judy Van der Veer, 5:101Ⓑ

SONG OF THE LITTLE DONKEY, THE, Alice Crew Gall and Fleming Crew, 1:214Ⓐ

SONG OF THE RABBITS OUTSIDE THE TAVERN, Elizabeth Coatsworth, 5:96Ⓓ

SPECTACLES, THE, Fredrika Shumway Smith, 5:42Ⓐ

SPELL, THE, Ruth Dixon, 5:166Ⓐ

SPERRY, ARMSTRONG, Forbidden Island, The, 9:345; Jambi and the Tiger, 14:184

SPICER, ANNE HIGGINSON, Christmas Path, The, 6:16

SPINDLEBERRIES AND PAM, Constance Savery, 6:78Ⓑ

SPLINTER, Carl Sandburg, 5:191Ⓓ

SPRING PASTURES, Judy Van der Veer, 5:100Ⓑ

SPRING RAIN, Marchette Chute, 5:14Ⓑ

SPRING SIGNS, Mildred Bowers Armstrong, 5:50Ⓑ

SPYRI, JOHANNA, Heidi's Adventures on the Mountain, 3:26

SQUEAK OF LEATHER, THE, Will James, 14:211Ⓒ

SQUIER, EMMA-LINDSAY, Pack Rat, The, 14:50

SQUIRREL, THE, Mildred Bowers Armstrong, 5:113Ⓐ

STAFFORD, LEONA, Forest Lullaby, 5:259

STALACTITE SURPRISE, L. R. Davis, 7:61Ⓑ

STAR, THE, Marjorie Barrows, 5:6Ⓑ

STAR DUCKS, THE, Bill Brown, 16:36Ⓑ

STEELMAN'S NERVE, William Heyliger, **13**:144Ⓒ

STEPHEN WANTS A MOUSE, Bertha Ten Eyck James, **5**:99Ⓑ

STEPHENS, JAMES, White Fields, **5**:198

STEVENS, ELEANOR ELIZABETH, Winter Wood, **5**:198

STEVENS, JAMES, Great Hunter of the Woods, The, **8**:103

STEVENS, WILLIAM OLIVER, Jane Addams, **15**:320

STEVENSON, ROBERT LOUIS, Celestial Surgeon, The, **15**:210; Farewell to the Farm, **5**:28; Man with the Belt of Gold, The, **12**:273; Vagabond, The, **5**:318

STILL IT IS WILDERNESS, Elizabeth Coatsworth, **14**:256Ⓓ

STINETORF, LOUISE A., First Lamb, The, **9**:49

STOCKTON, FRANK R., Mrs. Lecks and Mrs. Aleshine are Shipwrecked, **4**:283; Reformed Pirate, The, **2**:322

STODDARD, ANNE, Good Little Dog, A, **1**:178

STONG, PHIL, Waino and Ivar meet Honk the Moose, **6**:65

STOPPING BY WOODS ON A SNOWY EVENING, Robert Frost, **5**:357Ⓓ

STORM TIDE, Willis Lindquist, **13**:51Ⓑ

STORY HOUR, Siddie Joe Johnson, **6**:95Ⓑ

STORY OF ALADDIN; OR, THE WONDERFUL LAMP, THE, **2**:293Ⓒ

STORY OF BABAR, THE, Jean de Brunhoff, **1**:100Ⓐ

STORY OF DOBBIN, THE, Alice Dalgliesh, **1**:244Ⓐ

STORY OF MRS. TUBBS, THE, Hugh Lofting, **1**:119Ⓐ

STRANGE BEAST, A, Carl S. Junge, **5**:119Ⓓ

STRANGE HOLINESS, Robert P. Tristram Coffin, **5**:350Ⓓ

STRANGE PETTINGILL PUZZLE, THE, Augusta Huiell Seaman, **7**:108Ⓑ

STRANGER IN THE WOOD, THE, Margery Blair Perkins, **12**:169Ⓑ

STRANGERS IN THE WILDERNESS, Alexander Key, **11**:150Ⓒ

STREATFEILD, NOEL, Understudy, **13**:200

STREET, JULIAN, Theodore Roosevelt, **15**:288

STREET OF MEMORIES, Elizabeth Rhodes Jackson, **6**:1Ⓑ

STRICKLER, GERTRUDE, Our Street, **5**:31

STROBEL, MARION, Cross-Stitch Sampler, **5**:57

STRUGGLE, THE, Arthur Hugh Clough, **15**:273Ⓒ

SUMMER, Elizabeth-Ellen Long, **5**:185Ⓑ

SUN IS FIRST TO RISE, THE, Elizabeth Coatsworth, **5**:179Ⓓ

SWAN MAIDEN, THE, Howard Pyle, **2**:178Ⓑ

SWEET AFTON, Robert Burns, **5**:278Ⓓ

SWEET AND LOW, Alfred Tennyson, **5**:263Ⓓ

SWENSON, L. M., Mystery of No. 30, The, **7**:42

SWINGING, Marjorie Allen Anderson, **5**:32Ⓐ

327

TABBY'S TABLECLOTH, Louisa May Alcott, **11**:264Ⓑ

TALE OF CUSTARD, THE DRAGON, THE, Ogden Nash, **4**:1Ⓓ

TALE OF SIR GARETH, THE, Cornelia Meigs, **8**:309Ⓒ

TALE OF THE LAZY PEOPLE, THE, Charles J. Finger, **8**:129Ⓑ

TALE OF THREE TAILS, A, Charles J. Finger, **8**:241Ⓑ

TALK, Harold Courlander and George Herzog, **8**:17Ⓑ

TAMED, Nancy Byrd Turner, **5**:178Ⓑ

TANNER, RUTH E., Wild Dog, **14**:116

TAPPAN, EVA MARCH, Pathfinders: Lewis and Clark, The, **11**:289; Two Scenes from the Life of George Washington, **15**:196

TARR, ADELE JORDAN, Octopus, **5**:208; Song for Roberta, **5**:256; Song for Warren, **5**:110

TAZEWELL, CHARLES, Littlest Angel, The, **1**:350

TEASDALE, SARA, Barter, **5**:351; Night, **5**:354

TEDDY BEAR DANCE, Ruth Dixon, **5**:158Ⓐ

TEENIE WEENIE PICNIC, THE, William Donahey, **1**:132Ⓐ

TEN LITTLE PUSSYCATS, Elizabeth Jones, **1**:71Ⓐ

TENNYSON, ALFRED, Bugle Song, **5**:318; Eagle, The, **5**:304; Follow the Gleam, **8**:293; Lady Clare, **5**:322; Owl, The, **5**:279; Song of King Arthur's Knights, **8**:328; Sweet and Low, **5**:263

TERHUNE, ALBERT PAYSON, One Minute Longer, **14**:358

TEXAS TRAINS AND TRAILS, Mary Austin, **5**:26Ⓑ

THANK YOU, LORD, Marjorie Allen Anderson, **5**:265Ⓑ

THANKSGIVING, Judy Van der Veer, **5**:90Ⓑ

THANKSGIVING IS COMING, Elsie Melchert Fowler, **5**:91Ⓐ

THAT BOY!, Helen Coale Crew, **9**:96Ⓑ

THAYER, ERNEST LAWRENCE, Casey at the Bat, **5**:332

THEODORE ROOSEVELT, Julian Street, **15**:288Ⓒ

THERE ONCE WAS A PUFFIN, Florence Page Jaques, **5**:226Ⓐ

THERE WAS A ROARING IN THE WIND, William Wordsworth, **5**:275Ⓒ

THERE WAS TAMMIE!, Dorothy and Marguerite Bryan, **1**:145Ⓐ

THING OF BEAUTY, A, John Keats, **8**:270Ⓒ

THIRD OF JUNE ON ANNAPURNA, THE, Maurice Herzog, **13**:322Ⓒ

THIRD ROUND, THE, Owen Johnson, **10**:199Ⓒ

THIS LITTLE PIG, Helen and Alf Evers, **1**:72Ⓐ

328

THOMAS ALVA EDISON, Henry and Dana Lee Thomas, **15**:117ⓒ

THOMAS, HENRY and DANA LEE, Thomas Alva Edison, **15**:117

THOMAS JEFFERSON, Sonia Daugherty, **15**:274ⓒ

THOR'S WONDERFUL JOURNEY, Hamilton Wright Mabie, **8**:230ⓒ

THOUGHTS ABOUT GRASSHOPPERS, Florence Page Jaques, **1**:43Ⓑ

THREE–CORNERED HAT, THE, Russell Gordon Carter, **11**:189Ⓑ

THREE GOLDEN ORANGES, Mary Gould Davis and Ralph Steele Boggs, **8**:188Ⓑ

THREE–LEGGED STOOL, THE, Isa L. Wright, **2**:121Ⓐ

THREE LITTLE WITCHES, Marjorie Barrows, **5**:86Ⓐ

THREE SILLIES, THE, Joseph Jacobs, **2**:139Ⓑ

THREE WISHES, THE, Pauline Rosenberg, **2**:99Ⓑ

THURBER, JAMES, Great Quillow, The, **2**:195; Many Moons, **2**:1

TICKLY OSTRICH, THE, John Manning, **5**:236Ⓓ

TIDY TURTLE, Polly Chase, **5**:47Ⓐ

TIETJENS, EUNICE, April, **5**:179; Desert Adventure, **9**:307; Moving, **5**:44; Reflection, **5**:43

TIETJENS, EUNICE and JANET, D Is for Diplodocus, **5**:225; I Is for Ichthyosaurus, **5**:225

TILLYHEEHEE, THE, John Dukes McKee, **4**:51Ⓓ

TIM, Nancy Byrd Turner, **5**:51Ⓑ

TIPPETT, JAMES S., Familiar Friends, **5**:133; My Dog, **5**:120; Trains, **5**:44

TITIAN'S FIRST PICTURE, Mary Newlin Roberts, **15**:56Ⓑ

TO A VERY YOUNG CLOUD, Ruth Crary, **5**:179Ⓑ

TOBY TYLER AND MR. STUBBS, James Otis, **3**:93Ⓑ

TOM AND BECKY IN THE CAVE, Samuel Clemens, **3**:308ⓒ

TOM CHIST AND THE TREASURE BOX, Howard Pyle, **13**:247ⓒ

TOMMY THE TUGBOAT, Betty Martin, **1**:228Ⓐ

TOMORROW WILL BE BRIGHT, Mabel Leigh Hunt, **11**:26Ⓑ

TOOTH OF THE GREAT ONE, Dee Dunsing, **11**:346Ⓑ

TOUCH OF ARAB, A, Vivian Breck, **13**:178Ⓑ

TRAIL–MAKERS, Montgomery M. Atwater, **14**:301Ⓑ

TRAIL TO THE STARS, Burr W. Leyson, **16**:134ⓒ

TRAINS, James S. Tippett, **5**:44Ⓑ

TRAINS AT NIGHT, Frances Frost, **5**:40Ⓑ

TRAVEL, Edna St. Vincent Millay, **5**:356ⓒ

TREE–CHILDREN, Mary Carolyn Davies, **5**:9Ⓑ

TREE HOUSE, Mildred Bowers Armstrong, **5**:163Ⓑ

TREES, Joyce Kilmer, **5**:356Ⓓ

TREGARTHEN, ENYS, Bucca Boo's Little Merry Men, **8**:1

TRIAL BY BATTLE, Howard Pyle, **13**:278ⓒ

TRUST FULFILLED, A, Hubert Evans, **13**:125Ⓑ

TRUTH ABOUT PYECRAFT, THE, H. G. Wells, 16:102©

TUNGWA, Alice Crew Gall and Fleming H. Crew, 9:180®

TUNIS, JOHN R., Pass, The, 10:350; Two-Mile Race, 10:321

TURBULENT TIGER, THE, John Manning, 5:237®

TURNER, NANCY BYRD, Birthday of our Land, The, 5:84; First Thanksgiving of All, 5:89; Indian Children Long Ago, 5:90; Lincoln, 5:80; Planting a Tree, 5:82; Round the Maypole now We Dance, 5:83; Sea Child, 5:167; Shine, Star, 5:79; Sing, World, Sing!, 5:82; Song at Dusk, 5:252; Tamed, 5:178; Tim, 5:51; Washington, 5:81

TWIN SEALS, Inez Hogan, 1:84Ⓐ

TWO–MILE RACE, John R. Tunis, 10:321©

TWO SCENES FROM THE LIFE OF GEORGE WASHINGTON, Eva March Tappan, 15:196©

TYRANNICAL TOAD, THE, John Manning, 5:237®

UGLY DUCKLING, THE, Hans Christian Andersen, 2:149®

UNCLE REMUS AND THE TAR–BABY, Joel Chandler Harris, 8:20®

UNDERSTUDY, Noel Streatfeild, 13:200©

UNDERWOOD, ELEANOR, Bunny, The, 1:239; Christmas Song, 11:126

UNEXPECTED CHRISTMAS, AN, Louisa May Alcott, 3:113©

UNFORTUNATE GIRAFFE, THE, Oliver Herford, 5:243Ⓓ

UNNERSTAD, EDITH, Singing Saucepan, The, 9:65

UPON WESTMINSTER BRIDGE, William Wordsworth, 5:276©

UPPITY ORIOLES, William Donahey, 1:137Ⓐ

USCHOLD, MAUD E., Fawn's First Journey, 5:110

VACATION TIME, Ann Zelenka, 5:60®

VAGABOND, THE, Robert Louis Stevenson, 5:318©

VALENTINE TO MY DOLL, Helen Wing, 5:81Ⓐ

VAN DER VEER, JUDY, Christmas Calf, The, 5:126; Shares, 5:100; Song of the Herd, 5:101; Spring Pastures, 5:100; Thanksgiving, 5:90

VAN STOCKUM, HILDA, Hut, The, 5:66; Visit with Pierre, A, 9:85; Woman's Wit, A, 8:201

VANDEVERE, J. LILIAN, Seashore Gossip, 5:117; Song for Supper, 5:43

VELVETEEN RABBIT, THE, Margery Williams Bianco, 1:1Ⓐ

VILLAGE BLACKSMITH, THE, Henry Wadsworth Longfellow, 5:315®

VISION OF SIR LAUNFAL, FROM THE, James Russell Lowell, **5**:274Ⓑ

VISIT WITH PIERRE, A, Hilda Van Stockum, **9**:85Ⓑ

VOICE IN A HUNDRED YEARS, A, Constance Burnett, **15**:293Ⓑ

WAINO AND IVAR MEET HONK THE MOOSE, Phil Stong, **6**:65Ⓑ

WALD, MALVIN, Boy who Owned on Elephant, The, **1**:285

WALK ON THE RAINBOW TRAIL, Author Unknown, **9**:190Ⓒ

WALRUS AND THE CARPENTER, Lewis Carroll, **4**:206Ⓓ

WASHINGTON, Nancy Byrd Turner, **5**:81Ⓑ

WASHINGTON, BOOKER T., My Struggle for an Education, **15**:211

WASTED PHILANTHROPY, Carolyn Wells, **5**:212Ⓓ

WASTWYCH SECRET, THE, Constance Savery, **7**:49Ⓑ

WATSON, SIR WILLIAM, Beauty, **15**:99

WE GIVE OUR THANKS, Clara E. Randall, **5**:265Ⓐ

WELLES, WINIFRED, Dogs and Weather, **5**:104; Lucky Snail, The, **5**:124

WELLS, CAROLYN, Animals' Fair, The, **5**:204; Beast I Like, A, **5**:213; Camel, The, **5**:217; Discomfort, **5**:217; Flamingo, The, **5**:212; How to tell Wild Animals, **4**:162; Mishaps of Gentle Jane, The, **5**:216; Queer One, The, **5**:213; Wasted Philanthropy, **5**:212

WELLS, H. G., Truth about Pyecraft, The, **16**:102

WELLS, PETER, Camel Is a Mammal, The, **4**:145

WESLEY, CHARLES, Gentle Jesus, Meek and Mild, **5**:267

WEST WIND, THE, John Masefield, **5**:345Ⓓ

WESTERN WAGONS, Rosemary and Stephen Vincent Benét, **11**:82Ⓒ

WHALE, Geoffrey Dearmer, **5**:117Ⓑ

WHAT IS A GOOD SCIENCE BOOK?, Herman Schneider, **16**:162

WHAT I WOULD DO, Dorothy Aldis, **5**:9Ⓑ

WHAT TIME IS IT?, Richard M. Elam, Jr., **16**:1Ⓑ

WHEN MARK TWAIN WAS A BOY, Margaret Ford Allen, **15**:43Ⓑ

WHERE DOES MUSIC COME FROM?, Vivian G. Gouled, **5**:181Ⓑ

WHICH?, Joyce L. Brisley, **5**:52Ⓑ

WHITE, Elizabeth-Ellen Long, **5**:184Ⓑ

WHITE, ANNE H., Serapina Proves Herself, **4**:166

WHITE BLACKBIRD, THE, Padraic Colum, **2**:34Ⓑ

WHITE FIELDS, James Stephens, **5**:198Ⓓ

WHITE FLAG, George Cory Franklin, **14**:239Ⓒ

WHITE HORSE OF VOLENDAM, THE, Frances Carpenter, **8**:198Ⓑ

WHITE, WILLIAM C., Who Is Who?, 9:253

WHITEY AND THE RUSTLERS, Glen Rounds, 13:16Ⓑ

WHITMAN, WALT, From Miracles, 15:195; I Hear America Singing, 5:281

WHITTIER, JOHN GREENLEAF, Snowbound, 5:308

WHIZZ!, Clara E. Randall, 1:83Ⓐ

WHO GOES THERE?, Dorothy P. Lathrop, 14:17Ⓐ

WHO HAS SEEN THE WIND?, Christina Rossetti, 5:275Ⓓ

WHO IS WHO?, William C. White, 9:253Ⓑ

WHY BOTHER WITH LADDERS, L. R. Davis, 13:134Ⓒ

WHY THE CHIPMUNK'S BACK IS STRIPED, Frank B. Linderman, 8:50Ⓑ

WHY THE WINDS BLOW, Caroline S. P. Wild, 5:177Ⓑ

WIDDEMER, MARGARET, Family Dragon, The, 5:7; Hollow Tree House, The, 5:59; Secret Cavern, The, 5:66

WIGGIN, KATE DOUGLAS, Journey with Dickens, A, 15:100; Rebecca at the Brick House, 3:203; Ruggleses' Christmas Dinner, The, 4:217

WILD, CAROLINE P., Mountain, The, 5:56

WILD, CAROLINE S. P., Why the Winds Blow, 5:177

WILD DOG, Ruth E. Tanner, 14:116Ⓑ

WILD DUCK'S NEST, THE, Michael McLaverty, 14:81Ⓒ

WILD-HORSE ROUNDUP, Gladys Frances Lewis, 14:194Ⓑ

WILDE, OSCAR, Happy Prince, The, 2:346; Selfish Giant, The, 2:316

WILDER, LAURA INGALLS, Christmas Horses, 11:111

WILKINS, PERCY H., Is There Life on the Moon?, 16:132

WILLIE THE MOOSE, Adolph Regli, 14:7Ⓑ

WILLOUGHBY, BARRETT, One Alaska Night, 7:297

WILLOW BASKET, THE, Carol Ryrie Brink, 11:93Ⓑ

WILLSON, DIXIE, Mist and All, The, 5:194; Mr. Rabbit, 1:96; Politely, 1:107; Wing Dreams, 1:263

WILSON, ANTHONY C., Hunter's Moon, 7:315

WIND, Mildred Bowers Armstrong, 5:177Ⓑ

WIND ELVES, Ruth Dixon, 5:171Ⓐ

WING DREAMS, Dixie Willson, 1:263Ⓐ

WING, HELEN, Apple Blossoms, 1:301; Frogs, 5:132; Halloween, 5:88; Heroism, 5:104; Old Goose, The, 1:52; Said the Sandman, 1:338; Sensible Lobster, The, 5:208; Valentine to My Doll, 5:81

WINTERBOUND ADVENTURE, A, Margery Williams Bianco, 6:327Ⓒ

WINTER WOOD, Eleanor Elizabeth Stevens, 5:198Ⓓ

WISE, Aileen Fisher, 5:176Ⓑ

WISHES, Edith Franklin Wyatt, 5:57Ⓑ

WITCH CAT, Rowena Bennett, 5:87Ⓑ

WITCH OF WILLOWBY WOOD, THE, Rowena Bennett, 5:162Ⓑ

WITH THE FOREST RUNNERS, Joseph A. Altsheler, 11:295Ⓒ

WOLFE, FFRIDA, Choosing Shoes, 5:18

WOLFE, LOUIS, John Henry, Mighty Railroader, 8:26

WOLFGANG MOZART, Mary Newlin Roberts, **15**:94Ⓑ

WOMAN'S WIT, A, Hilda Van Stockum, **8**:201Ⓑ

WON'T–PICK–UP–TOYS CURE, THE, Betty MacDonald, **4**:136Ⓐ

WOODCHUCK HILL, Frances Frost, **5**:96Ⓑ

WOODEN HORSE AND THE FALL OF TROY, THE, Josephine Preston Peabody, **12**:355Ⓒ

WOODPECKER, THE, Elizabeth Madox Roberts, **5**:10Ⓑ

WOOLLEY, CATHERINE, Little Bear Takes His Nap, **1**:224; Puppy Who Wanted a Boy, The, **1**:332

WORDSWORTH, WILLIAM, Daffodils, **5**:272; Solitary Reaper, The, **5**:280; There Was a Roaring in the Wind, **5**:275; Upon Westminster Bridge, **5**:276

WORLD SECRETS, Marjorie H. Hayes, **5**:3Ⓓ

WORTH, KATHRYN, Penguin Summer, **5**:116; Circus Elephant, **14**:80

WRIGHT BROTHERS, THE, Joseph Cotter and Haym Jaffe, **15**:158Ⓑ

WRIGHT, ISA L., Three-Legged Stool, The, **2**:121

WYATT, EDGAR, Apache Warpath, **11**:338

WYATT, EDITH FRANKLIN, Wishes, **5**:57

WYNKEN, BLYNKEN, AND NOD, Eugene Field, **5**:262Ⓐ

WYNNE, ANNETTE, House Cat, The, **5**:136; I Keep Three Wishes Ready, **5**:153; I'm Wishing the Whole World Christmas, **5**:73; Little Folks in the Grass, **5**:114; Once When You Were Walking, **2**:120

YAK, THE, Hilaire Belloc, **4**:235Ⓓ

YE STARS, Lord Byron, **5**:277Ⓒ

YEAR'S AT THE SPRING, THE, Robert Browning, **5**:271Ⓓ

YEATS, WILLIAM BUTLER, Lake Isle of Innisfree, The, **5**:355

YOGI'S DARK HORSE, Howard M. Brier, **10**:361Ⓑ

YOU NEVER SAW SUCH AN EGG, Russell Carpenter, **4**:270Ⓑ

YOUNG, BARBARA, Being a Gipsy, **5**:5

YOUNG, ELLA, Ardan's Pooka, **2**:89; Ballor's Son Goes Riding, **2**:280; Faery Riders, **5**:155; Heron, **5**:109; Pooka, **5**:173; Rain, **5**:190

YOUNG LADY'S EYES, THE, Edward Lear, **4**:117Ⓓ

YOUR CHILD AND WORLD NEIGH-BORLINESS, Agatha L. Shea, **16**:159

YUKON TRAIL, Willis Lindquist, **13**:1Ⓑ

ZELENKA, ANN, Old Country, The, **5**:5; Vacation Time, **5**:60

SUBJECT INDEX

ADDAMS, Jane, **15**:320
ADVENTURE
Adam to the Rescue, **12**:240
Adventure at the Toll Bridge,
  7:279
Adventure in a Chimney, **12**:14
Adventure in Candle Street, **12**:179
Adventure of the Blue Carbuncle, The,
  7:254
Adventure on Mars, **16**:21
Alligator up the Bayou, **8**:60
Answering the Challenge, **14**:227
Baedeker Boy, The, **9**:116
Ballor's Son Goes Riding, **2**:280
Bears of Blue River, The, **11**:306
Bellerophon, **8**:93
Bim's Gift from the Forest, **9**:150
Black Pirate of the Peaks, **14**:202
Black Pits of Luna, The, **16**:115
Blaze and the Forest Fire, **14**:1
Bucca Boo's Little Merry Men, **8**:1
Buffalo Hunting, **11**:357
Calloway's Code, **7**:245
Carca, **14**:136
Case of the Sensational Scent, The,
  7:30
Climb High, **13**:8
Cream-Colored Pony, The, **6**:242
Cub Pilot on the River, **11**:321
Curse of Kaing, The, **9**:320
Dantès' Escape from the Château D'If,
  13:291
Desert Adventure, **9**:307

ADVENTURE—CONT.
Dinty—A Husky's Story, **14**:176
Don, the Story of a Lion Dog, **14**:330
Dungeon Deep, **12**:108
Eskimo Twins Go Coasting, The, **9**:20
False Summer, **6**:314
Farmer of Paimpol, **9**:7
Feather of the Northman, The, **11**:64
Fern Tiki, The, **9**:332
First Day of School, The, **4**:146
Follow Your Leader, **13**:315
Fools Walk In, **13**:302
Forbidden Island, The, **9**:345
Forgotten Island, **7**:1
For the Love of a Man, **14**:275
Freddy the Detective Solves a Mystery,
  4:71
Gang's All There, The, **6**:115
Going Up!, **9**:215
Gold Bug, The, **7**:201
Golden Cup of Kasimir, The, **12**:259
Gorillas and Lions, **13**:158
Guides with Wings, **13**:228
Horseshoe Nails, **11**:197
How Kari Saved Our Lives in the
  Jungle, **14**:76
Hunter's Moon, **7**:315
Hunting Old Slew Foot, **14**:314
Jambi and the Tiger, **14**:184
Kon-Tiki Adventure, A, **13**:354
Koyo, the Singer, **14**:98
Lancelot Biggs on the Saturn, **16**:70
Legacy of Canyon John, The, **7**:98

334

ADVENTURE—CONT.
Little Red, **13**:68
Man with the Belt of Gold, The, **12**:273
Mars and Miss Pickerell, **16**:36
Mary Silver, **11**:159
Miss Hinch, **7**:179
Mrs. Lecks and Mrs. Aleshine are Shipwrecked, **4**:283
Mystery of Number 30, The, **7**:42
Nanook, **14**:64
New York to Paris, **15**:246
Nurenberg Stove, The, **9**:36
Old Sly Eye, **11**:173
One Alaska Night, **7**:297
One Minute Longer, **14**:358
Penny Walk, The, **6**:59
Peter Pan and Captain Hook, **2**:225
Pippi Acts as a Lifesaver, **13**:94
Red-Headed League, The, **7**:346
Rikki-Tikki-Tavi, **14**:257
Robin Hood and the Shooting Match, **12**:227
Robinson Crusoe Is Shipwrecked, **3**:153
Sandpipers, The, **6**:37
Secret in the Snow, **13**:101
Secret of Rainbow Ridge, The, **7**:69
Secret Staircase, The, **9**:29
Silver Llama, The, **9**:171
Skeleton Windmill, The, **9**:127
Stalactite Surprise, **7**:61
Steelman's Nerve, **13**:144
Storm Tide, **13**:51
Story of Babar, The, **1**:100
Strange Pettingill Puzzle, The, **7**:108
Strangers in the Wilderness, **11**:150
Third of June on Annapurna, The, **13**:322
Tom Chist and the Treasure Box, **13**:247
Tooth of the Great One, **11**:346
Touch of Arab, A, **13**:178
Trust Fulfilled, A, **13**:125
Tungwa, **9**:180
What Time Is It?, **16**:1
White Flag, **14**:239
Why Bother with Ladders, **13**:134
Wild Dog, **14**:116
With the Forest Runners, **11**:295
Yukon Trail, **13**:1
AFTERNOON: *Afternoon*, **5**:181
AGASSIZ, Louis, **15**:354
ALASKA—see Many Lands
ALCOTT, LOUISA MAY: Early Days with Invincible Louisa, **15**:130
ALLIGATORS—see Reptiles
ANDERSEN, HANS CHRISTIAN: Boy Who Liked Puppets, The, **15**:69

ANDERSON, Marian: A Voice in a Hundred Years, **15**:293
ANIMALS—also see Birds, Fish and Creatures of the Sea, Insects, and Reptiles
FANCIFUL
Adventure on Mars, **16**:21
Animals' Fair, The, **5**:204
Dr. Dolittle and the Pushmi-Pullyu, **4**:158
Flanigan's Field, **5**:239
Mr. Scrunch, **4**:52
Pale Pink Tea, The, **5**:242
Story of Mrs. Tubbs, The, **1**:119
Tale of Three Tails, A, **8**:241
Baboons: *Big Baboon, The*, **4**:234
Bears: Cannery Bear, The, **4**:94
Five Little Bears Have Their Pictures Taken, The, **1**:269
How to Tell Wild Animals, **4**:162
Little Bear Takes His Nap, **1**:224
Politely, **1**:107
Teddy Bear Dance, **5**:158
Birds: *Purple-Eyed Pirate, The*, **5**:202
Camels: *Camel and the Cachelot, The*, **5**:228
Camel's Complaint, The, **5**:218
Cats: *Duel, The*, **5**:219
Genial Grimalkin, The, **1**:311
Owl and the Pussy Cat, The, **5**:232
Serapina Proves Herself, **4**:166
Ten Little Pussycats, **1**:71
Witch Cat, **5**:87
Chinchillas: *Aristocrat, The*, **5**:227
Chipmunks: Teenie Weenie Picnic, The, **1**:132
Why the Chipmunk's Back Is Striped, **8**:50
Cows: Cow Golden Horn, The, **8**:39
Coyotes: Pecos Bill and His Bouncing Bride, **8**:115
Crocodiles: Bertram and the Musical Crocodile, **4**:197
Deer: Littlest Reindeer, **1**:58
Dogs: Ashes That Made Trees Bloom, The, **8**:80
Duel, The, **5**:219
Good Little Dog, A, **1**:178
Great Hunter of the Woods, The, **8**:103
Otto at Sea, **1**:181
Donkeys: In Which Eeyore Has a Birthday and Gets Two Presents, **1**:186
Elephants: *Elephant in the Cinnamon Tree, The*, **5**:206

335

ANIMALS, FANCIFUL—CONT.
Elephant's Child, The, 4:4
Eletelephony, 4:14
Story of Babar, The, 1:100
Foxes: Fox Ferry, The, 2:218
Geese: Augusta Goose, 1:67
Giraffes: *Giraffe, The*, 1:213
  Pink Giraffe, The, 4:111
  Unfortunate Giraffe, The, 5:243
Gnu: *Neighborly Gnu, The*, 5:236
Horses: Bellerophon, 8:93
  Son of the South Wind, 8:86
  Velveteen Rabbit, The, 1:1
  White Horse of Volendam, The, 8:198
Kangaroos: *Duck and the Kangaroo, The*, 5:244
Lions: *Barber, The*, 1:311
  Bertram and the Lion, 4:102
Llamas: *Bedtime Story*, 5:202
Lobsters: *Lobster Quadrille, The*, 4:93
Mice: *Elf and the Dormouse, The*, 5:148
  Muggins Mouse at the Seashore, 1:240
Moles: Open Road, The, 2:20
Mongooses: Rikki-Tikki-Tavi, 14:257
Monkeys: *Organ Grinders Garden, The*, 5:174
  Ship of Rio, The, 4:70
  Tale of the Lazy People, The, 8:129
Owls: *Owl and the Pussy Cat, The*, 5:232
Pigs: Freddy the Detective Solves a Mystery, 4:73
  Melancholy Pig, The, 5:223
  This Little Pig, 1:72
Rabbits: *Easter Bunny, The*, 5:56
  Nine Rabbits and Another One, 1:234

ANIMALS, FANCIFUL—CONT.
Uncle Remus and the Tar-Baby, 8:20
Reindeer: Littlest Reindeer, 1:58
Seals: Oscar, the Trained Seal, 4:58
  Twin Seals, 1:84
Tigers: *Turbulent Tiger, The*, 5:237
Toads: *Tyrannical Toad, The*, 5:237
Walruses: *Walrus and the Carpenter, The*, 4:206
Wolves: Children of the Wolf, The, 8:34
Zebras: *Little Susan Zebra*, 5:219
PREHISTORIC
Beast I Like, A, 5:213
Creature Brontosaurus, The, 5:128
D Is for Diplodocus, 5:225
Dinosaur, The, 5:119
Dinosaur, The, 5:129
I Is for Ichthyosaurus, 5:225
Ichthyosaurus, The, 5:227
What Time Is It?, 16:1
You Never Saw Such An Egg, 4:270
REAL
Alligators: Alligator Up the Bayou, 8:60
Antelopes: Trail-Makers, 14:301
  White Flag, 14:239
Barnyard: All Through the Night, 1:360
  Christmas Calf, The, 5:126
  Familiar Friends, 5:133
  Farmers, 5:15
  Janie's Wish, 1:298
  Little Lamb, A, 1:97
  On the Farm, 5:28
Bats: Guides with Wings, 13:228
Bears: Bears of Blue River, The, 11:306
  Brown Bear, The, 5:112
  Cubby, 14:45
  Eskimo Twins Go Coasting, The, 9:20
  Hasty Pudding, 11:36
  Hunting Old Slew Foot, 14:314
  Mystery of the Bay, The, 13:190
  Nanook, 14:64
Boars: Boar Hunt, The, 12:61
Buffaloes: Buffalo Hunting, 11:357
  Flower-Fed Buffaloes, The, 14:75
  Trail-Makers, 14:301
Camels: *Camel Is a Mammal, The*, 4:145
  Camel, The, 5:132
  Camel, The, 5:217
  Desert Adventure, 9:307
Caribou: Trail-Makers, 14:301

336

ANIMALS, REAL—CONT.

Cats: *Adolfuss*, 5:135
  Bad Kittens, The, 5:41
  Bobo, 14:13
  Cat, 5:103
  Catalogue, 14:161
  Harper's Farm, The, 5:30
  House Cat, The, 5:136
  Kitten, A, 5:122
  Little Cats, 5:135
  Miranda, 5:123
  Mr. Murdle's Large Heart, 1:250
  Mrs. Tabby Gray, 1:210
  Mysterious Cat, The, 5:97
  Smoky, 6:104
Cattle: *Christmas Calf, The*, 5:126
  Familiar Friends, 5:133
  I Stare at the Cow, 5:136
  Look at the Grand Champ, A, 14:148
  Model for Me, 5:137
  Pasture, The, 5:136
  Song of the Herd, 5:101
  Spring Pastures, 5:100
  Whitey and the Rustlers, 13:16
Chipmunks: *Chant of the Chipmunk*, 5:135
  Who Goes There?, 14:17
Cougars: Carca, 14:136
Deer: Bambi Starts to See the World, 14:27
  Deer at Night, 14:41
  Fawn's First Journey, 5:110
  Night Song, 14:183
  Still It Is Wilderness, 14:256
  Trail-Makers, 14:301
Dogs: Adam to the Rescue, 12:240
  All Mutt, 6:126
  Angus and the Ducks, 1:49
  Animal Store, The, 5:98
  Benjamin Jones and His Dogs, 5:238
  Boozer, 5:132
  Cake at Midnight, 9:269

ANIMALS, REAL—CONT.

  Christmas Eve at Reginald's, 6:359
  Chums, 5:102
  Dinty—A Husky's Story, 14:176
  Dog, A, 5:123
  Dog's Dog, 14:86
  Dogs and Weather, 5:104
  Don, the Story of a Lion Dog, 14:330
  Fools Walk In, 13:302
  For the Love of a Man, 14:275
  Friendly Pup, The, 5:63
  Gang's All There, The, 6:115
  Ginger On the Fire Escape, 10:1
  Gratitude, 5:120
  Handsome Is, 6:234
  Heroism, 5:104
  Hunting Old Slew Foot, 14:314
  Mahogany Fox, The, 14:290
  Mr. Dooley Disgraces His Family, 6:202
  My Dog, 5:63
  My Dog, 5:111
  My Dog, 5:120
  My Puppy, 1:259
  One Minute Longer, 14:358
  Pixie, Dixie, Trixie, and Nixie, 1:206
  Puppies, 5:127
  Puppy Who Wanted a Boy, The, 1:332
  Rusty—Movie Star, 6:87
  There Was Tammie, 1:145
  Wild Dog, 14:116
  Yukon Trail, 13:1
Donkeys: Bridget on Fortune's Trail, 14:55
  Burro Bells in the Moonlight, 14:115
  Desert Adventure, 9:307
  Macdonald Plaid, The, 9:202
  Our Burro, 5:115
  Our Donkey, 5:104

ANIMALS, REAL—CONT.

Song of the Little Donkey, The, 1:214

Elephants: Boy Who Owned an Elephant, The, 1:285
Circus Elephant, 14:80
Curse of Kaing, The, 9:320
How Kari Saved Our Lives in the Jungle, 14:76
Jambi and the Tiger, 14:184

Elk: Answering the Challenge, 14:227
Trail-Makers, 14:301

Foxes: Fox and Geese, 11:10
Koyo, the Singer, 14:98
Little Fox, The, 14:300
Mahogany Fox, The, 14:290
Night of Wind, 14:111
Still It Is Wilderness, 14:256

Frogs: Frog, The, 5:110
Frogs, 5:132

Giraffes: Archie and the April Fools, 6:267

Goats: Heidi's Adventures on the Mountain, 3:26
Visit with Pierre, A, 9:85

Gorillas: Gorillas and Lions, 13:158

Horses: Black Stallion's Race, The, 14:162
Blaze and the Forest Fire, 14:1
Christmas Horses, 11:111
Climb High, 13:8
Coalie, 5:130
Coaly-Bay, the Outlaw Horse, 14:305
Cream-Colored Pony, The, 6:242
Dinner Horses, 5:130
Dolly Joins the Circus, 6:193
Flame, 14:251
Great Soldier: Robert E. Lee, A, 15:176
Horses, 5:105
Horse Who Lived Upstairs, The, 1:173
King of the Wind and the Queen's Plate, 14:123
Round Up, The, 13:80
Runaway, The, 5:131
Squeak of Leather, The, 14:211
Touch of Arab, A, 13:178
Whitey and the Rustlers, 13:16
Wild Horse Roundup, 14:194

Kangaroos: Kangaroo, The, 5:129

Lambs: First Lamb, The, 9:49
Little Lamb, A, 1:97

Lions: Gorillas and Lions, 13:158

Llamas: Animal Crackers, 5:217

ANIMALS, REAL—CONT.

Silver Llama, The, 9:171

Mice: Mice, 5:95
Musical Mice, The, 5:134
Stephen Wants a Mouse, 5:99
Who Goes There?, 14:17

Monkeys: Animal Store, The, 5:98
Curious George, 1:53
Jambi and the Tiger, 14:184
Monkey Spirit, The, 9:140
Pippi Acts As a Lifesaver, 13:94
Sara Crewe, 3:325
Toby Tyler and Mr. Stubbs, 3:93

Moose: Trail-Makers, 14:301
Waino and Ivar Meet Honk the Moose, 6:65
Willie the Moose, 14:7

Mountain Lions: Don, the Story of a Lion Dog, 14:330

Muskrat: Chisel Chin, 14:112

Ocelot: Ocelot, 5:203

Oxen: In a Covered Wagon, 11:72

Pack Rats: Pack Rat, The, 14:50

Panthers: Answering the Challenge, 14:227
Old Sly Eye, 11:73
Panther, The, 4:111

Porcupines: Who Goes There?, 14:17

Rabbits: Birthdays, 5:55
Bunny, The, 1:239
Bunny, The, 5:196
Mr. Rabbit, 1:96
Rabbit Tracks, 5:138
Song of the Rabbits Outside the Tavern, 5:96
Who Goes There?, 14:17

Raccoons: Cave, The, 5:10
Denny Puts in His Oar, 10:332
Song for Warren, 5:110

Rhinoceros: Rhinoceros, The, 4:111

Seals: Seal Lullaby, 5:258
Storm Tide, 13:51

Sheep: Rocky Mountain Sheep, The, 14:371

Skunks: Case of the Sensational Scent, The, 7:30
Frisbie Cures the Doctor, 6:71

ANIMALS, REAL—CONT.
Small Wild Animals: *Easter in the Woods,* 5:141
Eyes Are Lit Up, 5:92
Forest Lullaby, 5:259
Hiawatha's Childhood, 5:305
Remembering the Winter, 5:195
Shares, 5:100
Snails: *Lucky Snail, The,* 5:124
Squirrels: *Squirrel, The,* 5:113
Who Goes There?, 14:17
Tapir: *Strange Beast, A,* 5:119
Tigers: Bim's Gift from the Forest, 9:150
Jambi and the Tiger, 14:184
Toads: *Hoppity Toad, The,* 5:124
Wolverines: Carca, 14:136
Wolves: Feather of the Northman, The, 11:64
White Flag, 14:239
Woodchucks: *Little Woodchuck's Fright,* 5:99
Woodchuck Hill, 5:95
Yak: *Yak, The,* 4:235

APPLESEED, JOHNNY
Johnny Appleseed's Coat, 11:47
Johnny Appleseed Visits Licking Creek, 11:146

APRIL FOOL'S DAY—see Holidays

ARABIA—see Many Lands

ARBOR DAY—see Holidays

ARCTIC—see Many Lands

ARMADILLO—see Animals

ARTISTS
Antonio Van Dyck and His Master Rubens, 15:88
Benny and the Cat's Tail (Benjamin West), 15:62
Boy Who Loved Birds, The, (John James Audubon), 15:51
Howard Pyle: Great American Illustrator, 15:348
Leonardo da Vinci, 15:325
Michelangelo and the Snow Man, 15:1

ASPIRATION—see Character: Ambition

AUDUBON, JOHN JAMES: Boy Who Loved Birds, The, 15:51

AUSTRALIA—see Many Lands

AUTOMOBILES
Headlights, 5:27
Janie's Wish, 1:296
Song for a Blue Roadster, 5:27
There Was Tammie, 1:145

AUTUMN
Attic Trunk, 5:36
Autumn, 5:189
Autumn Song, 5:194

AUTUMN—CONT.
Corn in the Shocks, 5:191
Farewell to the Farm, 5:28
Field Flowers, 5:192
Great Craftsman, The, 5:193
Little Bear Takes His Nap, 1:224
Mist and All, The, 5:194
North Country, 5:39
Paths, 5:189
Remembering the Winter, 5:195
Silver Trees, 5:191
Something Told the Wild Geese, 5:187
Splinter, 5:191

AVIATION
Air Mail, 5:40
Best Ride of All, The, 6:276
Cocky, 1:150
Follow Your Leader, 13:315
High Flight, 5:352
Last of the Dragons, The, 2:11
New York to Paris, 15:246
Silver Ships, 5:67
Smoky, 6:104
Star Ducks, The, 16:59
Whizz, 1:83
Wright Brothers, The, 15:158

BABIES
Baby, The, 5:13
Little, 5:13
Lost Merbaby, The, 1:272
Patsy and the Leprechaun, 2:109

BALLOONS—see Play

BEARS—see Animals

BEETHOVEN, Ludwig van, 15:328

BIRDS
Blackbirds: White Blackbird, The, 2:34
Bluebirds: *Bluebird, A,* 2:39
Blue Jays: Bobo, 14:13
Canaries: House of the Singing Windows, 9:191
Condors: Legacy of Canyon John, The, 7:98
Cranes: *Sandhill Crane, The,* 14:54
Crows: Who Goes There?, 14:17
Ducks: Angus and the Ducks, 1:49
Janie's Wish, 1:296
Open Road, The, 2:20
Rainy Day, 5:133
Ugly Duckling, The, 2:149
Wild Duck's Nest, The, 14:81

BIRDS—CONT.

Eagles: Black Pirate of the Peaks, 14:202
  Climb High, 13:8
  Eagle, The, 5:304
Flamingos: *Flamingo, The,* 5:212
Geese: Adventure of the Blue Carbuncle, The, 7:254
  Fox and Geese, 11:10
  Goose, 5:47
  Goosie Gray, 1:74
  Something Told the Wild Geese, 5:187
  Trust Fulfilled, A, 13:125
Hawks: Black Pirate of the Peaks, 14:202
Herons: *Heron,* 5:109
Hornbills: *Hornbill Family, The,* 5:118
Hummingbirds: My Hummingbirds, 14:42
Larks: *Hark! Hark! the Lark,* 5:272
Loons: *Still It Is Wilderness,* 14:256
Mockingbirds: *Mockingbird, The,* 5:107
Nightingales: *Nightingale, The,* 5:6
  Nightingale, The, 2:358
Owls: *Owl, The,* 5:279
Parrots: *Song of Grandfather Thomas' Parrot,* 5:108
Penguins: Mr. Popper and Captain Cook, 4:30
  Penguin Summer, 5:116
  Polite Penguins, The, 5:116
Pigeons: *Pigeon, The,* 5:52
Rhea: *Ever See a Rhea?,* 5:242
Sandpipers: Sandpipers, The, 6:37
  School for Sandpipers, 5:109
Sea Gulls: *Sea Gull, The,* 5:108
Swans: King's Cygnet, The, 12:99
  Picnic Basket, The, 1:158
Woodpeckers: *Woodpecker, The,* 5:10

BIRTHDAYS

Bim's Gift from the Forest, 9:150
Birthday of Our Land, The, 5:84
Birthdays, 5:55
Boy Who Owned An Elephant, The, 1:285
Cake at Midnight, 9:269
Glass Hill, The, 2:44
In Which Eeyore Has a Birthday and Gets Two Presents, 1:186
Rocking-Horse Land, 1:304
Sandpipers, The, 6:37

BLACKBIRDS—see Birds
BLUEBIRDS—see Birds
BOATS AND BOATING
Boat, The, 5:25
Canadian Boat-Song, 5:278

BOATS AND BOATING—CONT.

False Summer, 6:314
Holiday Cup, The, 10:18
Iceboat Race, The, 10:60
Jacques Cartier, 15:315
Little Guy, The, 10:286
Sea Fever, 5:358
Tommy the Tugboat, 1:228
Trust Fulfilled, A, 13:125
BOOKS—see Reading, Love of
BOONE, Daniel, 11:369
BRAVERY—see Character
BRONTOSAURUS—see Animals: Prehistoric
BROWNIES
Adventures of a Brownie, 1:163
  Brownie's Ride, 2:102
  Browny, The, 2:93
BULGARIA—see Many Lands
BURMA—see Many Lands
BUTTERFLIES—see Insects
CANADA—see Many Lands
CANARIES—see Birds
CARROLL, Lewis, 15:8
CARTIER, Jacques, 15:315
CARVER, George Washington, 15:269
CATS—see Animals
CAVES
Cave, The, 5:10
Guides with Wings, 13:228
Last of the Dragons, The, 2:11
Little Dragon, The, 2:142
Secret Cavern, The, 5:66
Stalactite Surprise, 7:61
Storm Tide, 13:51
Tom and Becky in the Cave, 3:308
When Mark Twain Was a Boy, 15:43
CHAMELEONS—see Reptiles
CHARACTER
Ambition: Alligator up the Bayou, 13:60
  Baedeker Boy, The, 9:116
  Box the Bee Crept In, The, 12:52
  Charles Dickens: The Boy of the London Streets, 15:100
  Cinderella, 2:165
  Cuckoo in the Nest, The, 12:1
  Daniel Boone, 11:369
  Daniel Webster, 15:367
  Dobry's New Year, 9:294
  Feather of the Northman, The, 11:64
  First Lamb, The, 9:49
  Fisherman and His Wife, The, 2:133
  Golden Fleece, The, 8:148
  Great Soldier: Robert E. Lee, A, 15:176
  Jacques Cartier, 15:315
  Jane Addams, 15:320
  Journey with Dickens, A, 15:106

340

CHARACTER, AMBITION—CONT.

Kon-Tiki Adventure, A, **13**:354
Little Dragon, The, **2**:142
Look at the Grand Champ, A, **14**:148
Louis Agassiz, **15**:354
Louis Joseph, Marquis de Montcalm, **15**:332
Marian Anderson: A Voice in a Hundred Years, **15**:293
Marie Curie: Discoverer of a Hidden Treasure, **15**:264
Mystery—and the Race, **3**:261
My Struggle for an Education, **15**:211
Nurenberg Stove, The, **9**:36
On the Mayflower, **11**:1
Pathfinders: Lewis and Clark, The, **11**:289
Silver Belt, The, **9**:110
Silver Ships, **5**:67
Skeleton Windmill, The, **1**:127
Steelman's Nerve, **13**:144
Strangers in the Wilderness, **11**:150
Third of June on Annapurna, The, **13**:322
Understudy, **13**:200
Western Wagons, **11**:82
Why Bother with Ladders, **13**:134
Wolfgang Mozart, **15**:94
Bravery: *Admiral's Ghost, The*, **5**:338
Alexander Mackenzie: Hero of Canada, **15**:153
Apache Warpath, **11**:338
Bears of Blue River, The, **11**:306
Black Pits of Luna, The, **16**:115
Blaze and the Forest Fire, **14**:1
Climb High, **13**:8
Columbus, **5**:84
Dantès' Escape from the Château D'If, **13**:291
Desert Adventure, **9**:307
Disperse, Ye Rebels, **11**:238
Down in Davy Jones's Locker, **13**:334
Dungeon Deep, **12**:108

CHARACTER, BRAVERY—CONT.

Early Days with Invincible Louisa, **15**:130
False Summer, **6**:314
Farmer of Paimpol, **9**:7
Feather of the Northman, The, **11**:64
Fern Tiki, The, **9**:332
First Lamb, The, **9**:49
Follow Your Leader, **13**:315
Fools Walk In, **13**:302
Forbidden Island, The, **9**:345
Frontier Blockade Buster, **11**:229
Good Little Dog, A, **1**:178
Gorillas and Lions, **13**:158
Great Soldier: Robert E. Lee, A, **15**:176
Helen Keller, **15**:81
Jacques Cartier, **15**:315
Jane Addams, **15**:320
Last of the Dragons, The, **2**:11
Little Dog Star, **11**:102
Little Red, **13**:68
Louis Joseph, Marquis de Montcalm, **15**:332
Marian Anderson: A Voice in a Hundred Years, **15**:293
Marie Curie: Discoverer of a Hidden Treasure, **15**:264
Most Wonderful Thing in the World, The, **10**:69
New York to Paris, **15**:246
Patrick Henry Enters Public Life, **15**:337
Pearl Diver, The, **13**:347
Peter Pan and Captain Hook, **2**:225
Pippi Acts as a Lifesaver, **13**:94
Rikki-Tikki-Tavi, **14**:257
Round Up, The, **13**:80
Rule of Three, **6**:156
Secret in the Snow, **13**:101
Steelman's Nerve, **13**:144
Storm Tide, **13**:51
Tale of Sir Gareth, The, **8**:309
Tale of Three Tails, A, **8**:241
Theodore Roosevelt, **15**:288
Third of June on Annapurna, The, **13**:322
Thomas Jefferson, **15**:274
Tom and Becky in the Cave, **3**:308
Tommy the Tugboat, **1**:228
Touch of Arab, A, **13**:178
Trial by Battle, **13**:278
Trust Fulfilled, A, **13**:125
Two Scenes from the Life of George Washington, **15**:196
Whitey and the Rustlers, **13**:16

CHARACTER, BRAVERY—CONT.

Why Bother with Ladders, 13:134
Yukon Trail, 13:1
Carefulness and Carelessness: Hasty Pudding, 11:36
Jonathan Bing, 4:134
Kit and Kat Go Fishing, 1:75
Lady Who Put Salt in Her Coffee, The, 4:262
Little Lamb, A, 1:97
Mrs. Goose's Rubbers, 4:15
Pale Pink Tea, The, 5:242
Peter Pan and Captain Hook, 2:225
Punch Has an Adventure, 6:52
Purple-Eyed Pirate, The, 5:202
Sandpipers, The, 6:37
Smoky, 6:104
Won't-Pick-Up-Toys Cure, The, 4:136
Zany Zoo, The, 5:236
Cooperation: Antonio Van Dyck and His Master Rubens, 15:88
Archie and the April Fools, 6:269
Boy Who Owned an Elephant, The, 1:285
Christmas Horses, 11:111
Going Up!, 9:215
Great Quillow, The, 2:195
Last of the Dragons, The, 2:11
Life of William Shakespeare, A, 15:222
Marie Curie: Discoverer of a Hidden Treasure, 15:264
Pass, The, 10:350
Secret in the Snow, 13:101
Willow Basket, The, 11:93
Winterbound Adventure, A, 6:327
Courtesy: Cake at Midnight, 9:269
Deep Sea Song, 5:150
500 Hats of Bartholomew Cubbins, The, 1:16
Glass Hill, The, 2:44
Going Up!, 9:215
Gratitude, 5:120
Harper's Farm, The, 5:30
House of the Singing Windows, 9:191
My Dog, 5:120
Penny Walk, The, 6:59
Politely, 1:107
Polite Penguins, The, 5:116
Stranger in the Wood, The, 12:175
Street of Memories, 6:1
Curiosity: Angus and the Ducks, 1:49
Carca, 14:136
Curious George, 1:53
Elephant's Child, The, 4:4
Magic Glass, The, 4:65

CHARACTER, CURIOSITY—CONT.

Strange Pettingill Puzzle, The, 7:108
Foolishness: Bertram and the Lion, 4:102
Bertram and the Musical Crocodile, 4:197
Crazy Story of Dizzy Lizzie, 4:118
Dr. Dolittle Meets a Londoner in Paris, 4:210
Elizabeth Eliza's Piano, 4:135
Fisherman and His Wife, The, 2:133
Golden Touch, The, 8:62
House the Pecks Built, The, 4:18
King of the Golden River, The, 3:231
King's Wish, The, 4:24
Lady Who Put Salt in Her Coffee, The, 4:262
Little Dragon, The, 2:142
Phaeton, 8:144
Three Sillies, The, 2:139
Friendliness: *Abou Ben Adhem,* 5:328
Augusta Goose, 1:67
Boiling the Billy, 9:281
Ellen's Secret, 6:177
Going Up!, 9:215
Goody O'Grumpity, 1:223
Heidi's Adventures on the Mountain, 3:26
In Which Eeyore Has a Birthday and Gets Two Presents, 1:186
Island Christmas, An, 6:277
Jo Meets Laurie, 3:138
Living Christmas, 6:164
Macdonald Plaid, The, 9:202
Monkey Spirit, The, 9:140
Old Houses, 7:89
Open Road, The, 2:20
Story of Babar, The, 1:100
Unexpected Christmas, An, 3:113
Uppity Orioles, The, 1:137
Velveteen Rabbit, The, 1:1
Willow Basket, The, 11:93
Happiness: *April,* 5:179
Bellerophon, 8:93
Ben Franklin's First Adventures, 15:164
Cricket, The, 5:114
Dancer in the Sun, 5:257
God's World, 5:343
Good Morning, 5:1
Happiness, 5:3
Happy Day, 5:32
Happy Hen, The, 1:162
Happy Prince, The, 2:346
Heidi's Adventures on the Mountain, 3:26

342

CHARACTER, HAPPINESS—CONT.

High Flight, 5:352
Home Thoughts from Abroad, 5:274
How Birgit Danced in Her Red
 Shoes, 9:1
I Hear America Singing, 5:281
Jonathan Bing Dances for Spring,
 5:200
Light-Hearted Fairy, The, 5:170
Little Lamb, A, 1:97
Louis Agassiz, 15:354
Mockingbird, The, 5:107
Morning, 5:177
Morning, 5:180
Mrs. Lecks and Mrs. Aleshine Are
 Shipwrecked, 4:283
Rebecca at the Brick House, 3:203
Sing Ho!, 5:196
There Was a Roaring in the Wind,
 5:275
Vagabond, The, 5:318
Vision of Sir Launfal, From the,
 5:274
Year's at the Spring, The, 5:271
Heroism: Bellerophon, 8:93
 Blaze and the Forest Fire, 14:1
 Boot and Saddle, 5:319
 Bridgit on Fortune's Trail, 14:55
 Broken Note, The, 8:294
 Climb High, 13:8
 Clutch Man, 10:250
 Cuchulain in Shadow-Land, 8:329
 Don, the Story of a Lion Dog,
  14:330
 Follow Your Leader, 13:315
 Fools Walk In, 13:302
 Forbidden Island, The, 9:345
 Frontier Blockade Buster, 11:229
 Golden Cup of Kasimir, The,
  12:259
 Golden Fleece, The, 8:148
 Good Little Dog, A, 1:178
 Heroism, 5:104
 Highwayman, The, 5:289
 How Beowulf Rules the Geats, 8:97
 *How They Brought the Good News
  from Ghent to Aix,* 5:320
 Iceboat Race, The, 10:60
 King's Cygnet, The, 12:99
 Kon-Tiki Adventure, A, 13:354
 Little Red, 13:68
 Most Wonderful Thing in the World,
  The, 10:69
 One Minute Longer, 14:358
 Out of Defeat, 12:359
 Roland and His Horn, 8:355
 Round Up, The, 13:80

CHARACTER, HEROISM—CONT.

 Saving of Boonesborough, The,
  11:181
 Secret in the Snow, 13:101
 Song of King Arthur's Knights, 8:328
 Steelman's Nerve, 13:144
 Tale of Sir Gareth, The, 8:309
 Third of June on Annapurna, The,
  13:322
 Touch of Arab, A, 13:178
 Trial by Battle, 13:278
 Trust Fulfilled, A, 13:125
 Whitey and the Rustlers, 13:16
 Why Bother with Ladders, 13:134
 Wild Dog, 14:116
 Yukon Trail, 13:1
Honesty: Abraham Lincoln's Boyhood,
 15:25
 Antonio Van Dyck and His Master
  Rubens, 15:88
 Apache Warpath, 11:338
 Ben Franklin's First Adventures,
  15:164
 Broken Note, The, 8:294
 Caricature, 10:212
 Clutch Man, 10:251
 Emperor's New Clothes, The, 2:258
 Hit or Error?, 10:143
 Iceboat Race, The, 10:60
 Lady Clare, 5:322
 Little Guy, The, 10:286
 Secret Staircase, The, 9:29
 Theodore Roosevelt, 15:288
 Thomas Jefferson, 15:274
Hospitality: Cake for Company Dinner,
 4:185
 Christmas Eve at Reginald's, 6:359
 Guests, 5:40
 Island Christmas, An, 6:277
 Jam Session at Abbie's, 10:86
 Little Dog Star, 11:102
 Living Christmas, 6:164
 Nine Rabbits and Another One,
  1:234
 Our Street, 5:31
 Rebecca at the Brick House, 3:203
 Ruggleses' Christmas Dinner, The,
  4:217
 Stranger in the Woods, The, 12:169
Industry: Albert Schweitzer: The Doc-
 tor in the Jungle, 15:256
 Baedeker Boy, The, 9:116
 Ben Franklin's First Adventures,
  15:164
 Desirable Shawl, The, 9:14
 First Christmas Tree, The, 2:51
 George Washington Carver, 15:269

343

CHARACTER, INDUSTRY—cont.

Guglielmo Marconi, 15:189
Hasty Pudding, 11:36
Heidi's Adventures on the Mountain, 3:26
Henri Fabre: A Place of His Own, 15:308
Howard Pyle: Great American Illustrator, 15:348
Jane Addams, 15:320
Leonardo Da Vinci, 15:325
Life of William Shakespeare, A, 15:222
Louis Agassiz, 15:354
Ludwig Van Beethoven, 15:328
Marian Anderson: A Voice in a Hundred Years, 15:293
Marie Curie: Discoverer of a Hidden Treasure, 15:264
My Struggle for an Education, 15:211
Struggle, The, 15:173
Tale of the Lazy People, The, 8:129
Theodore Roosevelt, 15:288
Thomas Alva Edison, 15:117
Understudy, 13:200
Village Blacksmith, The, 5:315
Winterbound Adventure, A, 6:327
Wright Brothers, The, 15:158
Kindness: Albert Schweitzer: The Doctor in the Jungle, 15:256
Antonio Van Dyck and His Master Rubens, 15:88
Bellerophon, 8:93
Ben Franklin's First Adventures, 15:164
Black Pirate of the Peaks, 14:202
Caddie's Silver Dollar, 11:127
Celestial Surgeon, The, 15:210
Cinderella, 2:165
Don, the Story of a Lion Dog, 14:330
Down Down the Mountain, 1:108
Elves and the Shoemaker, The, 2:40
First Christmas Tree, The, 2:51
First Lamb, The, 9:49
Heidi's Adventures on the Mountain, 3:26
Henry Wadsworth Longfellow, 15:237
Johnny Appleseed's Coat, 11:47
Johnny Appleseed Visits Licking Creek, 11:146
Jo Meets Laurie, 3:138
Josie's Home Run, 10:49
King of the Golden River, The, 3:231
King's Cygnet, The, 12:99

CHARACTER, KINDNESS—cont.

King's Daughter, 15:33
Last of the Dragons, The, 2:11
Little Snow-White, 2:269
Monkey Spirit, The, 9:140
Mr. Murdle's Large Heart, 1:250
Mr. Scrunch, 4:52
Muggins Mouse at the Seashore, 1:214
Nine Rabbits and Another One, 1:234
Penny Walk, The, 6:59
Runaway Bus, The, 1:312
Sara Crewe, 3:325
Secret Staircase, The, 9:29
Selfish Giant, The, 2:316
Song of the Little Donkey, The, 1:214
Spectacles, The, 5:42
Story of Mrs. Tubbs, The, 1:119
Stranger in the Wood, The, 12:169
Street of Memories, 6:1
Tennie Weenie Picnic, The, 1:132
Three-Legged Stool, The, 2:121
Wild Dog, 14:116
Wild Duck's Nest, The, 14:81
Loyalty: Albert Schweitzer: The Doctor in the Jungle, 15:256
All Mutt, 6:126
At the Boar Hunt, 12:61
Baedeker Boy, The, 9:116
Black Pits of Luna, The, 16:115
Broken Note, The, 8:294
Follow Your Leader, 13:315
Fools Walk In, 13:302
For the Love of a Man, 14:275
Golden Fleece, The, 8:148
Great Soldier: Robert E. Lee, A, 15:176
Highwayman, The, 5:289
Jane Addams, 15:320
King of the Wind and the Queen's Plate, The, 14:123
King's Cygnet, The, 12:99
Knights of the Red Rose, The, 10:269
Little Red, 13:68

CHARACTER, LOYALTY—CONT.

Marian Anderson: A Voice in a Hundred Years, 15:293
My Struggle for an Education, 15:211
Nightingale, The, 2:358
Open Road, The, 2:20
Patrick Henry Enters Public Life, 15:337
Rikki-Tikki-Tavi, 14:257
Robert Louis Stevenson, 15:206
Robin Finds a Way, 12:26
Roland and His Horn, 8:355
Santa Filomena, 15:244
Secret in the Snow, 13:101
Song of King Arthur's Knights, 8:328
Story of Dobbin, The, 1:244
Story of Mrs. Tubbs, The, 1:119
Tale of Sir Gareth, The, 8:329
Thomas Jefferson, 15:274
Tooth of the Great One, 11:346
Trial by Battle, 13:278
Trust Fulfilled, A, 13:125
Twin Seals, 1:84
Two Scenes from the Life of George Washington, 15:196
Washington, 5:81
Wild-Horse Roundup, 14:194
Obedience: Ashes That Made Trees Bloom, The, 8:80
Bambi Starts To See the World, 14:27
Bellerophon, 8:93
Bim's Gift from the Forest, 9:150
Cocky, 1:150
Don, the Story of a Lion Dog, 14:330
Five Little Bears Have Their Pictures Taken, The, 1:269
For the Love of a Man, 14:275
Little Bear Takes His Nap, 1:224
Louis Joseph, Marquis de Montcalm, 15:332
My Dog, 5:11
One Minute Longer, 14:358
Rebecca at the Brick House, 3:203
Rule of Three, 6:156
Shepherd Left Behind, The, 5:72
Unexpected Christmas, An, 3:113
Why Bother with Ladders?, 13:134
Patience: Anybody Can Ski, 10:95
Fir Tree, The, 1:339
Guglielmo Marconi, 15:189
Henri Fabre: A Place of His Own, 15:308
"Hoot!" Said the Owl, 10:110
Littlest Reindeer, The, 1:58
Thomas Alva Edison, 15:117

CHARACTER, PATIENCE—CONT.

Ugly Duckling, The, 2:149
Wright Brothers, The, 15:158
Penitence: Adventure in Candle Street, 12:179
Augusta Goose, 1:67
Cocky, 1:150
Cream-Colored Pony, The, 6:242
Dungeon Deep, 12:108
Fern Tiki, The, 9:332
Fox and Geese, 11:10
Fox Ferry, The, 2:218
Going Up!, 9:215
Golden Touch, The, 8:62
Little Lamb, A, 1:97
Mason Children on the Roof, The, 6:137
Nightingale, The, 2:358
Pied Piper of Hamelin, The, 5:294
Selfish Giant, The, 2:316
Spindleberries and Pam, 6:78
Steelman's Nerve, 13:144
Tale of the Lazy People, 8:129
Unexpected Christmas, An, 3:113
Uppity Orioles, The, 1:132
Willow Basket, The, 11:93
Perseverance: Adam to the Rescue, 12:240
Adventure of the Blue Carbuncle, The, 7:254

CHARACTER, PERSEVERANCE—CONT.

Anybody Can Ski, **10**:95
At the Fall of Pompeii, **12**:301
Baedeker Boy, The, **9**:116
Black Stallion's Race, The, **14**:162
Columbus, **5**:84
Cuchulain in Shadow-Land, **8**:329
Cutter Race, The, **10**:301
Dantès' Escape from the Chateau D'If, **13**:291
Desert Adventure, **9**:307
Desirable Shawl, The, **9**:14
Down in Davy Jones's Locker, **13**:334
First Lamb, The, **9**:49
Forbidden Island, The, **9**:345
For the Love of a Man, **14**:275
George Washington Carver, **15**:269
Georg Handel and the Duke, **15**:76
Glass Hill, The, **2**:195
Gold Bug, The, **7**:201
Golden Fleece, The, **8**:148
Guglielmo Marconi, **15**:189
Helen Keller, **15**:81
Hit or Error?, **10**:143
Holiday Cup, The, **10**:18
Hoop Hokum, **10**:236
Hunter's Moon, **7**:315
John Henry, Mighty Railroader, **8**:26
Kon-Tiki Adventure, A, **13**:354
Little Guy, The, **10**:286
Little Red, **13**:68
Little Steam Engine, The, **1**:247
Louis Agassiz, **15**:354
Marian Anderson: A Voice in a Hundred Years, **15**:293
Marie Curie: Discoverer of a Hidden Treasure, **15**:264
Miss Hinch, **7**:179
My Struggle for an Education, **15**:211
New York to Paris, **15**:246
Nurenberg Stove, The, **9**:36
Puppy Who Wanted a Boy, The, **1**:332
Red-Headed League, The, **7**:346
Robinson Crusoe Is Shipwrecked, **3**:153
Steelman's Nerve, **13**:144
Strange Pettingill Puzzle, The, **7**:108
Tale of Sir Gareth, The, **8**:309
Theodore Roosevelt, **15**:288
There Was Tammie, **1**:145
Third of June on Annapurna, The, **13**:322
Thomas Alva Edison, **15**:117
Three Golden Oranges, **8**:188
Tommy the Tugboat, **1**:228
Understudy, **13**:200

CHARACTER, PERSEVERANCE—CONT.

Whitey and the Rustlers, **13**:16
Wright Brothers, The, **15**:158
Resourcefulness: Adventure at the Toll Bridge, The, **7**:279
Albert Schweitzer: The Doctor in the Jungle, **15**:256
Cake for Company Dinner, **4**:185
Calloway's Code, **7**:245
Caricature, **10**:212
Climb High, **13**:8
Clutch Man, **10**:251
Cow Golden Horn, The, **8**:39
Dantès' Escape from the Château D'If, **13**:291
Denny Puts in His Oar, **10**:332
Dungeon Deep, **12**:108
Fox Ferry, The, **2**:218
Funny Thing, The, **1**:90
Glorious Whitewasher and His Friends, The, **3**:1
Great Quillow, The, **2**:195
Guides with Wings, **13**:228
Hercules, **1**:200
Homer Price and the Doughnuts, **4**:360
"Hoot!" Said the Owl, **10**:110
Horse Mackerel, **10**:79
Horseshoe Nails, **11**:197
Hunter's Moon, **7**:315
King's Cygnet, The, **12**:99
Kon-Tiki Adventure, A, **13**:354
Lancelot Biggs on the Saturn, **16**:70
Mahogany Fox, The, **14**:290
Many Moons, **2**:1
Marian Anderson: A Voice in a Hundred Years, **15**:293
Mason Children on the Roof, The, **6**:137
Master's Footstool, The, **11**:20
Might of a Song, The, **12**:331
Miss Hinch, **7**:179
Most Wonderful Thing in the World, The, **10**:69
Mrs. Lecks and Mrs. Aleshine Are Shipwrecked, **4**:283
Mrs. Tabby Gray, **1**:210
Mystery of Number 30, The, **7**:42
Old Woman and the Tramp, The, **4**:112
Out of Defeat, **12**:359
Picnic Basket, The, **1**:158
Robinson Crusoe Is Shipwrecked, **3**:153
Sandpipers, The, **6**:37
Secret in the Snow, **13**:101
Strange Pettingill Puzzle, The, **7**:108

CHARACTER, RESOURCEFULNESS—CONT.
Thomas Alva Edison, 15:117
Tom Chist and the Treasure Box, 13:247
Uncle Remus and the Tar-Baby, 8:20
Winterbound Adventure, A, 6:327
Self-Reliance: Abraham Lincoln's Boyhood, 15:25
Baedeker Boy, The, 9:116
Boar Hunt, The, 12:61
Caddie's Silver Dollar, 11:127
Cuckoo in the Nest, The, 12:1
Daniel Boone, 11:369
Down in the Wolf Pit, 13:38
Dungeon Deep, 12:108
First Lamb, The, 9:49
Guides with Wings, 13:228
Hasty Pudding, 11:36
Holiday Cup, The, 10:18
Horse Mackerel, 10:79
Iceboat Race, The, 10:60
Independence Day for Davy, 6:42
Josie's Home Run, 10:40
Little Guy, The, 10:286
Most Wonderful Thing in the World, The, 10:69
Nurenberg Stove, The, 9:36
Randy at the Art Gallery, 6:211
Robin Finds a Way, 12:26
Robinson Crusoe Is Shipwrecked, 3:153
Rococco Skates, 6:30
The Round Up, 13:80
Secret in the Snow, 13:101
Six Bells, 6:152
Winterbound Adventure, A, 6:327
Service: Albert Schweitzer: The Doctor in the Jungle, 15:256
Boy Who Voted for Abe Lincoln, The, 11:83
Caddie's Silver Dollar, 11:127
Celestial Surgeon, 15:210
Farmer of Paimpol, 9:7
Farmers, 5:126
Fern Tiki, The, 9:332
For the Love of a Man, 14:275
George Washington Carver, 15:269
Happy Prince, The 2:346
Heidi's Adventures on the Mountain, 3:26
How Birgit Danced in Her Red Shoes, 9:1
Hunter's Moon, 7:315
Island Christmas, An, 6:277
Jane Addams, 15:320
Johnny Appleseed's Coat, 11:47

CHARACTER, SERVICE—CONT.
Johnny Appleseed Visits Licking Creek, 11:146
King's Cygnet, The, 12:99
King's Daughter, 15:33
Living Christmas, 6:164
Louis Joseph, Marquis de Montcalm, 15:332
Marian Anderson: A Voice in a Hundred Years, 15:293
Marie Curie: Discoverer of a Hidden Treasure, 15:264
Might of a Song, The, 12:331
My Struggle for an Education, 15:211
One Minute Longer, 14:358
Otto At Sea, 1:181
Rikki-Tikki-Tavi, 14:257
Robert Louis Stevenson, 15:206
Robin Finds a Way, 12:26
Santa Filomena, 15:244
Secret in the Snow, 13:101
Shares, 5:100
Skeleton Windmill, The, 9:127
Tale of Sir Gareth, The, 8:309
Trust Fulfilled, A, 13:125
Unexpected Christmas, An, 3:113
Winterbound Adventure, A, 6:277
Sportsmanship: Cuchulain in Shadow-Land, 8:329
Farmer of Paimpol, 9:7
Gang's All There, The, 6:115
Hit or Error?, 10:143
Holiday Cup, The, 10:18
Horse Mackerel, 10:79
House of the Singing Windows, 9:191
Iceboat Race, The, 10:60
Knights of the Red Rose, 10:269
Little Guy, The, 10:286
Living Christmas, 6:164
Mystery and the Race, 3:261
Pass, The, 10:350
Third Round, The, 10:199
Thor's Wonderful Journey, 8:230
Unselfishness: *Abou Ben Adhem,* 5:328
Adventure in Candle Street, 12:179
At the Fall of Pompeii, 12:301
Bellerophon, 8:93
Caddie's Silver Dollar, 11:127
Child's Prayer for Other Children, 5:270
Cratchits' Christmas Dinner, The, 12:292
Desirable Shawl, The, 9:14
Don, the Story of a Lion Dog, 14:330
Down in the Wolf Pit, 13:38
Flame, 14:251

347

CHARACTER, UNSELFISHNESS—CONT.
Fools Walk In, 13:302
For the Love of a Man, 14:275
Fox and Geese, 11:10
Happy Prince, The, 2:346
Horseshoe Nails, 11:197
How Birgit Danced in Her Red Shoes, 9:1
Island Christmas, An, 6:277
Jane Addams, 15:320
Johnny Appleseed's Coat, 11:47
Johnny Appleseed Visits Licking Creek, 11:146
King of the Golden River, The, 3:231
Little Dog Star, 11:102
Little Red, 13:68
Living Christmas, 6:164
Marie Curie: Discoverer of a Hidden Treasure, 15:264
Most Wonderful Thing in the World, The, 10:69
Mystery and the Race, 3:261
Nine Rabbits and Another One, 1:234
Penny Walk, The, 6:59
Pine Tree Song, 5:73
Sara Crewe, 3:325
Selfish Giant, The, 2:316
Shares, 5:100
Street of Memories, 6:1
Three-Legged Stool, The, 2:121
Tooth of the Great One, 11:346
Trust Fulfilled, A, 13:125
Unexpected Christmas, An, 3:113
White Horse of Volendam, The, 8:198
Wild Dog, 14:116
Wild-Horse Roundup, 14:194
Willow Basket, The, 11:93
CHINA—see Many Lands
CHIPMUNK—see Animals
CHRISTMAS—see Holidays
CIRCUSES AND FAIRS
Adventure in Candle Street, 12:179
Animals' Fair, The, 5:204
Benjamin Jones and His Dogs, 5:238
Benjy Goes to the Circus, 5:239
Bertram and the Lion, 4:102
Boy Who Owned An Elephant, The, 1:285
Bug and Beetle Circus, The, 5:124
Circus, 5:22
Circus, 5:55
Circus, The, 5:23
Circus, The, 5:48
Circus Drums, 6:201
Circus Elephant, 14:80
Clown, The, 5:17

CIRCUSES AND FAIRS—CONT.
Dippy, The, 2:94
Dolly Joins the Circus, 6:193
Down, Down the Mountain, 1:108
Forgotten Island, 7:1
How Birgit Danced in Her Red Shoes, 9:1
Look at the Grand Champ, A, 14:148
Mystery—and the Race, 3:261
Oliver at the Circus, 13:26
Oscar, the Trained Seal, 4:58
Pixie, Dixie, Trixie, and Nixie, 1:206
Randy at the Art Gallery, 6:211
Toby Tyler and Mr. Stubbs, 3:93
COLUMBUS:
Columbus, 5:84
Columbus Discovers America, 15:12
COMPASSION—see Character: Kindness
CONDOR—see Birds
CONTENTMENT—see Character: Happiness
COOPERATION—see Character
COURAGE—see Character: Bravery
COWS—see Animals: Cattle
COYOTES—see Animals
CRICKETS—see Insects
CURIE, Marie: Discoverer of a Hidden Treasure, 15:264
DANCING
Catch Me Caddy, 5:243
Cinderella, 2:165
Cream-Colored Pony, The, 6:242
Dancer in the Sun, 5:257
Dippy, The, 2:94
Ellen's Secret, 6:177
Fairy Lore, 5:166
Flanigan's Field, 5:221
How Birgit Danced in Her Red Shoes, 9:1
Island Christmas, An, 6:277
Jonathan Bing Dances for Spring, 5:200
Light-Hearted Fairy, The, 5:170
Living Christmas, 6:164

DANCING—CONT.
Owl and the Pussycat, 5:232
Road to Raffydiddle, The, 5:144
Teddy Bear Dance, 5:158
Understudy, 13:200
DEDUCTION—see Mystery
DETERMINATION—see Character: Perseverance
DICKENS, CHARLES
Charles Dickens: The Boy of the London Streets, 15:100
Journey with Dickens, A, 15:106
DINOSAUR—see Animals: Prehistoric
DIPLODOCUS—see Animals: Prehistoric
DOGS—see Animals
DOLLS
Good Little Dog, A, 1:178
Hitty's Shipwreck, 12:81
Hollow Tree House, The, 5:59
Long-Ago Doll, The, 5:37
Mishaps of Gentle Jane, The, 5:216
Pale Pink Tea, The, 5:242
Sara Crewe, 3:325
Self-Control, 5:61
Valentine to My Doll, 5:81
DONKEYS—see Animals
DRAGONS
Dippy, The, 2:94
Family Dragon, The, 5:7
How Beowulf Ruled the Geats, 8:97
Last of the Dragons, The, 2:11
Little Dragon, The, 2:142
Tale of Custard the Dragon, The, 4:1
DRAKE, Sir Francis: *Admiral's Ghost, The,* 5:338
DRAMATICS
Boy Who Liked Puppets, The, 15:69
Cuckoo in the Nest, The, 12:1
Early Days with Invincible Louisa, 15:130
Fisherman's Luck, 12:348
Gift from the Queen, A, 12:69
Life of William Shakespeare, A, 15:222
Middle Bear, The, 6:144
Understudy, 13:200
Unexpected Christmas, An, 3:113
DRYAD
Dryad, The, 5:152
Song for Summer, 2:50
DUCKS—see Birds
DWARFS—see Elves, Dwarfs, Gnomes, and Pixies
EAGLES—see Birds
EASTER—see Holidays
EDISON, Thomas Alva, 15:117
ELEPHANT—see Animals
ELIZABETH II: King's Daughter, 15:33

ELK—see Animals: Real
ELVES, DWARFS, GNOMES, AND PIXIES
Apple Rhyme, The, 5:172
Elf, The, 2:127
Elf and the Dormouse, The, 5:48
Elves and the Shoemaker, The, 2:40
I Wish I Lived in Elfland, 5:152
King of the Golden River, The, 3:231
Little Elf, The, 2:19
Little Gnome, The, 5:168
Little Snow-White, 2:269
Poppy, 2:54
Queer One, The, 5:213
Rip Van Winkle, 8:252
Rumpelstiltskin, 2:252
Wind Elves, 5:171
ENGLAND—see Many Lands
EVERYDAY FUN
Attic Trunk, 5:36
Away We Go, 5:69
Balloon, 5:62
Belongings, 5:53
Boat, The, 5:25
Butterbean Tent, The, 5:11
Cross-Stitch Sampler, 5:57
Galoshes, 5:14
Harper's Farm, The, 5:30
Hilly Little Town, A, 5:4
Hollow Tree House, The, 5:59
Home-Made Ship, The, 5:58
Hut, The, 5:66
I Caught a Fish, 5:68
Merry-Go-Round, 5:34
Mrs. Brown, 5:29
Mud, 5:14
My New Roller Skates, 5:47
My Teddy Bear, 5:33
On the Farm, 5:102
Over the Garden Wall, 5:2
Pet Show, 5:102
Pirate, The, 5:54
Playhouse Key, The, 5:35
Policemen on Parade, 5:53
Rain Toys, The, 5:190

EVERYDAY FUN—CONT.
Rainy Days, 5:188
Roads, 5:51
Rolling Down a Hill, 5:8
Round the Maypole Now We Dance,
   5:83
Sammy Snowman, 5:64
Sandpile Town, 5:4
Secret Place, The, 5:17
Slide, The, 1:295
Spring Signs, 5:50
Swinging, 5:32
EXPLORERS
Alexander Mackenzie: Hero of Canada,
   15:153
Columbus, 5:84
Columbus Discovers America, 15:12
Daniel Boone, 11:369
Jacques Cartier, 15:315
Louis Agassiz, 15:354
New York to Paris, 15:246
Pathfinders: Lewis and Clark, The,
   11:289
Western Wagons, 11:82
With the Forest Runners, 11:295
FABRE, Henri: A Place of His Own,
   15:308
FAIR PLAY—see Character: Sportsmanship
FAIRIES
Boredom, 5:149
Candlebright, Candlelight!, 5:172
Child and the Fairies, The, 5:175
Cinderella, 2:165
City Fairies, 2:224
Consolation, 5:149
Enchanted Garden, The, 2:327
Fairies, 5:166
Fairy and I, 5:156
Fairy Lore, 5:166
Fairy Phone, 5:160
Fairy Riders, 5:155
Fairy School, The, 2:148
*Fairy Who Didn't Believe in Children,
   The*, 2:128
Fidgity Fairy, The, 5:163
First Christmas Tree, The, 2:51
Glass Hill, The, 2:44
If I Were Thumbelina, 2:88
I Keep Three Wishes Ready, 5:153
Lady Slipper, The, 5:161
Light-Hearted Fairy, The, 5:170
Little Snow-White, 2:269
Magic Fishbone, 4:38
Offer, 5:142
Once When You Were Walking, 2:120
Peter Pan and Captain Hook, 2:225
Playing at the Waterfall, 5:160

FAIRIES—CONT.
Please, 5:149
Poppy, 2:54
Puck's Song, 2:43
Questions, 5:158
Reformed Pirate, The, 2:322
Roses, 5:161
Rumpelstiltskin, 2:252
Second-Hand Shop, The, 5:147
Sleeping Beauty, The, 2:289
Snowflake Fun, 5:170
Spell, The, 5:166
Swan Maiden, The, 2:178
Three Wishes, The, 2:99
Tree House, 5:163
FAMILY RELATIONSHIP
All Mutt, 6:126
Archie and the April Fools, 6:267
Away We Go, 5:69
Benny and the Cat's Tail, 15:62
Big Moment, 10:185
Box the Bee Crept In, The, 12:52
Caddie's Silver Dollar, 11:127
Cake at Midnight, 9:269
Cake for Company Dinner, 5:185
Case of the Sensational Scent, The,
   7:30
Christmas Eve at Reginald's, 6:359
Christmas Horses, 11:111
Christmas Path, The, 6:16
Clarinda, 1869, 6:297
Cratchits' Christmas Dinner, The, 4:217
Cuckoo in the Nest, The, 12:1
Dinner Horses, 5:130
Down, Down the Mountain, 1:108
Early Days with Invincible Louisa,
   15:130
Five Little Bears Have Their Pictures
   Taken, 1:269
Forgotten Island, 7:1
Fox and Geese, 11:10
Gallons of Guppies, 6:17
Ginger on the Fire Escape, 10:1
Handsome Is, 6:234
Happily Ever After, 5:39
Hasty Pudding, 11:36
Heidi's Adventures on the Mountain,
   3:26
Hitty's Shipwreck, 12:81
Horseshoe Nails, 11:197
House of the Mouse, The, 5:138
House of the Singing Windows, 9:191
Hunting Old Slewfoot, 14:314
In a Covered Wagon, 11:72
Independence Day for Davy, 6:42
Island Christmas, An, 6:277
Jam Session at Abbie's, 10:86

FAMILY RELATIONSHIP—CONT.

Jo Meets Laurie, **3**:138
Journey with Dickens, A, **15**:106
Little, **5**:13
Little Dog Star, The, **11**:102
Little Red, **13**:68
Little Woodchuck's Fright, **5**:99
Living Christmas, **6**:164
Macdonald Plaid, The, **9**:202
Mason Children on the Roof, The, **6**:137
Most Wonderful Thing in the World, The, **10**:69
Mr. Dooley Disgraces His Family, **6**:202
Mumps, The, **5**:49
My House, **5**:42
Mystery and the Race, **3**:261
Nine Rabbits and Another One, **1**:234
North Country, **5**:39
Old Houses, **7**:89
Oliver at the Circus, **13**:26
Pioneer Wedding, A, **11**:314
Punch Has an Adventure, **6**:52
Randy at the Art Gallery, **6**:211
Rebecca at the Brick House, **3**:203
Ruggleses' Christmas Dinner, The, **4**:217
Rule of Three, **6**:156
Rusty—Movie Star, **6**:87
Santa Fe, New Mexico, **5**:45
Secret of Rainbow Ridge, The, **7**:69
Silver Llama, The, **9**:171
Singing Saucepan, The, **9**:65
Small Homes, **5**:115
Smoky, **6**:104
Spindleberries and Pam, **6**:78
Strange Pettingill Puzzle, The, **7**:108
Street of Memories, **6**:1
There Was Tammie, **1**:145
Tomorrow Will Be Bright, **11**:26
Touch of Arab, A, **13**:178
Trial By Battle, **13**:278
Two-Mile Race, **10**:321
Unexpected Christmas, An, **3**:113
Visit with Pierre, A, **9**:85
Wastwych Secret, The, **7**:49
Willow Basket, The, **11**:93
Winterbound Adventure, A, **6**:327

FARM LIFE

Angus and the Ducks, **1**:49
Augusta Goose, **1**:67
Cake for Company Dinner, **4**:185
Christmas Calf, The, **5**:126
Corn in the Shocks, **5**:191
Dinner Horses, **5**:130
Easter Eggs, **9**:76
Familiar Friends, **5**:133

FARM LIFE—CONT.

Farewell to the Farm, **5**:28
Farmer of Paimpol, **9**:7
Farmers, **5**:15
Farmers, **5**:126
Harper's Farm, The, **5**:30
Janie's Wish, **1**:298
Knights of the Red Rose, **10**:269
Look at the Grand Champ, A, **14**:148
Model for Me, **5**:137
On the Farm, **5**:28
Pasture, The, **5**:136
Round Up, The, **13**:80
Solitary Reaper, The, **5**:280
Spring Pastures, **5**:100
Thanksgiving, **5**:90
What I Would Do, **5**:9

FATHER

Baedeker Boy, The, **9**:116
Boy Who Voted for Abe Lincoln, The, **11**:83
Dancer in the Sun, **5**:257
Dungeon Deep, **12**:108
First Lamb, The, **9**:49
Five Little Bears Have Their Pictures Taken, The, **1**:269
Gang's All There, The, **6**:115
Golden Touch, The, **8**:62
Hunting Old Slew Foot, **14**:314
I Caught a Fish, **5**:68
It Was, **5**:68
Jam Session at Abbie's, **10**:86
Little Red, **13**:68
Marshall at Bat, **10**:313
Most Wonderful Thing in the World, The, **10**:69
North Country, **5**:39
Wishes, **5**:57

FAWN—see Animals

FIRE

At the Fall of Pompeii, **12**:301
Blaze and the Forest Fire, **14**:1
Cream-Colored Pony, The, **6**:242
Follow Your Leader, **13**:315
Fools Walk In, **13**:302
Hercules, **1**:200
Pippi Acts as a Lifesaver, **13**:94
Punch Has an Adventure, **6**:52
Willie the Moose, **14**:7

FISH AND CREATURES OF THE SEA

At the Aquarium, **13**:353
Bears of Blue River, The, **11**:306
Belinda, **5**:208
Camel and the Cachelot, The, **5**:228
Deep Sea Adventure, A, **5**:151
Deep Sea Song, **5**:150
Fisherman and His Wife, The, **2**:133

351

FISH AND CREATURES OF THE SEA—CONT.
Forbidden Island, The, **9**:345
Gallons of Guppies, **6**:17
Guppies Are Best, **6**:29
Horse Mackerel, **10**:110
I Caught a Fish, **5**:68
In from the Sea, **5**:192
Kit and Kat Go Fishing, **1**:75
Kon-Tiki Adventure, A, **13**:354
Koyo, the Singer, **14**:98
Maybe, **4**:261
McElligot's Pool, **1**:323
Moon Song, **5**:250
Naturally Enough, **5**:164
Octopus, **5**:208
Pearl Diver, The, **13**:347
Sea Horse, The, **5**:24
Seal Lullaby, **5**:258
Seashore Gossip, **5**:117
Sensible Lobster, The, **5**:208
Shark, The, **5**:210
Storm Tide, **13**:51
There Once Was a Puffin, **5**:226
Walrus and the Carpenter, The, **4**:206
Whale, **5**:117
FLAMINGO—see Birds
FLOWERS AND GARDENS
Afternoon, **5**:181
April, **5**:179
April Rain, **5**:178
Bluebells, **2**:186
Country Church, **5**:353
Daffodils, **5**:272
Down, Down the Mountain, **1**:108
Farmers, **5**:126
Field Flowers, **5**:192
Garden Fancy, **5**:33
Home Thoughts from Abroad, **5**:274
In Grandmother's Garden, **5**:180
In the Garden, **5**:183
Lady Slipper, The, **5**:161
Morning, **5**:180
Rhodora, The, **5**:276
Roses, **5**:161
Small Homes, **5**:115
Song for Summer, **5**:182
Spindleberries and Pam, **6**:78
Summer, **5**:185
Vision of Sir Launfal, **5**:274
Winterbound Adventure, A, **6**:327
FOLK TALES
Ballor's Son Goes Riding, **2**:280
Cow Golden Horn, The, **8**:39
Elves and the Shoemaker, The, **2**:40
Fisherman and His Wife, The, **2**:133
Lad Who Went to the North Wind, The, **2**:264

FOLK TALES—CONT.
Man with the Bag, The, **2**:171
Old Woman and the Tramp, The, **4**:112
Tale of the Lazy People, The, **8**:129
Tale of Three Tails, A, **8**:241
Talk, **8**:17
Three Golden Oranges, **8**:188
Uncle Remus and the Tar-Baby, **8**:20
White Horse of Volendam, The, **8**:198
Woman's Wit, A, **8**:201
FOOD
Birthdays, **5**:55
Boat, The, **5**:25
Boiling the Billy, **9**:281
Cake at Midnight, **9**:269
Cake for Company Dinner, **4**:185
Cannery Bear, The, **4**:94
Cratchits' Christmas Dinner, The, **12**:292
First Thanksgiving of All, **5**:89
Forgotten Island, **7**:1
Fox Ferry, The, **2**:218
Goody O'Grumpity, **1**:223
Guests, **5**:140
Halloween, **5**:88
Hasty Pudding, **11**:36
Heidi's Adventures on the Mountain, **3**:26
Homer Price and the Doughnuts, **4**:360
King of the Golden River, The, **3**:231
King's Breakfast, The **1**:44
Lady Who Put Salt in Her Coffee, The, **4**:262
Macdonald Plaid, The, **9**:202
Magic Fishbone, **4**:38
Old Woman and the Tramp, The, **4**:112
Oliver at the Circus, **13**:26
Parade of the Animal Crackers, **5**:157
Picnic Basket, The, **1**:158
Robinson Crusoe Is Shipwrecked, **3**:153
Ruggleses' Christmas Dinner, The, **4**:217

FOOD—CONT.
Runaway Bus, The, 1:312
Sara Crewe, 3:325
Shares, 5:100
Singing Saucepan, The, 9:65
Song for Supper, 5:43
Strange Pettingill Puzzle, The, 7:108
Tale of Sir Gareth, The, 8:309
Teenie Weenie Picnic, The, 1:132
Thanksgiving Is Coming, 5:91
Toby Tyler and Mr. Stubbs, 3:93
Truth about Pyecraft, The, 16:102
Unexpected Christmas, An, 3:113
Uppity Orioles, The, 1:137
Who Goes There?, 14:17
Wind Elves, 5:171
FOOLISHNESS—see Character
FOXES—see Animals
FRANKLIN, BENJAMIN: Ben Franklin's
First Adventures, 15:164
FREEDOM
Abraham Lincoln Walks at Midnight,
5:346
At the Fall of Pompeii, 12:301
Black Pirate of the Peaks, 14:202
Coaly Bay, the Outlaw Horse, 14:305
Daniel Boone, 11:369
Daniel Webster, 15:367
Flame, 14:251
On the Mayflower, 11:1
Our America, 5:83
Patrick Henry Enters Public Life,
15:337
Rocky Mountain Sheep, The, 14:371
Song for Warren, 5:110
Song of Sherwood, A, 5:348
*Song of the Rabbits Outside the Tav-
ern,* 5:96
Thomas Jefferson, 15:274
White Blackbird, The, 2:34
FROGS—see Animals: Real
GALILEO, 15:74
GARDENS—see Flowers and Gardens
GEESE—see Birds
GENEROSITY—see Character: Kindness,
Service, Unselfishness
GEOGRAPHY—see Many Lands
GIANTS
Fox Ferry, The, 2:218
Great Quillow, The, 2:195
Selfish Giant, The, 2:316
Woman's Wit, A, 8:201
GIFTS
About Christmas, 5:79
Bim's Gift from the Forest, 9:150
Birthdays, 5:55
Christmas Eve at Reginald's, 6:359

GIFTS—CONT.
Christmas Gifts, 5:74
Cream-Colored Pony, The, 6:242
Desirable Shawl, The, 9:14
Dobry's New Year, 9:294
Down, Down the Mountain, 1:108
Gallons of Guppies, 6:17
Gift from the Queen, A, 12:69
Happy Prince, The, 2:346
Heidi's Adventures on the Mountain,
3:26
How Birgit Danced in Her Red Shoes,
9:1
I Caught a Fish, 5:68
In Which Eeyore Has a Birthday and
Gets Two Presents, 1:186
Island Christmas, An, 6:277
Little Gnome, The, 5:168
Littlest Angel, The, 1:350
Living Christmas, 6:164
My Gift, 5:74
Nightingale, The, 2:358
Packages, 5:18
Parchment Door, The, 12:140
Penny Walk, The, 6:59
Pine Tree Song, 5:73
Rocking-Horse Land, 1:302
Sara Crewe, 3:325
Sleeping Beauty, The, 2:289
Spindleberries and Pam, 6:78
Street of Memories, 6:1
Unexpected Christmas, An, 3:113
Velveteen Rabbit, The, 1:1
Whitey and the Rustlers, 13:16
Winterbound Adventure, A, 6:327
GIRAFFE—see Animals
GNOMES—see Elves, Dwarfs, Gnomes, and
Pixies
GNU—see Animals
GOATS—see Animals
GOBLINS—see Witches, Wizards, and Gob-
lins
GRANDFATHER
Bim's Gift from the Forest, 9:150
Dobry's New Year, 9:294
Heidi's Adventures on the Mountain,
3:26
Jo Meets Laurie, 3:138
Kit and Kat Go Fishing, 1:75
Macdonald Plaid, The, 9:202
Silver Belt, The, 9:110
Song of Grandfather Thomas' Parrot,
5:108
Strange Pettingill Puzzle, The, 7:108
Visit with Pierre, A, 9:85
GRANDMOTHER
Down, Down the Mountain, 1:108

353

GRANDMOTHER—CONT.
Grandmother's Brook, 5:2
Heidi's Adventures on the Mountain, 3:26
In Grandmother's Garden, 5:180
Spectacles, The, 5:42
Thanksgiving Is Coming, 5:91
Visit with Pierre, A, 9:85

GYPSY
At Night, 5:187
Being a Gypsy, 5:5
Caravan, The, 5:54
Cream-Colored Pony, The, 6:242
Dobry's New Year, 9:294
Little Dragon, The, 2:142
Old Country, The, 5:5
Summer, 5:185

HALLOWEEN—see Holidays
HANDEL, GEORG: Georg Handel and the Duke, 15:76
HELICOPTER—see Aviation
HENRY, PATRICK: Patrick Henry Enters Public Life, 15:337
HENS—see Birds
HERON—see Birds
HISTORICAL BACKGROUND
Abraham Lincoln's Boyhood, 15:25
Adam to the Rescue, 12:240
Adventure in a Chimney, 12:14
Alexander Mackenzie: Hero of Canada, 15:153
Antonio Van Dyck and His Master Rubens, 15:88
Apache Warpath, 11:338
At the Boar Hunt, 12:61
At the Fall of Pompeii, 12:301
Ben Franklin's First Adventures, 15:164
Box a Bee Crept In, The, 12:52
Boy Who Loved Birds, The, 15:51
Boy Who Voted for Abe Lincoln, The, 11:83
Buffalo Hunting, 11:357
Children of the Wolf, The, 8:34
Columbus Discovers America, 15:12

HISTORICAL BACKGROUND—CONT.
Cuckoo in the Nest, The, 12:1
Daniel Webster, 15:367
Dantès' Escape from the Chateau D'If, 13:291
Disperse, Ye Rebels, 11:238
Dungeon Deep, 12:108
Feather of the Northman, The, 11:64
Fisherman's Luck, 12:348
Frontier Blockade Buster, 11:229
Georg Handel and the Duke, 15:76
Gift from the Queen, A, 12:69
Golden Cup of Kasimir, The, 12:259
Great Soldier: Robert E. Lee, A, 15:176
Horseshoe Nails, 11:197
Jacques Cartier, 15:315
Johnny Appleseed's Coat, 11:47
Johnny Appleseed Visits Licking Creek, 11:146
King's Cygnet, The, 12:99
Leonarda da Vinci, 15:325
Life of William Shakespeare, A, 15:222
Louis Joseph, Marquis de Montcalm, 15:332
Ludwig van Beethoven, 15:328
Man with the Belt of Gold, The, 12:273
Master's Footstool, The, 11:20
Message for Washington, A, 11:255
Michelangelo and the Snow Man, 15:1
Might of a Song, The, 12:331
Mystery of the Bay, The, 13:190
On Kublai Khan's Service, 12:313
On the Mayflower, 11:1
Out of Defeat, 12:359
Parchment Door, The, 12:140
Pathfinders: Lewis and Clark, The, 11:289
Patrick Henry Enters Public Life, 15:337
Ride with Tom Thumb, A, 11:56
River and Beasts Betray, 11:277
Robin Finds a Way, 12:26
Robin Hood and the Shooting Match, 12:227
Saving of Boonesborough, The, 11:181
Six Bells, 12:152
Stranger in the Wood, The, 12:169
Tabby's Tablecloth, 11:264
Thomas Jefferson, 15:274
Three-Cornered Hat, The, 11:189
Titian's First Picture, 15:56
Tom Chist and the Treasure Box, 13:247
Trial by Battle, 13:278
Two Scenes from the Life of George Washington, 15:196

HISTORICAL BACKGROUND—CONT.
With the Forest Runners, 11:295
Wolfgang Mozart, 15:94
Wooden Horse and the Fall of Troy, The, 12:355

HOLIDAYS
April Fool's Day: Archie and the April Fools, 6:267
Arbor Day: *Apple Blossoms,* 1:301
Morning Exercises, 5:33
Planting a Tree, 5:82
Tree Children, 5:9
Trees, 5:356

Christmas: *About Christmas,* 5:76
Adventure of the Blue Carbuncle, The, 7:254
All through the Night, 1:360
Christmas Calf, 5:126
Christmas Eve, 5:75
Christmas Eve at Reginald's, 6:359
Christmas Gifts, 5:74
Christmas Horses, 11:111
Christmas in the Woods, 5:77
Christmas Morning, 5:70
Christmas Path, The, 6:16
Christmas Song, 5:76
Christmas Song, 11:126
Cratchits' Christmas Dinner, The, 12:292
Fires, 5:76
First Christmas Tree, The, 2:51
First Night, The, 5:75
Fir Tree, The, 1:339
Flamingo, The, 5:212
Great Hunter of the Woods, 8:103
I'm Wishing the Whole World Christmas, 5:73
Island Christmas, An, 6:277
Jest 'Fore Christmas, 5:312
Littlest Angel, The, 1:350
Living Christmas, 6:164
Long, Long Ago, 5:71
Penny Walk, The, 6:59
Pine Tree Song, 5:73
Piping on Christmas Eve, The, 2:187

HOLIDAYS—CONT.
Puppy Who Wanted a Boy, The, 1:332
Ruggleses' Christmas Dinner, The, 4:217
Runaway Bus, The, 1:312
Shepherd Left Behind, The, 5:72
Shine, Star, 5:79
Street of Memories, 6:1
Unexpected Christmas, An, 3:113
Velveteen Rabbit, The, 1:1
Columbus Day: *Columbus,* 5:84
Columbus Discovers America, 15:12
Easter: *Easter Bunny, The,* 5:56
Easter Eggs, 9:76
Easter in the Woods, 5:141
In Grandmother's Garden, 5:180
Loveliest of Trees, 5:357
Nine Rabbits and Another One, 1:234
Sing, World, Sing!, 5:82
White Blackbird, The, 2:34
Flag Day: *America the Beautiful, From,* 9:201
Our America, 5:83
Halloween: *Bad Kittens, The,* 5:41
Goblin Gadgets, 5:88
Halloween, 5:88
Three Little Witches, 5:86
Witch Cat, 5:87
Witch of Willoughby Wood, 5:162
Independence Day: *America the Beautiful, From,* 9:201
Birthday of Our Land, The, 5:84
Independence Day for Davy, 6:42
Our America, 5:83
Rule of Three, 6:156
Labor Day: Little Guy, The, 10:286
Lincoln's Birthday: Abraham Lincoln's Boyhood, 15:25
Abraham Lincoln Walks at Midnight, 5:346
Boy Who Voted for Abe Lincoln, The, 11:83

355

HOLIDAYS—CONT.
Lincoln, 5:80
Our America, 5:83
May Day: *Dippy, The*, 2:94
Round the May Pole Now We Dance, 5:83
New Year's Day: *Morning*, 5:80
Dobry's New Year, 9:294
St. Patrick's Day: Basketball Mystery, The, 10:32
Thanksgiving: *First Thanksgiving of All*, 5:89
Little Dog Star, The, 11:102
Thanksgiving, 5:90
Thanksgiving Is Coming, 5:91
Valentine's Day: *Snowflake Fun*, 5:170
Valentine to My Doll, 5:81
Washington's Birthday: Cutter Race, The, 10:301
Out of Defeat, 12:359
Strangers in the Wilderness, 11:150
Two Scenes from the Life of George Washington, 15:196
Washington, 5:81
HOME—see Family Relationship
HORSE—see Animals
HUMOR
Animal Crackers, 5:217
Animals' Fair, The, 5:204
Anybody Can Ski, 10:95
Archie and the April Fools, 6:267
Aristocrat, The, 5:227
At the Zoo, 5:49
Ballad of the Oysterman, 5:282
Barber, The, 1:311
Beast I Like, A, 5:213
Beauty's Sister, 10:125
Belinda, 5:208
Benjy Goes to the Circus, 5:239
Bertram and the Lion, 4:102
Bertram and the Musical Crocodile, 4:197
Big Baboon, The, 4:234
Big Music, 8:338
Camel, The, 5:217
Camel Is a Mammal, The, 4:145
Camel's Complaint, The, 5:218
Can a Mouse Keep House?, 5:223
Case of the Sensational Scent, The, 7:30
Casey at the Bat, 5:332
Catastrophe, 5:206
Catch Me Caddy, 5:243
Crazy Story of Dizzy Lizzie, The, 4:118
Cremation of Sam McGee, The, 5:329
Dinosaur, The, 5:119
Discomfort, 5:217

HUMOR—CONT.
Dr. Dolittle and the Pushmi-Pullyu, 4:158
Dr. Dolittle Meets a Londoner in Paris, 4:210
Duck and the Kangaroo, The, 5:244
Elephant's Child, The, 4:4
Eletelephony, 4:14
Elizabeth Eliza's Piano, About, 4:135
Ellen's Secret, 6:117
Father William, 5:240
500 Hats of Bartholomew Cubbins, The, 1:16
Forty Singing Seamen, 5:334
Fox Ferry, The, 2:218
Frisbie Cures the Doctor, 6:71
Fun, 4:13
Funny Thing, The, 1:90
Gallons of Guppies, 6:17
Giraffe, The, 1:213
Glorious Whitewasher and His Friends, The, 3:1
Great Hunter of the Woods, 8:103
Gregory Griggs, 1:118
Hannibal the Cannibal, 5:224
"Hoot!" Said the Owl, 10:110
House the Pecks Built, The, 4:18
How to Get to Italy, 5:206
How to Tell Wild Animals, 4:162
Huckabuck Family, The, 4:47
Ichthyosaurus, The, 5:227
Johnny Fife and Johnny's Wife, 5:222
Jonathan Bing, 4:134
Jonathan Bing Dances for Spring, 5:200
Juggler, The, 4:196
King's Breakfast, The, 1:44
King's Wish, The, 4:24
Kudu, The, 5:227
Lady Who Put Salt in Her Coffee, The, 4:262
Magic Glass, The, 4:65
Maid of Timbuctoo, The, 5:207
Master Mind, 10:220
Maybe, 4:248
McElligot's Pool, 1:323
Melancholy Pig, The, 5:223
Middle Bear, The, 6:144

356

HUMOR—CONT.

More About Jonathan Bing, 5:246
Mr. Dooley Disgraces His Family, 6:202
Mr. Popper and Captain Cook, 4:30
Mr. Scrunch, 4:52
Mrs. Goose's Rubbers, 4:15
Mrs. Lecks and Mrs. Aleshine Are Shipwrecked, 4:283
Nautical Ballad, A, 4:164
Nautical Extravaganza, A, 4:267
Neighborly Gnu, The, 5:236
New Song to Sing About Jonathan Bing, A, 5:247.
Nonsense Limericks, 4:266
Octopus, 5:208
Odorous Owl, The, 5:237
Old Goose, The, 1:52
Old Woman and the Tramp, The, 4:112
Oscar, the Trained Seal, 4:58
Otto at Sea, 1:181
Owl and the Pussy Cat, The, 5:232
Pale Pink Tea, The, 5:242
Panther, The, 4:111
Peaceful Pirate, The, 1:172
Pecos Bill and His Bouncing Bride, 8:115
Pink Giraffe, The, 4:111
Playful Puma, The, 5:236
Purple-Eyed Pirate, The, 5:202
Queen of the Orkney Islands, The, 4:100
Queer One, The, 5:213
Ransom of Red Chief, The, 4:248
Rhinoceros, The, 4:111
Road to Raffydiddle, The, 5:144
Robinson Crusoe's Story, 4:236
Sensible Lobster, The, 5:208
Serapina Proves Herself, 4:166
Shark, The, 5:210
Ship of Rio, The, 4:70
Singing Saucepan, The, 9:65
Sir Peter Bombazoo, 4:358
Story of Babar, The, 1:100
Tale of Custard the Dragon, The, 4:1
Talk, 8:17
Tickly Ostrich, The, 5:236
Tillyheehee, 4:51
Turbulent Tiger, The, 5:237
Tyrannical Toad, The, 5:237
Waino and Ivar Meet Honk the Moose, 6:65
Walrus and the Carpenter, The, 4:206
Wasted Philanthropy, 5:212
Who Is Who?, 9:253
Woman's Wit, A, 8:201
Won't-Pick-Up-Toys Cure, The, 4:136

HUMOR—CONT.

Yak, The, 4:235
You Never Saw Such An Egg, 4:270
Young Lady's Eyes, The, 4:117

INDEPENDENCE DAY—see Holidays

INDIANS

Apache Warpath, 11:338
Caddie's Silver Dollar, 11:127
Dancer in the Sun, 5:257
Desirable Shawl, The, 9:14
Hiawatha's Childhood, 5:305
Indian Boy, 5:56
Indian Children Long Ago, 5:90
Indian Song, 5:258
Jacques Cartier, 15:315
Legacy of Canyon John, The, 7:98
Louis Joseph, Marquis de Montcalm, 15:332
Mary Silver, 11:159
Mystery of the Bay, The, 13:190
Pack Rat, 14:50
Silver Belt, The, 9:110
Strangers in the Wilderness, 11:150
Tooth of the Great One, 11:346
Tungwa, 9:180
Two Scenes from the Life of George Washington, 15:196
Walk on the Rainbow Trail, 9:190
With the Forest Runners, 11:295
Yukon Trail, 13:1

INDUSTRY—see Character

INITIATIVE—see Character: Resourcefulness, Self-Reliance

INSECTS

Bug and Beetle Circus, The, 5:124
Cricket, The, 5:114
Gold Bug, The, 7:201
Grasshoppers, The, 5:94
Henri Fabre: A Place of His Own, 15:308
Johnny and the Monarch, 1:260
Small Homes, 5:115
Splinter, 5:191
Thoughts about Grasshoppers, 1:43
Wing Dreams, 1:263

INTEGRITY—see Character: Honesty

Inventors
   Ben Franklin's First Adventures, 15:164
   Galileo, 15:74
   George Washington Carver, 15:269
   Guglielmo Marconi, 15:189
   Leonardo da Vinci, 15:325
   Thomas Alva Edison, 15:117
   Thomas Jefferson, 15:274
   Wright Brothers, The, 15:158
Islands
   If Once You Have Slept on an Island,
      5:188
   Island Christmas, An, 6:277
   Koyo, the Singer, 14:98
Jefferson, Thomas, 15:274
Kangaroo—see Animals
Keller, Helen, 15:81
Kindness—see Character
Kings—see Princes and Royal Family
Knights
   Adam to the Rescue, 12:240
   Broken Note, The, 8:294
   Dungeon Deep, 12:108
   Glove and the Lions, The, 12:347
   Might of a Song, The, 12:331
   Roland and His Horn, 8:355
   Song of King Arthur's Knights, 8:328
   Tale of Sir Gareth, The, 8:309
   Trial by Battle, 13:278
Labor Day—see Holidays
Lambs—see Animals
Larks—see Birds
Lee, Robert E., A Great Soldier,
      15:176
Legends—see Myths and Legends
Leprechauns and Pookas
   Ardan's Pooka, 2:89
   Patsy and the Leprechaun, 2:109
   Pooka, 5:173
Lewis and Clark
   Pathfinders: Lewis and Clark, The,
      11:289
   River and Beasts Betray, 11:277
Library—see Reading, Love of
Lighthouse
   Farmer of Paimpol, 9:7
   I'd Like To Be a Lighthouse, 5:29
   If Once You Have Slept on an Island,
      5:188
   Storm Tide, 13:51
Lincoln, Abraham
   Abraham Lincoln's Boyhood, 15:25
   Abraham Lincoln Walks at Midnight,
      5:346
   Boy Who Voted for Abe Lincoln, The,
      11:38
   Lincoln, 5:80

Lindbergh, Charles A.
   Lindbergh Flies Alone, 15:255
   New York to Paris, 15:246
Lions—see Animals
Lizards—see Reptiles
Llamas—see Animals
Lobsters—see Fish and Creatures of the
      Sea
Longfellow, Henry Wadsworth, 15:237
Loyalty—see Character

Lullabies
   All through the Night, 5:268
   Cradle Hymn, 5:255
   Cradle Song, 5:252
   Dream Song, 5:261
   Forest Lullaby, 5:257
   Harbor of Hushaby Ho, The, 5:254
   Indian Song, 5:258
   Lady Button-Eyes, 5:248
   Little Blue Pigeon, 5:256
   Moon Song, 5:250
   On Our Way to Dreamland, 5:253
   Rock-A-By Lady, The, 5:255
   Said the Sandman, 1:338
   Seal Lullaby, 5:258
   Sleep, Baby, Sleep, 5:267
   Song at Dusk, 5:252
   Sweet and Low, 5:263
   Wynken, Blynken, and Nod, 5:262
Machinery
   Guglielmo Marconi, 15:189
   Power Plant, A, 13:143
   Thomas Alva Edison, 15:117
   Why Bother with Ladders, 13:134
Machinery, Personified
   Cocky, 1:150
   Hercules, 1:200
   Little Steam Engine, The, 1:247
   Tommy the Tugboat, 1:228
Mackenzie, Alexander: Hero of Canada,
      15:153
Many Lands
   Africa: Albert Schweitzer: The Doctor
      in the Jungle, 15:256
   Curious George, 1:53

Many Lands—cont.

Desert Adventure, **9**:307
First Lamb, The, **9**:49
Gorillas and Lions, **13**:158
Alaska: Cake at Midnight, **9**:269
For the Love of a Man, **14**:275
One Alaska Night, **7**:297
Yukon Trail, **13**:1
Antarctic: Dinty—A Husky's Story, **14**:176
Arctic: Eskimo Twins Go Coasting, The, **9**:20
Geography Lesson, **5**:203
Nanook, **14**:64
Twin Seals, **1**:84
Australia: Boiling the Billy, **9**:281
Secret of Rainbow Ridge, The, **7**:69
Austria: Ludwig van Beethoven, **15**:328
Belgium: Antonio Van Dyck and His Master Rubens, **15**:88
Bermuda: Stalactite Surprise, **7**:61
Bulgaria: Dobry's New Year, **9**:294
Burma: Curse of Kaing, The, **9**:320
Canada: Alexander Mackenzie: Hero of Canada, **15**:153
Canadian Boat-Song, **5**:278
Jacques Cartier, **15**:315
Knights of the Red Rose, **10**:269
Louis Joseph, Marquis de Montcalm, **15**:332
Mary Silver, **11**:159
Trust Fulfilled, A, **13**:125
Visit with Pierre, A, **9**:85
China: Capture of the Shen, The, **8**:300
Hok-Hwa of the Waterfront, **9**:58
Little Red, **13**:68
Monkey Spirit, The, **9**:140
Nightingale, The, **2**:358
On Kublai Khan's Service, **12**:319
Denmark: Boy Who Liked Puppets, The, **15**:69
How Birgit Danced in Her Red Shoes, **9**:1
England: Adam to the Rescue, **12**:240
Adventure in Candle Street, **12**:179
Adventure of the Blue Carbuncle, The, **7**:254
Baedeker Boy, The, **9**:116
Charles Dickens: The Boy of the London Streets, **15**:100
Cratchits' Christmas Dinner, The, **12**:292
Cuckoo in the Nest, The, **12**:1
Dungeon Deep, **12**:108
Fisherman's Luck, **12**:348
Gift from the Queen, A, **12**:61

Many Lands—cont.

Home Thoughts from Abroad, **5**:274
Hunter's Moon, **7**:315
King of the Wind and the Queen's Plate, **14**:123
King's Cygnet, The, **12**:99
King's Daughter, **15**:33
Lewis Carroll, **15**:8
Life of William Shakespeare, A, **15**:222

Red-Headed League, The, **7**:346
Robin Finds a Way, **12**:26
Robin Hood and the Shooting Match, **12**:227
Robin Hood Turns Beggar, **8**:205
Sara Crewe, **3**:325
Song of Sherwood, A, **5**:348
Spindleberries and Pam, **6**:28
Trial by Battle, **13**:278
Understudy, **13**:200
Upon Westminster Bridge, **5**:276
Wastwych Secret, The, **7**:49
France: At the Boar Hunt, **12**:61
Dantès' Escape from the Château D'If, **13**:291
Farmer of Paimpol, **9**:7
Henri Fabre: A Place of His Own, **15**:308
Marie Curie: Discoverer of a Hidden Treasure, **15**:264
Parchment Door, The, **12**:140
Germany: Box a Bee Crept In, The, **12**:52
Georg Handel and the Duke, **15**:76
House of the Singing Windows, **9**:191
Nurenberg Stove, The, **9**:36
Pied Piper of Hamelin, The, **5**:294
Greece: Skeleton Windmill, The, **9**:127
Greenland: Nanook, **14**:64
Holland: Kit and Kat Go Fishing, **1**:75
Little Toy Land of the Dutch, The, **9**:306

MANY LANDS—CONT.

Mystery and the Race, 3:261

White Horse of Volendam, The, 8:198

Hungary: Easter Eggs, 9:76

Round Up, The, 13:80

India: Bim's Gift from the Forest, 9:150

Cow Golden Horn, The, 8:39

How Kari Saved Our Lives in the Jungle, 14:76

Rikki-Tikki-Tavi, 14:257

Ireland: Ardan's Pooka, 2:89

Ballor's Son Goes Riding, 2:280

Cuchulain in Shadow-Land, 8:329

First Harp, The, 8:44

Lake Isle of Innisfree, The, 5:355

Patsy and the Leprechaun, 2:109

Woman's Wit, A, 8:201

Italy: At the Fall of Pompeii, 12:301

Children of the Wolf, The, 8:34

Leonardo da Vinci, 15:325

Michelangelo and the Snow Man, 15:1

That Boy, 9:96

Wolfgang Mozart, 15:94

Japan: Ashes That Made Trees Bloom, The, 8:80

Mexico: Secret Staircase, The, 9:29

Nepal: Third of June on Annapurna, The, 13:322

New Zealand: Fern Tiki, The, 9:332

Norway: Secret in the Snow, 13:101

Poland: Broken Note, The, 8:294

Golden Cup of Kasimir, The, 12:259

Scotland: Lochinvar, 5:316

Macdonald Plaid, The, 9:202

Solitary Reaper, The, 5:280

Sweet Afton, 5:278

South America: Silver Llama, The, 9:171

South Seas: Forbidden Island, The, 9:345

Pearl Diver, The, 13:347

Robert Louis Stevenson, 15:206

Spain: Stranger in the Wood, The, 12:169

Three Golden Oranges, 8:188

MANY LANDS—CONT.

Sumatra: Jambi and the Tiger, 14:184

Sweden: Singing Saucepan, The, 9:65

Switzerland: Going Up!, 9:215

Heidi's Adventures on the Mountain, 3:26

West Indies: Who Is Who?, 9:253

MARCONI, GUGLIELMO, 15:189

MARCO POLO: On Kublai Khan's Service, 12:313

MAY DAY—see Holidays

MERMAIDS AND MERMEN

Ballad of the Oysterman, 5:282

Bucca Boo's Little Merry Men, 8:1

Deep Sea Adventure, A, 5:151

Deep Sea Song, 5:150

Little John Bottlejohn, 5:234

Lost Merbaby, The, 1:272

Mermaidens, The, 5:167

Minnie the Mermaid, 1:35

Sea Child, 5:167

Sea-Shell, 2:251

Song for Summer, 2:50

MICE—see Animals

MICHELANGELO and the Snow Man, 15:1

MOCKINGBIRDS—see Birds

MOLES—see Animals

MONKEYS—see Animals

MONTCALM, Louis Joseph, Marquis de, 15:332

MOON

Bad Kittens, The, 5:41

Bedtime for a Baby Brook, 5:193

Cradle Song, 5:252

Dryad, The, 5:152

Flanigans Field, 5:221

Highwayman, The, 5:289

Hunter's Moon, 7:315

Indian Song, 5:258

Many Moons, 2:1

Moon Song, 5:250

Night Will Never Stay, The, 5:185

On Our Way to Dreamland, 5:253

Radio Wish, 5:38

Road to Raffydiddle, The, 5:144

Silver, 5:38

Song of the Rabbits Outside the Tavern, 5:96

Wind Elves, The, 5:171

Wise, 5:176

MOOSE—see Animals

MORNING

Christmas Morning, 5:70
Crimson Dawn, The, 5:277
Good Morning, 5:1
Happy Day, 5:32
Hark! Hark! the Lark!, 5:272
Hie Away, Hie Away, 5:271
Home-Thoughts, from Abroad, 5:274
Hunting Song, 12:258
Morning, 5:177
Morning, 5:180
Morning Exercises, 5:33
Sun Is First to Rise, The, 5:179
There Was a Roaring in the Wind,
  5:275
Upon Westminster Bridge, 5:276

MOTHER

All through the Night, 1:360
Away We Go, 5:69
Bambi Starts To See the World, 14:27
Bim's Gift from the Forest, 9:150
Boy Who Owned an Elephant, The,
  1:285
Christmas Path, The, 6:16
Cow Golden Horn, The, 8:39
Desert Adventure, 9:307
Desirable Shawl, The, 9:14
Fawn's First Journey, 5:110
Five Little Bears Have Their Pictures
  Taken, The, 1:269
Gallantry Bower, 5:46
Goosie Gray, 1:74
Hok-Hwa of the Waterfront, 9:58
House of the Singing Windows, 9:191
Little Bear Takes His Nap, 1:224
Little Woodchuck's Fright, 5:99
Lost Merbaby, The, 1:272
Mary Silver, 11:159
Mrs. Brown, 5:29
Mrs. Tabby Gray, 1:210
My House, 5:42
Nine Rabbits and Another One, 1:234
Patsy and the Leprechaun, 2:109
Runaway Bus, The, 1:312
Strange Pettingill Puzzle, The, 7:108
Sweet and Low, 5:263
There Was Tammie, 1:145
Tomorrow Will Be Bright, 11:26
Twin Seals, 1:84
Unexpected Christmas, 3:113
Wishes, 5:57
Won't-Pick-Up-Toys Cure, The, 4:136

MOZART, Wolfgang, 15:94

MUSIC

Alphorn, The, 8:47
Away We Go, 5:69

MUSIC—CONT.

Bells, The, 5:284
Bertram and the Musical Crocodile,
  4:197
Big Music, 8:338
Broken Note, The, 8:294
Canadian Boat-Song, 5:278
Deep Sea Song, 5:150
Elizabeth Eliza's Piano, About, 4:135
Faery Riders, 5:155
First Harp, The, 8:44
Follow the Gleam, 8:293
Gift from the Queen, A, 12:69
Happily Ever After, 5:39
Happy Day, 5:32
Hunting Song, 12:258
If Once You Have Slept on an Island,
  5:188
I Hear America Singing, 5:281
Ironing, 5:16
Island Christmas, An, 6:277
It Was, 5:68
Jam Session at Abbie's, 10:86
Merry-Go-Round, 5:34
Might of a Song, The, 12:331
Morning, 5:180
Most Wonderful Thing in the World,
  The, 10:69
Nightingale, The, 2:358
Piping on Christmas Eve, The, 2:187
Rain, 5:190
Sing, World, Sing!, 5:82
Sleigh Bells at Night, 5:64
Solitary Reaper, The, 5:280
Song at Dusk, 5:252
Splinter, 5:191
Sweet Afton, 5:278
Where Does Music Come From?, 5:181

MUSICIANS
Albert Schweitzer: The Doctor in the Jungle, **15**:256
Georg Handel and the Duke, **15**:76
Ludwig van Beethoven, **15**:328
Marian Anderson: A Voice in a Hundred Years, **15**:293
Wolfgang Mozart, **15**:94

MYSTERY
Adventure at the Toll Bridge, The, **7**:279
Adventure of the Blue Carbuncle, The, **7**:254
Calloway's Code, **7**:245
Case of the Sensational Scent, The, **7**:30
Forgotten Island, **7**:1
Gold Bug, The, **7**:201
Hunter's Moon, **7**:315
Legacy of Canyon John, The, **7**:98
Miss Hinch, **7**:179
Mystery of No. 30, The, **7**:42
Old Houses, **7**:89
One Alaska Night, **7**:297
Red-Headed League, The, **7**:346
Secret of Rainbow Ridge, The, **7**:69
Stalactite Surprise, **7**:61
Strange Pettingill Puzzle, The, **7**:108
Wastwych Secret, The, **7**:49

MYTHS AND LEGENDS
Alphorn, The, **8**:47
Apples of Iduna, The, **8**:226
Ashes That Made Trees Bloom, The, **8**:80
Bellerophon, **8**:93
Broken Note, The, **8**:294
Bucca Boo's Little Merry Men, **8**:1
Capture of the Shen, **8**:300
Children of the Wolf, The, **8**:34
Cuchulain in Shadow-Land, **8**:329
Dobry's New Year, **9**:294
First Harp, The, **8**:44
Golden Fleece, The, **8**:148
Golden Touch, The, **8**:62
Great Hunter of the Woods, The, **8**:103
Great Stone Face, The, **8**:271
How Beowulf Rules the Geats, **8**:97
I Hear Paul Bunyan, **8**:197
John Henry, Mighty Railroader, **8**:26
One You Don't See Coming, The, **8**:56
Pecos Bill and His Bouncing Bride, **8**:115
Phaeton, **8**:144
Rip Van Winkle, **8**:252
Robin Hood Turns Beggar, **8**:205
Roland and His Horn, **8**:355
Son of the South Wind, **8**:86

MYTHS AND LEGENDS—CONT.
Song of King Arthur's Knights, **8**:328
Song of Sherwood, **5**:348
Tale of Sir Gareth, The, **8**:309
Thor's Wonderful Journey, **8**:230
Why the Chipmunk's Back Is Striped, **8**:50

NATURE
Afternoon, **5**:181
All Things Beautiful, **5**:268
Apple Blossoms, **1**:301
April, **5**:179
April Rain, **5**:178
At Night, **5**:187
Autumn Song, **5**:194
Bambi Starts to See the World, **14**:27
Bedtime for a Baby Brook, **5**:193
Being a Gypsy, **5**:5
Chambered Nautilus, The, **5**:287
Cool, **5**:183
Corn in the Shocks, **5**:191
Country Church, **5**:353
Crimson Dawn, The, **5**:277
Daffodils, **5**:272
Dream-Song, **5**:261
Easter in the Woods, **5**:141
Field Flowers, **5**:192
First Snowfall, **5**:199
Fog, **5**:193
George Washington Carver **15**:269
God's World, **5**:343
Good Morning, **5**:1
Grandmother's Brook, **5**:2
Great Craftsman, The, **5**:193
Happiness, **5**:3
Hark! Hark! the Lark!, **5**:272
Henri Fabre, A Place of His Own, **15**:308
Hiawatha's Childhood, **5**:305
Hie Away, Hie Away, **5**:271
High Flight, **5**:352
Home-Thoughts, from Abroad, **5**:274
If Once You Have Slept on an Island, **5**:188

NATURE—CONT.

Indian Song, 5:258
I Never Saw a Moor, 5:182
In from the Sea, 5:192
Inquisitive Barn, 5:197
In the Garden, 5:183
It's Snowing, 5:199
Johnny and the Monarch, 1:260
King Quiet, 5:196
Lake Isle of Innisfree, The, 5:355
Louis Agassiz, 15:354
Loveliest of Trees, 5:357
Ludwig van Beethoven, 15:328
May Morning, 5:180
Miracles, From, 5:195
Mist and All, The, 5:194
Morning, 5:177
Morning, 5:180
Morning Exercises, 5:33
Mountain, The, 5:56
New Snow, 5:197
Night, 5:38
Night, 5:354
Night Will Never Stay, The, 5:185
Nocturne, 5:182
North Country, 5:39
Old Country, 5:5
Planting a Tree, 5:82
Rabbit Tracks, 5:138
Radio Wish, 5:38
Rain, 5:190
Remembering the Winter, 5:195
Rhodora, The, 5:276
Roads, 5:51
Sea-Fever, 5:358
Sea-Shell, 2:251
Sea Song, A, 5:273
Silver, 5:38
Silver Ships, 5:67
Silver Trees, 5:191
Sing Ho!, 5:196
Sing, World, Sing!, 5:82
Sniff, 5:60
Snowbound, 5:308
Snow by Night, 5:21
Snowfall, 6:326
Snowy Morning, 5:195
Something Told the Wild Geese, 5:187

NATURE—CONT.

Song at Dusk, 5:252
Song for a Country Night, 5:125
Song for a Summer Evening, 2:33
Song for Summer, 2:50
Song for Summer, 5:182
Song of Gray Things, 5:184
Star, The, 5:6
Stopping by Woods on a Snowy Evening, 5:357
Summer, 5:185
Sun Is First to Rise, The, 5:179
There Was a Roaring in the Wind, 5:275
To a Very Young Cloud, 5:179
Tree-Children, 5:9
Trees, 5:356
Vision of Sir Launfal, From the, 5:274
West Wind, The, 5:345
Where Does Music Come From?, 5:181
Which?, 5:52
White, 5:184
White Fields, 5:198
Who Has Seen the Wind?, 5:275
Why the Winds Blow, 5:177
Wind, 5:177
Winter Wood, 5:198
Wise, 5:176
World Secrets, 5:3
Year's at the Spring, The, 5:271
NELSON, HORATIO, LORD: Admiral's Ghost, The, 5:338
NEW YEAR'S DAY—see Holidays
NEW ZEALAND—see Many Lands
NIGHT
All through the Night, 5:268
At Night, 5:187
Christmas Eve, 5:75
Eyes Are Lit Up, 5:92
Fawn's First Journey, 5:110
First Night, The, 5:75
Many Moons, 2:1
Night, 5:38
Night, 5:354
Night Prayer for Wild Things, 5:139
Night Will Never Stay, The, 5:185
Nocturne, 5:182
One Alaska Night, 7:297
Shine Star, 5:79
Six Bells, 12:152
Song at Dusk, 5:252
Song for a Country Night, 5:125
Star, The, 5:6
Stopping by Woods on a Snowy Evening, 5:357
Tom Chist and the Treasure Box, 13:247

NIGHT—CONT.
  Trains at Night, 5:40
  Wynken, Blynken, and Nod, 5:262
  Ye Stars, 5:277
NIGHTINGALE—see Birds
NONSENSE—see Humor and Nonsense
OBEDIENCE—see Character
OCELOT—see Animals
OCTOPUS—see Fish and Creatures of the
  Sea
ORIOLES—see Birds
OSTRICH—see Birds
OWL—see Birds
PANTHER—see Animals
PARROTS—see Birds
PASSING OF TIME
  Clarinda, 1869, 6:297
  Fern Tiki, The, 9:332
  Grandmother's Brook, 5:2
  Indian Children Long Ago, 5:90
  In the Garden, 5:183
  Long-Ago Doll, The, 5:37
  Mystery of the Bay, The, 13:190
  Old Coach Road, The, 6:313
  Snow by Night, 5:21
  Still It Is Wilderness, 14:256
  World Secrets, 5:3
PATIENCE—see Character
PATRIOTISM
  Abraham Lincoln's Boyhood, 15:25
  America the Beautiful, From, 9:201
  Ben Franklin's First Adventures, 15:164
  Birthday of Our Land, The, 5:84
  Boot and Saddle, 5:319
  *Breathes There a Man with Soul So
    Dead,* 5:281
  Broken Note, The, 8:294
  Daniel Webster, 15:367
  Dear Land of All My Love, 5:277
  Disperse Ye Rebels, 11:238
  Golden Cup of Kasimir, The, 12:259
  Home-Thoughts, from Abroad, 5:274
  Horseshoe Nails, 11:197
  House of the Singing Windows, 9:191
  I Hear America Singing, 5:281
  Little Red, 13:68
  Message for Washington, A, 11:255
  Our America, 5:83
  Out of Defeat, 12:359
  Patrick Henry Enters Public Life,
    15:337
  Rule of Three, 6:156
  Secret in the Snow, 13:101
  Six Bells, 12:152
  Theodore Roosevelt, 15:288
  Thomas Jefferson, 15:274
  Three-Cornered Hat, The, 11:189

PATRIOTISM—CONT.
  Two Scenes from the Life of George
    Washington, 15:196
  Washington, 5:81
PEACE
  Abraham Lincoln Walks at Midnight,
    5:346
  Jane Addams, 15:320
  Lake Isle of Innisfree, 5:355
  Night, 5:354
  Seal Lullaby, 5:258
  Song at Dusk, 5:252
  West Wind, The, 5:345
PENITENCE—see Character
PERSEVERANCE—see Character
PETS
  Adam to the Rescue, 12:240
  Adolfuss, 5:135
  All Mutt, 6:126
  Angus and the Ducks, 1:49
  Benjamin Jones and His Dogs, 5:238
  Birthdays, 5:55
  Blaze and the Forest Fire, 14:1
  Bobo, 14:13
  Boozer, 5:132
  Case of the Sensational Scent, 7:30
  Cat, 5:103
  Christmas Eve at Reginald's, 6:359
  Chums, 5:102
  Coalie, 5:130
  Crazy Story of Dizzy Lizzie, 4:118
  Cream-Colored Pony, The, 6:242
  Cubby, 14:45
  Denny Puts in His Oar, 10:332
  Dinty—A Husky's Story, 14:176
  Dog, A, 5:123
  Dog's Dog, 14:86
  Don, the Story of a Lion Dog, 14:330
  Dr. Dolittle and the Pushmi-Pullyu,
    4:158
  Dungeon Deep, 12:108
  Field Mouse, 5:139
  Forbidden Island, The, 9:345
  For the Love of a Man, 14:275
  Friendly Pup, The, 5:63

PETS—CONT.

Frisbie Cures the Doctor, 6:71
Gallons of Guppies, 6:17
Ginger on the Fire Escape, 10:1
Good Little Dog, A, 1:178
Gratitude, 5:120
Guppies Are Best, 6:29
Handsome Is, 6:234
Heidi's Adventures on the Mountain, 3:26
Heroism, 5:104
House Cat, The, 5:136
Hunting Old Slew Foot, 14:314
Janie's Wish, 1:296
Johnny Fife and Johnny's Wife, 5:222
Kitten, A, 5:122
Look at the Grand Champ, A, 14:148
Miranda, 5:123
Monkey Spirit, The, 9:140
Mr. Dooley Disgraces His Family, 6:202
Mr. Popper and Captain Cook, 4:30
Mrs. Tabby Gray, 1:210
My Dog, 5:63
My Dog, 5:111
My Dog, 5:120
My Hummingbirds, 14:42
Mysterious Cat, The, 5:97
One Minute Longer, 14:358
Oscar, the Trained Seal, 4:58
Our Burro, 5:115
Pet Show, 5:102
Pirate Don Durk of Dowdee, 5:230
Puppies, 5:127
Puppy Who Wanted a Boy, The, 1:332
Rikki-Tikki-Tavi, 14:257
Sara Crewe, or What Happened at Miss Minchin's, 3:325
Serapina Proves Herself, 4:166
Smoky, 6:104
Song of Grandfather Thomas' Parrot, 5:108
Squeak of Leather, The, 14:211
Street of Memories, 6:1
Tale of Custard, the Dragon, The, 4:1
There Was Tammie, 1:145
Tidy Turtle, 5:47
Tim, 5:51
You Never Saw Such an Egg, 4:270

PICNICS

Boiling the Billy, 9:281
Cake at Midnight, 9:269
Picnic Basket, The, 1:158
Teenie Weenie Picnic, The, 1:132
There Was Tammie, 1:145
Who Goes There?, 14:17

PIGS—see Animals

PIONEER

Abraham Lincoln's Boyhood, 15:25
Alexander Mackenzie: Hero of Canada, 15:153
Apache Warpath, 11:338
Bears of Blue River, The, 11:306
Caddie's Silver Dollar, 11:127
Christmas Horses, 11:111
Daniel Boone, 11:369
Feather of the Northman, The, 11:64
Flower-Fed Buffaloes, The, 14:75
Hasty Pudding, 11:36
In a Covered Wagon, 11:72
Johnny Appleseed's Coat, 11:47
Johnny Appleseed Visits Licking Creek, 11:146
Little Dog Star, The, 11:102
Mary Silver, 11:159
Old Sly Eye, 11:173
Out of Defeat, 12:359
Pathfinders: Lewis and Clark, The, 11:289
Pioneer Wedding, A, 11:314
Ride with Tom Thumb, A, 11:56
River and Beasts Betray, 11:277
Saving of Boonesborough, The, 11:181
Still It Is Wilderness, 14:256
Strangers in the Wilderness, 11:150
Tomorrow Will Be Bright, 11:26
Tooth of the Great One, 11:346
Western Wagons, 11:82
Willow Basket, The, 11:93
With the Forest Runners, 11:295

PIRATES

If I Were a One-Legged Pirate, 5:214
Lancelot Biggs on the Saturn, 16:70
Peaceful Pirate, The, 1:172
Peter Pan and Captain Hook, 2:225
Pirate, The, 5:54
Pirate Don Durk of Dowdee, 5:230
Purple-Eyed Pirate, The, 5:202
Reformed Pirate, The, 2:322
Secret Cavern, The, 5:66
Sir Peter Bombazoo, 4:358

PIRATES—CONT.

Tom Chist and the Treasure Box, 13:247

When Mark Twain Was a Boy, 15:43

PIXIES—see Elves, Dwarfs, Gnomes, Pixies

POLITENESS—see Character

POOKAS—see Leprechauns and Pookas

PRINCES AND ROYAL FAMILY

Broken Note, The, 8:294

Children of the Wolf, The, 8:34

Cinderella, 2:165

Dippy, The, 2:94

First Harp, The, 8:44

Gift from the Queen, A, 12:69

Glass Hill, The, 2:44

Glove and the Lions, The, 12:347

Golden Fleece, The, 8:148

Golden Touch, The, 8:62

Happy Prince, The, 2:346

How Beowulf Rules the Geats, 8:97

King of the Golden River, The, 3:231

King of the Wind and the Queen's Plate, 14:123

King's Breakfast, The, 1:44

King's Cygnet, The, 12:99

King's Daughter, 15:33

King's Wish, The, 4:24

Last of the Dragons, The, 2:11

Magic Fishbone, 4:38

Man with the Bag, The, 2:171

Many Moons, 2:1

Nightingale, The, 2:358

On Kublai Khan's Service, 12:313

Queen of the Orkney Islands, The, 4:100

Rocking-Horse Land, 1:302

Roland and His Horn, 8:355

Sleeping Beauty, The, 2:289

Story of Aladdin; or, the Wonderful Lamp, The, 2:293

Stranger in the Wood, The, 12:169

Swan Maiden, The, 2:178

Tale of Sir Gareth, The, 8:309

PRINCESSES—see Princes and Royal Family

PUFFIN—see Birds

PYLE, HOWARD: Howard Pyle: Great American Illustrator, 15:348

QUEENS—see Princes and Royal Family

RABBITS—see Animals

RACCOONS—see Animals

RAIN

April Rain, 5:178

Attic Trunk, 5:36

Cross-Stitch Sampler, 5:57

Mist and All, The, 5:194

Mrs. Goose's Rubbers, 4:15

Playhouse Key, The, 5:35

RAIN—CONT.

Rain, 5:190

Rain Toys, The, 5:190

Rainy Day, 5:133

Rainy Day, 5:188

Spring Rain, 5:14

RAT—see Animals

READING, LOVE OF

Abraham Lincoln's Boyhood, 15:25

Adventure at the Toll Bridge, The, 7:279

Baedeker Boy, The, 9:116

Ben Franklin's First Adventures, 15:164

Early Days with Invincible Louisa, 15:130

Fisherman's Luck, 12:348

Forgotten Island, 7:1

Happily Ever After, 5:39

Happy Day, 5:32

Hasty Pudding, 11:36

Journey with Dickens, A, 15:106

Lincoln, 5:80

Macdonald Plaid, 4:136

Naturally Enough, 5:164

Parchment Door, The, 12:140

Rebecca at the Brick House, 3:203

Sara Crewe, or What Happened at Miss Minchin's, 3:325

Story Hour, 6:95

REGIONAL

East: Adventure in a Chimney, 12:14

Ben Franklin's First Adventures, 15:164

Christmas Horses, 11:111

Daniel Webster, 15:367

Forgotten Island, 7:1

Fox and Geese, 11:10

Guides with Wings, 13:228

Hasty Pudding, 11:36

Henry Wadsworth Longfellow, 15:237

REGIONAL, EAST—CONT.

Howard Pyle: Great American Illustrator, 15:348
Island Christmas, 6:277
Jo Meets Laurie, 3:138
Journey with Dickens, A, 15:106
Mahogany Fox, The, 14:290
Miss Hinch, 7:179
Old Houses, 7:89
Oliver at the Circus, 13:26
Randy at the Art Gallery, 6:211
Rebecca at the Brick House, 3:203
Steelman's Nerve, 13:144
Strangers in the Wilderness, 11:150
Street of Memories, 6:1
Tom Chist and the Treasure Box, 13:247
Unexpected Christmas, 3:113
Midwest: Abraham Lincoln's Boyhood, 15:25
Bears of Blue River, The, 11:306
Boy Who Voted for Abe Lincoln, The, 11:83
Caddie's Silver Dollar, 11:127
Christmas Horses, 11:111
Cub Pilot on the River, 11:321
Glorious Whitewasher and His Friends, The, 3:1
Jane Addams, 15:320
Johnny Appleseed's Coat, 11:47
Johnny Appleseed Visits Licking Creek, 11:146
Little Dog Star, The, 11:102
Ride with Tom Thumb, A, 11:56
Saving of Boonesborough, The, 11:181
Tom and Becky in the Cave, 3:308
Tomorrow Will Be Bright, 11:26
Waino and Ivar Meet Honk the Moose, 6:65
When Mark Twain Was a Boy, 15:43
Willow Basket, The, 11:93
With the Forest Runners, 11:295
Northwest: Feather of the Northman, The, 11:64
Koyo, the Singer, 14:98
South: Alligator up the Bayou, 13:60
Down, Down the Mountain, 1:108
George Washington Carver, 15:269
Helen Keller, 15:81
My Struggle for an Education, 15:211
Patrick Henry Enters Public Life, 15:337
Robert E. Lee, 15:176
Story Hour, 6:95
Thomas Jefferson, 15:274

REGIONAL, SOUTH—CONT.

Tooth of the Great One, 11:346
Whitey and the Rustlers, 13:16
Southwest: Apache Warpath, 11:338
Burro Bells in the Moonlight, 14:115
Carca, 14:136
Cubby, 14:45
Desirable Shawl, The, 9:14
Legacy of Canyon John, 7:98
Silver Belt, The, 9:110
Tungwa, 9:180
West: Adventure at the Toll Bridge, The, 7:279
Coaly-Bay, the Outlaw Horse, 14:305
Don, the Story of a Lion Dog, 14:330
Mystery of the Bay, The, 13:190
Pack Rat, The, 14:50
Pathfinders: Lewis and Clark, The, 11:289
River and Beasts Betray, 11:277
Smoky, 6:104
Touch of Arab, A, 13:178
Trail-Makers, 14:301
REINDEER—see Animals
REPTILES
Alligators: Alligator up the Bayou, 13:60
Lizards: Lizard, The, 5:115
Snakes: Bim's Gift from the Forest, 9:150
Elephant's Child, The, 4:4
Rikki-Tikki-Tavi: 14:257
White Flag, 14:239
Turtles: Little Turtle, The, 5:95
Tidy Turtle, 5:47
REVERENCE
Abraham Lincoln's Boyhood, 15:25
Abou Ben Adhem, 5:328
Adventure in Candle Street, 12:179
Albert Schweitzer: The Doctor in the Jungle, 15:256
All Things Beautiful, 5:268
All through the Night, 1:360
All through the Night, 5:268
America the Beautiful, From, 9:201
Cake for Company Dinner, 4:185
Canticle of the Sun, 5:354
Child's Prayer, 5:266
Child's Prayer for Other Children, 5:270
Christmas Eve, 5:75
Christmas Gifts, 5:74
Christmas in the Woods, 5:77
Christmas Morning, 5:70
Christmas Path, The, 6:16
Christmas Song, 5:76
Christmas Song, 11:126

367

REVERENCE—CONT.
Country Church, 5:353
Cradle Hymn, 5:255
Dantès' Escape from the Château D'If, 13:291
Easter in the Woods, 5:141
Elizabeth Eliza's Piano, About, 4:135
Ever Very Near, 5:75
Eyes Are Lit Up, 5:92
Farmers, 5:126
Field Flowers, 5:192
First Night, The, 5:75
First Thanksgiving of All, 5:89
Gentle Jesus, Meek and Mild, 5:267
God Is Like This, 5:269
God's World, 5:343
Great Craftsman, The, 5:193
Great Stone Face, The, 8:271
Happy Prince, The, 2:346
Heidi's Adventures on the Mountain, 3:26
He Prayeth Best, 5:266
He Whom a Dream Hath Possessed, 5:352
High Flight, 5:352
House the Pecks Built, The, 4:18
I'm Wishing the Whole World Christmas, 5:73
In Church, 5:266
I Never Saw a Moor, 5:182
Lady Who Put Salt in Her Coffee, The, 4:262
Littlest Angel, The, 1:350
Long, Long Ago, 5:71
Ludwig van Beethoven, 15:328
Magic Fishbone, 4:38
Marian Anderson: A Voice in a Hundred Years, 15:293
Might of a Song, The, 12:331
Mountain, The, 5:56
My Gift, 5:74
Mystery—and the Race, 3:261
New York to Paris, 15:246
Night Prayer for Wild Things, 5:139
On the Mayflower, 11:1
Rebecca at the Brick House, 3:203

REVERENCE—CONT.
Recessional, 5:288
Robinson Crusoe Is Shipwrecked, 3:153
Rocky Mountain Sheep, The, 14:371
Selfish Giant, The, 2:316
Shepherd Left Behind, The, 5:72
Shine, Star, 5:79
Sleep, Baby, Sleep, 5:266
Something Told the Wild Geese, 5:187
Song of King Arthur's Knights, 8:328
Strange Holiness, 5:350
Thanksgiving, 5:90
Thank You, Lord, 5:265
Thomas Alva Edison, 15:117
Trees, 5:356
Unexpected Christmas, 3:113
Upon Westminster Bridge, 5:276
Winter Wood, 5:198
We Give Our Thanks, 5:265
Willow Basket, The, 11:93
Wise, 5:176
Year's at the Spring, The, 5:271
Ye Stars, 5:277
RHEA—see Birds
RHINOCEROS—see Animals
ROOSEVELT, THEODORE
Buffalo Hunting, 11:357
Theodore Roosevelt, 15:288
SANDPIPERS—see Birds
SCHOOL LIFE
Adventure in Candle Street, 12:179
Anybody Can Ski, 10:95
Basketball Mystery, The, 10:32
Beauty's Sister, 10:125
Big Moment, 10:185
First Day of School, The, 4:146
Ginger on the Fire Escape, 10:1
"Hoot!" Said the Owl, 10:110
Most Wonderful Thing in the World, The, 10:69
Prize, The, 10:48
Sara Crewe, 3:325
Third Round, The, 10:199
Yogi's Dark Horse, 10:361
SCHWEITZER, Albert: The Doctor in the Jungle, 15:256
SCIENCE FICTION
Adventure on Mars, 16:20
Black Pits of Luna, The, 16:115
Lancelot Biggs on the Saturn, 16:70
Mars and Miss Pickerell, 16:36
Star Ducks, The, 16:59
What Time Is It?, 16:1
SEA
Ballad of the Oysterman, 5:282
Chambered Nautilus, The, 5:287
Columbus, 5:84

SEA—CONT.
Down in Davy Jones' Locker, **13**:334
False Summer, **6**:314
Farmer of Paimpol, **9**:7
Forty Singing Seamen, **5**:334
In from the Sea, **5**:192
Letters from the Sea, **2**:64
Life on the Ocean Wave, A, **12**:272
Minnie the Mermaid, **1**:35
Nautical Ballad, A, **4**:164
Nautical Extravaganza, A, **4**:267
On the Mayflower, **11**:1
Otto at Sea, **1**:181
Pearl Diver, The, **13**:347
Robinson Crusoe Is Shipwrecked, **3**:153
Sea Child, **5**:167
Sea-Fever, **5**:358
Sea Gull, The, **5**:108
Sea Horse, The, **5**:24
Seal Lullaby, **5**:258
Sea-Shell, **2**:251
Seashore Gossip, **5**:117
Sea Song, A, **5**:273
SEA GULLS—see Birds
SEA HORSE—see Fish and Creatures of the Sea
SEALS—see Fish and Creatures of the Sea
SELF-SACRIFICE—see Character: Heroism, Unselfishness
SELFISHNESS—see Character: Unselfishness
SELF-RELIANCE—see Character
SERVICE—see Character
SHAKESPEARE, WILLIAM
Cuckoo in the Nest, The, **12**:1
Fisherman's Luck, **12**:348
Life of William Shakespeare, A, **15**:222
Shakespeare, **15**:236
SHARK—see Fish and Creatures of the Sea
SKUNK—see Animals
SNAILS—see Animals
SNAKES—see Reptiles
SNOW
Anybody Can Ski, **10**:95
Bridget on Fortune's Trail, **14**:55

SNOW—CONT.
Bunny, The, **5**:196
Clarinda, 1869, **6**:297
Cutter Race, The, **10**:301
First Christmas Tree, The, **2**:51
First Snowfall, **5**:195
Inquisitive Barn, **5**:197
It's Snowing!, **5**:199
King Quiet, **5**:196
Little Bear Takes His Nap, **1**:224
Little Dog Star, **11**:102
New Snow, **5**:197
Remembering the Winter, **5**:195
Sammy Snowman, **5**:64
Secret in the Snow, **13**:101
Sing Ho!, **5**:196
Snowbound, **5**:308
Snow by Night, **5**:21
Snowfall, **6**:326
Snowflake Fun, **5**:170
Snowy Morning, **5**:195
Stopping by Woods on a Snowy Evening, **5**:357
White Fields, **5**:198
Winterbound Adventure, A, **6**:327
Winter Wood, **5**:198
SOUTHWEST—see Regional
SPORTS
Anybody Can Ski, **10**:95
At the Boar Hunt, **12**:61
Basketball Mystery, The, **10**:32
Bears of Blue River, The, **11**:306
Black Stallion's Race, The, **14**:162
Casey at the Bat, **5**:332
Clutch Man, **10**:251
Cutter Race, The, **10**:301
Denny Puts in His Oar, **10**:332
Fisherman's Luck, **12**:348
Gawk, The, **10**:168
Going Up!, **9**:215
Hit or Error?, **10**:143
Holiday Cup, The, **10**:18
Hoop Hokum, **10**:236
Horse Mackerel, **10**:79
Hunting Old Slew Foot, **14**:314
Hunting Song, **12**:258
I Caught a Fish, **5**:68
Iceboat Race, The, **10**:60
Josie's Home Run, **10**:40
King of the Wind and the Queen's Plate, **14**:123
Knights of the Red Rose, **10**:269
Little Guy, The, **10**:286
Mahogany Fox, The, **14**:290
Marshall at Bat, **10**:313
Master Mind, **10**:220
My New Roller Skates, **5**:47

SPORTS—CONT.
Mystery and the Race, 3:261
Pass, The, 10:350
Rococo Skates, 6:30
Skating, 5:65
Third of June on Annapurna, The, 13:322
Third Round, The, 10:199
Two-Mile Race, 10:321

SPRING
Apple Blossoms, 1:301
April, 5:179
April Rain, 5:178
Brown Bear, The, 5:112
Daffodils, 5:272
Home-Thoughts, from Abroad, 5:274
In Grandmother's Garden, 5:180
Jonathan Bing Dances for Spring, 5:200
Mockingbird, The, 5:107
Morning, 5:180
Rhodora, The, 5:276
Robin Hood Turns Beggar, 8:205
Selfish Giant, The, 2:316
Spring Pastures, 5:100
Spring Rain, 5:14
Spring Signs, 5:50
Tamed, 5:178
There Was a Roaring in the Wind, 5:275
West Wind, The, 5:345
Year's at the Spring, The, 5:271

STARS
About Christmas, 5:76
All through the Night, 5:268
Christmas Eve, 5:75
Christmas Gifts, 5:74
Crimson Dawn, The, 5:277
Dream-Song, 5:261
First Night, The, 5:75
Indian Song, 5:258
Little Dog Star, The, 11:102
Littlest Angel, The, 1:350
Night Will Never Stay, The, 5:185
Nocturne, 5:182
Radio Wish, 5:38
Shepherd Left Behind, The, 5:72

STARS—CONT.
Shine, Star, 5:79
Star, The, 5:6
Wynken, Blyken, and Nod, 5:262
Ye Stars, 5:277

STEVENSON, Robert Louis, 15:206

STORY POEMS
Abou Ben Adhem, 5:328
Abraham Lincoln Walks at Midnight, 5:346
Admiral's Ghost, The, 5:338
Ballad of the Oysterman, 5:282
Boot and Saddle, 5:319
Casey at the Bat, 5:332
Cremation of Sam McGee, The, 5:329
Forty Singing Seamen, 5:334
Glove and the Lions, The, 12:347
Hiawatha's Childhood, 5:305
Highwayman, The, 5:289
How They Brought the Good News from Ghent to Aix, 5:320
Jest 'Fore Christmas, 5:312
King's Breakfast, The, 1:44
Lady Clare, 5:322
Listeners, The, 5:344
Little Orphant Annie, 5:310
Lochinvar, 5:316
Maid of Timbuctoo, The, 5:207
Mishaps of Gentle Jane, The, 5:216
Pied Piper of Hamelin, The, 5:294
Pirate Don Durk of Dowdee, 5:230
Raggedy Man, The, 5:311
Robin Hood and Allen-A-Dale, 5:325
Song of Sherwood, A, 5:348
Village Blacksmith, The, 5:315

SUMMER
Afternoon, 5:181
Cool, 5:183
Nocturne, 5:182
Small Homes, 5:115
Song for Summer, 5:182
Song of the Herd, 5:101
Summer, 5:185

SWALLOWS—see Birds
SWANS—see Birds

SWITZERLAND—see Many Lands
TALL TALES
  Big Music, 8:338
  Great Hunter of the Woods, The, 8:103
  John Henry, Mighty Railroader, 8:26
  Pecos Bill and His Bouncing Bride, 8:115
TAPIR—see Animals
THANKSGIVING—see Holidays
THOROUGHNESS—see Character: Industry
THOUGHTFULNESS—see Character: Kindness
THOUGHTS
  At Night, 5:187
  Barter, 5:351
  Canticle of the Sun, 5:354
  Country Church, 5:353
  God's World, 5:343
  He Whom a Dream Hath Possessed, 5:352
  High Flight, 5:352
  Lake Isle of Innisfree, The, 5:355
  Night, 5:354
  Night Will Never Stay, The, 5:185

  Reflection, 5:43
  Stopping by Woods on a Snowy Evening, 5:357
  Strange Holiness, 5:350
  Walk on the Rainbow Trail, 9:190
  World Secrets, 5:3
TIGER—see Animals
TITIAN'S First Picture, 15:56
TOADS—see Animals
TOLERANCE—see Character: Friendliness
TOYS—also see Dolls
  Acorns, 5:34
  Balloon, 5:62
  Duel, The, 5:219
  Funny Thing, The, 1:90
  Good Little Dog, A, 1:178
  Hitty's Shipwreck, 12:81
  Hollow Tree House, The, 5:59
  In Which Eeyore Has a Birthday and Gets Two Presents, 1:186
  Long-Ago Doll, The, 5:37
  Magic Glass, The, 4:65
  Muggins Mouse at the Seashore, 1:240
  My Teddy Bear, 5:33
  Over the Garden Wall, 5:2
  Pale Pink Tea, The, 5:242

TOYS—CONT.
  Pirate, The, 5:54
  Present, The, 5:19
  Rain Toys, The, 5:190
  Rainy Day, 5:133
  Rock-A-By Lady, The, 5:255
  Rocking-Horse Land, 1:302
  Self-Control, 5:61
  Story of Dobbin, The, 1:244
  Teddy Bear Dance, 5:158
  Valentine to My Doll, 5:81
  Velveteen Rabbit, 1:1
  Won't-Pick-Up-Toys Cure, The, 4:136
TRAINS
  Journey with Dickens, A, 15:106
  Little Steam Engine, The, 1:247
  On the Train, 5:50
  Ride with Tom Thumb, A, 11:56
  Texas Trains and Trails, 5:26
  Trains, 5:44
  Trains at Night, 5:40
  Travel, 5:356
TREES
  Apple Blossoms, 1:301
  Apple Rhyme, The, 5:172
  Elephant in the Cinnamon Tree, The, 5:206
  Loveliest of Trees, 5:357
  May Morning, 5:180
  Mexican Palm, 5:46
  Morning Exercises, 5:33
  North Country, 5:39
  Pine Tree Song, 5:73
  Planting a Tree, 5:82
  Secret Place, The, 5:17
  Silver Trees, 5:191
  Stopping by Woods on a Snowy Evening, 5:357
  Tree-Children, 5:9
  Tree House, 5:163
  Trees, 5:356
  Winter Wood, 5:198
TURTLES—see Reptiles
TWINS
  Children of the Wolf, The, 8:34
  Eskimo Twins Go Coasting, The, 9:20
  Josie's Home Run, 10:40
  Kit and Kat Go Fishing, 1:75
  Twin Seals, 1:84

UNSELFISHNESS—see Character
VAGABONDING
Being a Gypsy, 5:5
Caravan, The, 5:54
Life on the Ocean Wave, A, 12:272
Roads, 5:51
Robin Hood and the Shooting Match, 12:227
Sea-Fever, 5:358
Singing Saucepan, The, 9:65
Sniff, 5:60
Vagabond, The, 5:318
West Wind, The, 5:345
VALENTINE'S DAY—see Holidays
VAN DYCK, Antonio, and His Master Rubens, 15:88
VINCI, Leonardo da, 15:325
WALRUS—see Animals
WASHINGTON, BOOKER T.: My Struggle for an Education, 15:211
WASHINGTON, GEORGE
Message for Washington, A, 11:255
Out of Defeat, 12:359
Strangers in the Wilderness, 11:150
Two Scenes from the Life of George Washington, 15:196
Washington, 5:81
WASHINGTON'S BIRTHDAY—see Holidays
WEBSTER, Daniel, 15:367
WEST, BENJAMIN: Benny and the Cat's Tail, 15:62
WEST INDIES—see Many Lands
WHALES—see Fish and Creatures of the Sea
WIND
False Summer, 6:314
Happiness, 5:3
Tamed, 5:178
There Was a Roaring in the Wind, 5:275
West Wind, The, 5:345
Who Has Seen the Wind?, 5:275
Why the Winds Blow, 5:177
Wind, 5:177
Wind Elves, 5:171
WINTER
Cross-Stitch Sampler, 5:57
First Snowfall, 5:195
It's Snowing!, 5:199
King Quiet, 5:196
Looking In, 5:16
New Snow, 5:197
Remembering the Winter, 5:195
Sing Ho!, 5:196
Skating, 5:65
Sleigh Bells at Night, 5:64
Snowbound, 5:30

WINTER—CONT.
Snow by Night, 5:21
Snowy Morning, 5:195
White Fields, 5:198
Winterbound Adventure, A, 6:327
Winter Wood, 5:198
WISHING AND PRETENDING
Ardan's Pooka, 2:89
Ashes That Made Trees Bloom, The, 8:80
Augusta Goose, 1:67
Being a Gypsy, 5:5
Bellerophon, 8:93
Birthdays, 5:55
Bucca Boo's Little Merry Men, 8:1
Caravan, The, 5:54
Child and the Fairies, The, 5:175
Choosing Shoes, 5:18
Cinderella, 2:165
Cuchulain in Shadow-Land, 8:329
Deep Sea Song, 5:150
Down, Down the Mountain, 1:108
Elf, The, 2:127
Emperor's New Clothes, The, 2:258
Fisherman and His Wife, The, 2:133
General Store, 5:61
Golden Fleece, The, 8:148
Golden Touch, The, 8:62
Good Little Dog, A, 1:178
Great Hunter of the Woods, The, 8:103
Great Quillow, The, 2:195
Great Stone Face, The, 8:271
Happy Hen, The, 1:162
Horse Who Lived Upstairs, The, 1:173
House of the Singing Windows, 9:191
I Can Be a Tiger, 5:24
If I Were Otherwise, 5:52
If I Were Thumbelina, 2:88
If Only, 5:25
I Wish I Lived in Elfland, 5:152
Janie's Wish, 1:296
John Henry, Mighty Railroader, 8:26
King's Breakfast, The, 1:44
King's Wish, The, 4:24
Little Dragon, The, 2:142
Little Snow-White, 2:269
Little Steam Engine, The, 1:247
Littlest Angel, The, 1:350

WISHING AND PRETENDING—CONT.
Littlest Reindeer, The, 1:58
Lost Merbaby, The, 1:272
Many Moons, 2:1
McElligot's Pool, 1:323
Mrs. Brown, 5:29
My Plan, 5:15
One You Don't See Coming, The, 8:56
Patsy and the Leprechaun, 2:109
Phaeton, 8:144
Piping on Christmas Eve, The, 2:187
Pirate, The, 5:54
Pixie, Dixie, Trixie, and Nixie, 1:206
Puppy Who Wanted a Boy, The, 1:332
Radio Wish, 5:38
Ranger Wishes, 5:45
Reformed Pirate, The, 2:322
Sara Crewe, or What Happened at Miss Minchin's, 3:325
Sea-Fever, 5:358
Secret Cavern, The, 5:66
Skeleton Windmill, The, 9:127
Sleeping Beauty, The, 2:289
Story of Aladdin; or, The Wonderful Lamp, 2:293
Tale of Sir Gareth, The, 8:309
Three Golden Oranges, 8:188
Three Wishes, The, 2:99
Tommy the Tugboat, 1:228
Travel, 5:356
Tree-Children, 5:9
Ugly Duckling, The, 2:149
Vagabond, The, 5:318
Velveteen Rabbit, The, 1:1
What I Would Do, 5:9
Why the Chipmunk's Back Is Striped, 8:50
Wishes, 5:57

WITCHES, WIZARDS, GOBLINS
Goblin Gadgets, 5:88
Halloween, 5:88
King's Wish, The, 4:24
Little Orphant Annie, 5:310
Little Snow-White, 2:269
Many Moons, 2:1
Reformed Pirate, The, 2:322
Sleeping Beauty, The, 2:289
Swan Maiden, The, 2:178
Tale of Three Tails, A, 8:241
Three Golden Oranges, 1:188
Three Little Witches, 5:86
Witch Cat, 5:87
Witch of Willowby Wood, The, 5:162
WOLVES—see Animals
WOODCHUCK—see Animals
WOODPECKER—see Birds
WORSHIP—see Reverence
WREN—see Birds
WRIGHT BROTHERS, The, 15:158
WRITERS
Ben Franklin's First Adventures, 15:164
Charles Dickens: The Boy of the London Streets, 15:100
Early Days with Invincible Louisa, 15:130
Henry Wadsworth Longfellow, 15:237
Lewis Carroll, 15:8
Life of William Shakespeare, A, 15:222
Robert Louis Stevenson, 15:206
When Mark Twain Was a Boy, 15:43
YAK—see Animals
ZEBRA—see Animals
ZOO
At the Zoo, 5:49
Boy Who Owned an Elephant, The, 1:285
Curious George, 1:53

373

ILLUSTRATORS FOR THE CHILDREN'S HOUR

ANDERSON, C. W., 14:1

AYER, MARGARET, 15:33

BACHARACH, H. I., 4:262

BAHNC, SALCIA, 9:96; 11:264

BENNETT, JUANITA, 5:263, 267

BIANCA, 1:67; 2:149

BIERS, CLARENCE, 1:150, 228, 247, 332; 2:121; 4:58, 102, 197; 5:x, 1, 3, 8, 19, 58, 98, 142, 143, 164, 165, 176, 269, 279; 9:49, 127, 140, 191; 10:236; 12:1, 169; 15:76, 94

BIRCH, REGINALD, 12:69

BJORKLUND, LORENCE, 10:301; 11:173, 277; 14:227, 330

BONNARD, CECILE, 5:121

BREUER, MATILDA, 4:136; 6:1, 95, 242; 9:116, 171; 10:212; 11:1, 111; 12:108, 292; 13:8, 51; 14:148; 15:211, 293

BROCK, C. E., 8:36, 68, 292; 12:294, 358; 15:134

BROCK, H. M., 8:100, 260, 356

BRYAN, MARGUERITE, 1:145, 206

BUEHRIG, ROSEMARY, 1:285; 4:14, 70, 100, 134, 234, 235; 5:204, 205, 232, 233, 244, 245, 262; 8:201; 9:294

BURNE, HARRY H. A., 9:320; 14:76, 184

BUSONI, RAFAELLO, 12:273; 15:176

CAMPBELL, ELEANOR, 13:38

CARROLL, BETTY, 1:250

CHAPMAN, FREDERICK, 11:64, 338

CHOATE, FLORENCE, 12:14

CHUTE, MARCHETTE, 5:12, 13, 15, 28, 45, 50, 51, 55, 63, 68, 69

CRANE, DONN P., 2:34; 8:144; 14:176, 301

CREDLE, ELLIS, 1:108

DARLING, LOUIS, 6:17, 177

DAVIDOW, ANN, 14:50, 251; 16:132

DAVIS, MARGUERITE, 3:26; 6:156, 359; 9:215; 10:18

DE ANGELI, MARGUERITE, 7:49; 12:26

DE BRUNHOFF, JEAN, 1:100

DENNIS, WESLEY, 14:123, 162

DERWINSKI, BEATRICE, 4:146

DOANE, PELAGIE, 5:6, 38, 70; 15:237

DONAHEY, WILLIAM, 1:132, 137

DU BOIS, WILLIAM PÈNE, 1:181

DUVOISIN, ROGER, 8:47; 15:12

EADIE, ELEANOR OSBORNE, 6:104; 9:332

ECKART, FRANCES, 1:172, 173; 2:133, 258; 4:145, 162, 262; 5:7, 48, 84, 90, 105, 282, 283; 6:267; 8:86, 198; 9:65; 12:69; 14:194; 15:51

ELGIN, JILL, 2:322; 6:277

ELSTAD, RUDOLPH, 14:239

ERNST, CLARA, 2:128, 316

EVANS, KATHERINE, 1:350

EVERS, HELEN, 1:72, 97, 162; 4:18, 52

FIELD, RACHEL, 5:188

FINK, BOB, 10:220, 269; 13:134

FITZGERALD, BARBARA, 2:109; 3:26; 5:152, 153, 156

FLEISHMAN, SEYMOUR, 4:270; 6:30; 10:110, 361; 16:21

FOSTER, GENEVIEVE, 6:115; 7:108

FRANCIS, J. G., 1:311

FRAZEE, HAZEL, 1:234; 9:307

FRIEND, ESTHER, 1:210; 2:11, 218; 4:94; 5:9, 77, 147, 158, 220, 248, 252, 257, 258, 259, 310; 6:89; 9:1; 12:81; 14:27; 15:8

FROMMHOLZ, HILDA, 10:125, 321; 13:200; 15:81

FROST, A. B., 8:20

GÁG, FLAVIA, 6:52

GÁG, WANDA, 1:90; 2:269

GALDONE, PAUL, 16:47

GEE, JOHN, 1:240, 269, 312; 2:94; 4:47; 5:72, 74, 145, 207, 212, 213, 215, 219, 222, 223, 226, 228, 229; 8:39; 15:1, 56, 88

GELLER, TODROS, 5:251

GIRAUD, DENISE, 5:17, 30, 43, 61, 128, 159, 160; 15:244

GLANZMAN, LOUIS, 13:94

GRAMATKY, HARDIE, 1:200; 2:195; 10:286; 12:259; 13:68, 101, 322; 15:117, 256; 16:1, 36

HADDOW, JAMES MURRAY, 3:1

HADER, BERTA, 14:55

HADER, ELMER, 14:55

HAGGANDER, SYLVIA, 9:269; 10:32, 86, 185

HAMLIN, PAUL, 5:314

HEILBRON, I., 7:245; 9:14, 110; 11:83

HOGAN, INEZ, 1:84

HOLLAND, JANICE, 6:37

HOOPES, FLORENCE, 6:78, 193; 7:89

HOOPES, MARGARET, 6:78, 193; 7:89

HUNTER, FRANCES TIPTON, 5:102, 270

HURFORD, MIRIAM, 1:178

JAMES, WILL, 14:211

JAQUES, FRANCIS LEE, 14:202

JAYNE, DeWITT WHISTLER, 12:152, 331; 13:247, 291, 302; 14:86, 116; 15:164, 337

JONES, ELIZABETH ORTON, 1:1, 35; 5:134, 166, 264; 14:13

KEY, ALEXANDER, 2:280; 11:102, 150, 359; 13:60; 15:158, 189

KLEP, ROLF, 15:74

KREDEL, FRITZ, 3:231

LATHROP, DOROTHY, 2:89; 5:21, 92, 93, 140, 141, 154, 155, 187, 260, 261; 12:99; 14:17, 81

LAWSON, MARIE, 2:40, 90, 252, 264, 289; 12:52

LAWSON, ROBERT, 2:142, 171, 187; 4:30; 5:246, 247; 12:240

LEHMAN, MAHREA CRAMER, 5:122

LEITZ, JOAN, 5:4, 18, 35, 316

LILSTROM, STAN, 7:245

LOFTING, HUGH, 1:119; 4:118, 158, 210

LOUDEN, CLAIRE, 8:226

LOUDEN, GEORGE, 8:226

LOVELACE, KAY, 3:93; 4:248; 7:297; 8:329; 9:253, 294; 11:189; 12:140, 301; 13:228; 15:308, 320

MALVERN, CORRINE, 7:1

MASTRI, FIORE, 1:260; 9:36

MAYNARD, BARBARA, 11:47, 146

McCLOSKEY, ROBERT, 4:238, 360; 7:30; 8:115

McKEE, JOHN DUKES, 5:57, 118, 119, 168, 169, 209, 216, 221, 224, 225, 234, 235, 238, 239, 345, 353, 355; 8:1, 50, 103, 205; 11:20, 238, 306, 369; 12:227; 15:196; 16:70, 102

MERRYWEATHER, JOHN, 4:111, 164, 236, 267, 358; 5:289, 290, 293, 305, 306, 307, 319, 320, 324, 336, 338, 341, 347, 348, 349, 359; 8:26, 129, 241; 12:272; 13:144, 334; 14:305; 15:274, 288, 315, 332, 367; 16:134

MERWIN, DECIE, 1:272; 5:36, 37, 60, 62, 167, 180, 253; 8:44; 12:179; 15:100, 106

MILLER, MARY, 4:135

MORSE, DOROTHY BAILEY, 10:332; 13:125

MORTON, ELISE, 2:44, 165

NEWELL, DAVID M., 14:45

PALAZZO, TONY, 4:166

PAULL, GRACE, 1:71

PECK, GLADYS, 6:104; 9:332; 14:275

PERKINS, LUCY FITCH, 1:75; 9:20

PETERSHAM, MAUD, 5:78, 79, 106; 8:252

PETERSHAM, MISKA, 5:78, 79, 106; 8:252

PITZ, HENRY C., 2:293, 346; 7:315; 8:309, 355; 11:181, 197; 13:278; 15:153, 328

PONTER, JAMES, 3:113, 138; 10:199, 313; 11:159, 229, 314; 15:25, 130

POWELL, JAMES D., 8:164, 228

PRICKETT, HELEN, 6:327; 7:69; 8:17, 34, 56, 62; 9:7, 202, 281; 10:69; 12:355; 13:178; 15:264

PYLE, HOWARD, 15:348

RACKHAM, ARTHUR, 2:258

RADER, EVELINE, 5:89, 109, 117, 272

REY, H. A., 1:53

RICHARDS, GEORGE, 4:283

RODERICK, JACK, 11:255, 289

ROGNAN, LLOYD NORMAN, 10:251

ROSS, JANET, 4:185; 11:56

ROUNDS, GLEN, 13:16

ROUSSEFF, MINNIE, 4:24, 65

RUTH, ROD, 10:168; 13:1, 158; 14:136; 15:269

SABEL, WALTER R., 3:308; 5:326, 332; 7:179; 8:97, 230, 271; 10:95, 143; 11:295; 13:315; 15:43

ST. JOHN, J. ALLEN, 7:254, 346

SCOTT, JANET LAURA, 9:58; 11:10

375

SEREDY, KATE, 9:76; 13:80

SEUSS, DR. (Theodore S. Geisel), 1:16, 323

SEWELL, HELEN, 1:360

SHEPARD, ERNEST H., 1:44, 186; 2:20

SHORT, DOROTHY, 1:264; 2:178; 3:261

SINNOTT, ROBERT, 5:87, 199, 343, 356; 7:98, 201; 8:80, 93, 148, 188, 330; 11:321, 357; 12:313; 13:190, 347; 14:64, 98; 15:222, 325

SLOBODKIN, LOUIS, 2:1

SMALLEY, JANET, 1:296; 3:325; 4:217; 6:42, 59, 137, 211, 297; 10:40; 11:93, 127; 13:26

SMITH, EUNICE YOUNG, 10:48; 11:26

SMITH, JESSIE WILCOX, 3:138

SMYTHE, WILLARD, 5:83

SNIDER, SUZIE, 5:22, 47, 53, 64, 65, 81, 103, 171, 185, 191, 194, 195, 217, 223; 14:161

SPERRY, ARMSTRONG, 6:314; 9:345; 13:354

STOAKS, CAROL, 7:61; 9:29; 11:72

STOSSEL, ANNE, 5:210, 211, 236, 237

STRAYER, PAUL, 14:42, 314, 358; 15:246, 348

TARBOX, HASCY, 6:71; End Papers for All Volumes

TARRANT, MARGARET W., 2:225; 5:294, 295, 296, 297, 299, 301, 303, 304

TAVRIDES, CHRYSIE, 5:11

TENNIEL, JOHN, 4:93, 206; 5:240, 241

THORNE, DIANA, 5:111, 131

TREYBAL, BEVERLY, 5:66, 135, 174, 183

TURKLE, BRINTON, 7:279; 11:346; 16:115

UNWIN, NORA, 1:58

VAN STOCKUM, HILDA, 9:85

VAN TELLINGEN, RUTH, 1:49, 158, 163, 214, 244, 302, 339; 2:51, 102, 139, 160; 4:15, 112; 5:151; 6:144, 202; 10:1; 15:69

VAUGHN, ANN, 9:150

VERPILLEUX, EMILE ANTOINE, 3:153

WALLEEN, HANS, 10:350

WALTHER, CAROLYN, 5:190

WARD, KEITH, 4:1, 4; 5:101, 113, 127, 137; 6:126, 164, 234; 7:42; 9:180; 10:60, 79; 11:36; 12:61; 14:257; 15:62

WARD, LYND, 2:358; 8:294, 338; 14:290; 15:206, 354

WEBER, WALTER, 14:112

WEST, BENTON, 2:54

WIESE, KURT, 4:71; 6:65; 14:7

WILDING, DOROTHY, 15:38

WISE, MARILOU, 4:38; 12:348

WUERFEL, LILLIAN B., 3:203; 5:49

WYETH, N. C., 12:227